PHYSICAL BEHAVIOUR
IN GEOTECHNICS

PHYSICAL BEHAVIOUR IN GEOTECHNICS

Fethi Azizi
University of Plymouth, UK

Published by F. Azizi

First published 2007 by F. Azizi
School of Engineering, University of Plymouth
Plymouth, PL1 8AA
fazizi@plymouth.ac.uk

British Library Cataloguing in Publication Data
A catalogue record for this book is available from the British Library.

ISBN 978-0-9555996-2-0 (pb)

Printed in Great Britain by T J International Ltd, Cornwall England

In memory of a beloved sister

...Mais quand, d'un passé ancien rien ne subsiste, après la mort des êtres, après la destruction des choses, seules, plus frêles mais plus vivaces, plus immaterielles, plus persistantes, plus fidèles, l'odeur et la saveur restent encore longtemps, comme des âmes, à se rappeler, à attendre, à espérer, sur la ruine de tout le reste, à porter sans fléchir, sur leur gouttelette presque impalpable, l'édifice immense du souvenir.

Marcel Proust
À la recherche du temps perdu

Contents

Preface

Initially, I intended to write a comprehensive book on Geotechnical engineering that encompasses several aspects such as engineering geology, modelling of soil and rock behaviour and engineering design. I quickly realised that such an ambitious task cannot be achieved under the cover of one book, and so a decision needed to be made as to the best way to present these topics without watering down the content or the analysis. I also came to the conclusion very early on that writing one book in two volumes was not the answer; instead I have elected to write two separate books (with an almost identical preface), which can be read independently, but which can be complementary since they are written in the same style using the same philosophy: *Physical Behaviour in Geotechnics* and *Engineering Design in Geotechnics*. The content of this first book relates (rather unsurprisingly) to physical aspects of soil and rock behaviour, and is written in a logical congruent way.

I have endeavoured to make the book enjoyable to read, but in this respect, only your judgement matters.

I am assuming that the reader has a working knowledge of engineering mechanics, especially on stresses and strains, Mohr's circle representation of stresses and strains, equilibrium equations in terms of moments and forces, elasticity and plasticity.

Although I have some sympathy with the view that an engineer should be literate and numerate, I do believe that a design engineer *must* be able to translate a physical behaviour into mathematical equations; after all that is what design *is* about. In this respect, I am aware that part of the analysis in some sections of the book may appear somewhat mathematically involved. In fact, you would be surprised to realise how easy they are once you have reread them: it is only by reading about it time and time again that an intellectual skill can be mastered. The book contains more than 50 worked examples and in excess of 320 state-of-the-art illustrations which are presented in a clear and detailed way that can only enhance the understanding of the principles involved.

By the time you have read through this book, you would have hopefully understood, learned and mastered its content. In addition, you would have been able to satisfy some of your curiosity through some detailed derivations of formulae and equations which are otherwise presented as a *fait accompli* in other textbooks. You would have also noticed the rather lengthy process related to the detailed calculations of some worked examples. In practice, these calculations are almost exclusively undertaken numerically, since not only specialised software packages dealing with different themes in geotechnics are widely available, but a designer can always develop a software to suit his or her needs. So, do not despair if you find the hand calculations in some instances long and tedious because that was the feeling I had when I wrote them! However, as a learning experience, every example presents you with an opportunity to see how these details are handled, and more to the point, helps you develop your engineering judgement, in that the outcome of any computation always reflects the choice made vis à vis the soil parameters. One has to realise that geotechnics is *not* an exact science; rather, it can be described as an art in which the artist (*i.e.* the engineer) has to rely sometimes, if only partly, on his or her intuition (*i.e.* judgement).

Moreover, you will be able to appreciate that, although in practice calculations may be undertaken in a different way, the fundamental thinking is similar to what you would have learned throughout the book. If anything, once you have assimilated the basic knowledge and principles, you will find it much easier to make the *appropriate assumptions* with confidence. This reinforces the statement made earlier about mastering an intellectual skill; and so do not be put off if you do not fully understand what you have read: go through it again bearing in mind that the last reading *is* the one that matters.

This book is also meant to be useful to a postgraduate student who seeks a deeper understanding and a specialised knowledge about different subjects in geotechnics. In addition, practising engineers may find the book valuable since most of the mathematical formalisms can be forgone, provided that the assumptions of the formulation are well understood, so that it is not used in a perfunctory way as a recipe: bear in mind this book is meant to make you think, then act.

Fethi Azizi
June 2007

Acknowledgements

Reasonable effort has been made to seek copyright permission and to include acknowledgements where appropriate, and any omission notified will be rectified at the earliest opportunity.

I am thankful to the many friends and colleagues who contributed, in their own ways, to the improvement of the content of this book. In particular, I am grateful to my friends Robert Saxton and John Summerscales for making valuable constructive comments.

Finally, on a personal note, I am so thankful to have had the privilege of meeting two dear friends who passed away of late: Kenneth Fleming and Henri Josseaume. Not only have I learned my trade from these generous men, but I also learnt a great deal from them in terms of humility and dignity.

List of main symbols

a	radius, area, amplitude
A	amplitude, air content, activity, area, porewater pressure coefficient
B	width, porewater pressure coefficient
b	width
c	speed of light, apparent cohesion
c_h	coefficient of horizontal consolidation
c_u	undrained shear strength
c_v	coefficient of vertical consolidation
C_c	compression index
C_g	coefficient of gradation
C_s	swelling index
C_u	coefficient of uniformity
C_α	slope of secondary consolidation graph
CSL	critical state line
D, d	diameter, depth, depth factor, depth of embedment
d_w	drawdown
$[D]$	elasticity matrix
e	void ratio,
E	stiffness (elasticity modulus)
E_b	soil secant modulus
E_m	pressuremeter modulus
δE	work done by an external load
f	motion frequency
F	force, factor of safety, flux density
f_o	correction factor
$\{F\}$	vector of nodal forces
g	acceleration due to gravity, intercept of Hvorslev surface,
G	shear modulus
G^*	modified shear modulus
G_s	specific gravity
h, H	height, total head, length of drainage path, slope of Hvorslev surface
h_c	capillary rise
h_e	elevation head
h_p	pressure head
h_s	capillary saturation level
i	hydraulic gradient
i_{cr}	critical hydraulic gradient

i_e	exit hydraulic gradient
I_L	liquidity index
I_P	plasticity index
I_σ	influence factor
J	cross modulus
k	permeability
k_h	equivalent horizontal permeability
k_v	equivalent vertical permeability
k_t	transformed permeability
K	kurtosis, ratio of horizontal to vertical effective stresses, bulk modulus,
$[K]$	stiffness matrix
K^*	modified bulk modulus
K_a	coefficient of active pressure
K_o	coefficient of active pressure at rest
K_p	coefficient of passive pressure
L	length
M	mass, mean, moment, magnitude of an earthquake
m	soil creep parameter
m_α	slope constant
m_v	coefficient of volume compressibility
n	porosity
N	normal force
N_f	number of flow channels
N_d	number of equipotential drops
NCL	normal consolidation line
OCR	overconsolidation ratio
p	mean stress
p'_e	equivalent mean effective pressure
P_c	creep pressure
P_l	limit pressure
PBP	prebored pressuremeter
q	load, rate of flow, deviator stress
Q	load, rate of flow
R, r	radius
r_u	pore pressure ratio
R_e	Reynolds number
R_o	radius of influence
RC	relative compaction
S	degree of saturation, skewness, sensitivity, spacing, total settlement
s	reduced mean stress
SBP	self-boring pressuremeter
SBS	state boundary surface
ΔS	stress error

t	time, reduced deviator stress, thickness
T	surface tension force, torque, shear force per linear metre
T_v, T_r	time factors
u	porewater pressure, lateral displacement
u_g	pore gas pressure
U	degree of consolidation
$\{U\}$	vector of nodal unknowns
v	velocity, specific volume, vertical displacement
V	volume, model centrifuge in flight velocity
V_a	volume of air
V_p	primary wave velocity
V_s	volume of solids, shear wave velocity
V_w	volume of water
w	water content, weight, radial displacement
w_L	liquid limit
w_P	plastic limit
w_S	shrinkage limit
W	weight
δW	work dissipated per unit volume
z	depth, complex variable
α	thermal diffusivity
γ	unit weight
γ'	effective unit weight
ε	strain
ε_1	collapse potential
η	dynamic viscosity, ratio of total heads, drainage coefficient, ratio of deviator stress to mean effective stress,
θ	temperature
$\Gamma, \kappa, \lambda, M$	critical state parameters
Γ_c	Coriolis acceleration
Γ_h	horizontal shaking
Γ_v	vertical acceleration
λ, μ	Lame parameters
ν	Poisson's ratio
ξ	correction factor, strength ratio
ρ	density
σ	total stress, standard deviation
σ'	effective stress
σ_a	active pressure
σ_h, σ_3	horizontal stress
σ_p	preconsolidation pressure
σ_v, σ_1	vertical stress
σ_{vm}	centrifugal force
τ	shear stress
τ_{mob}	mobilised shear stress

υ	angle of dilation
∇	nabla operator
∇^2	Laplacian operator
ϕ	angle of shearing resistance, form factor
ϕ_p, ϕ_c, ϕ_r	peak, critical and residual angles of shearing resistance
Φ	stress function, velocity potential
χ	constant
Ψ	stream function
ω	angular velocity, complex potential

Conversion factors

- **Multiplication factors**

10^9	giga	G
10^6	mega	M
10^3	kilo	k
10^{-3}	milli	m
10^{-6}	micro	μ
10^{-9}	nano	n

- **Length**

  $1\,cm = 0.3937\,in$ $1\,in = 2.54\,cm$

  $1\,m = 3.28\,ft$ $1\,ft = 30.48\,cm$

- **Area**

  $1\,m^2 = 10.76\,ft^2$ $1\,ft^2 = 929\,cm^2$

- **Volume**

  $1\,l = 1000\,cm^3 = 61.02\,in^3$ $1\,in^3 = 16.388\,cm^3$

  $1\,m^3 = 35.32\,ft^3$ $1\,ft^3 = 0.02832\,m^3$

- **Mass**

  $1\,g = 0.0022\,p$ $1\,p = 453.6\,g$

- **Density**

  $1\,g/cm^3 = 1\,Mg/m^3 = 62.43\,p/ft^3$ $1\,p/ft^3 = 0.01602\,Mg/m^3$

- **Energy**

  $1\,J = 1\,Nm = 1\,kg\,m^2/s^2$

- **Force**

  $1\,N = 102\,g = 0.2248\,p$ $1\,p = 4.448\,N$

- **Pressure**

  $1\,N/m^2 = 1\,Pa$ $1\,bar = 100\,kPa$

  $1\,kN/m^2 = 20.89\,p/ft^2$ $1\,p/ft^2 = 0.04787\,kN/m^2$

  $1\,kN/m^2 = 0.1450\,psi$ $1\,psi = 6.895\,kN/m^2$

- **Angle**

  $1\,rad = 57.296°$ $1° = 0.017453\,rad$

- **Temperature**

  $°C = 0.555\,°F - 17.778$ $°F = 1.8\,°C + 32$

The Greek alphabet

Lower case	(selected) Capital	Name
α		alpha
β		beta
γ	Γ	gamma
δ	Δ	delta
ε		epsilon
ζ		zeta
η		eta
θ		theta
ι		iota
κ		kappa
λ	Λ	lambda
μ		mu
ν		nu
ξ		xi
ο		omicron
π	Π	pi
ρ		rho
σ (ς)	Σ	sigma (at end of word)
τ		tau
υ		upsilon
φ	Φ	phi
χ		chi
φ	Ψ	psi
ω	Ω	omega

CHAPTER 1

Practical aspects of geology

1.1 The planet Earth: formation and constitution

As early as 1644, René Descartes suggested in his vortex theory that circular eddies of all sizes were formed at the beginning of the solar system in a primordial gas, then eventually settled down to become the various celestial bodies. This theory did not prove to be as sound as Descartes famous edict *"je pense donc je suis"*, and in 1755, Immanual Kant postulated that the Sun and the planets were formed by the same process. In 1779, Pierre Simon Laplace (also known for his mathematical work) suggested a theory similar to Kant's, in which the Sun and the planets were formed from an interstellar spinning cloud of gas called *nebula*. In the process, the spinning gas threw off rings that eventually condensed to become the planets we know.

The latest thinking seems to follow Kant and Laplace theories. It is now thought that around 4.6 billion years ago (some eight billion years after the galaxies began to form), smaller clouds of gas and dust began to contract out of interstellar space. Shock waves, possibly from nearby supernova, set off the collapse of gas to form the solar system. This, in turn, would have engendered a net spin of the primeval solar nebula. As it contracted, the solar nebula would have started to spin faster because of the conservation of angular momentum. Gravity would have contracted the spinning nebula into a disk where the nebula collapsed towards its centre (one may think of the flaring out of the skirt of a female ice skater spinning faster and faster as she draws her arms in). In the process, most of the solar nebula collapsed to become the Sun itself. Around the Sun, material left behind would have started to form bodies that increased in size, combining under the force of gravity over tens of millions of years to form different planets. As the Sun condensed, the heat generated from contraction at its centre reached a temperature at which nuclear fusion was triggered. The planets on the other hand were not big enough in size to heat up sufficiently to allow such nuclear process to take place. Some of the material in the solar nebula may have become comets with orbits such that collisions with planets relatively early after the formation of the solar system were inevitable. This may explain the formation of the Moon and the tilt of the axis of rotation of the Earth (refer to Figure 1.1). Cosmologists seem to favour the model based on a Mars-size comet colliding with the planet Earth, some time after its formation, causing matter to be ejected in gaseous form. The pressure difference could have caused the ejected matter to start spinning rapidly enough to go into orbit forming a disk of orbiting material. This material eventually coalesced into the Moon. Carbon dating of rock samples collected from the Moon surface suggests that the Moon was borne about 4.4 billion years ago, some 200 million years after the formation of Earth. This early activity resulted in a molten Earth planet, in which the denser material sank towards the centre as illustrated in figure 1.1. A *dynamo effect* was then generated from a combination of thermal convection effects and rotation in the spinning liquid upper core (which consists of iron and nickel). The electrical currents thus produced engendered the Earth magnetic field, an event without which life on Earth could not be sustained. Remarkably, the Earth is shielded by its magnetic field from much of the solar wind emanating from the Sun with variable intensity and velocities of up to 400 km/s. On reaching the Earth magnetic field, most of the solar wind is deflected much in the way water is deflected around the bow of a ship. Only a small amount of high energy particles from the solar wind become trapped in the Earth magnetic field, resulting in the northern and southern lights known as the *aurora*.

Referring to figure 1.1[1], as the denser material sank towards the centre, less dense silicates floated to the surface forming a magma ocean. Eventually, the upper surface layer cooled to form a (relatively) thin crust. The surface of the Earth was then continuously bombarded with different comets consisting of ice and dust, coming from outside the solar system. These comets, with sizes ranging between a few metres and several kilometres in width melted as they went through the Earth upper atmosphere, producing continuous rain, the essential ingredient of life. It is now thought that this process was at the origin of the early Earth atmosphere and the formation of oceans. In fact, some of the oldest crystals found recently in the Australian desert were carbon-dated to about 4.4 billion years ago. More importantly, the chemical analysis of these crystals revealed some traces of heavy oxygen ^{18}O, proving the presence of liquid water on the Earth surface, just 200 million years after its formation. Initially, oceans contained virtually no salt, but within a relatively short period of (geological) time, rivers carrying weathered products on land generated the salt. Very early after the oceans were formed, the salinity of sea water reached a level remarkably similar to what it is today. This is due to the natural control mechanism consisting of the precipitation of salt from sea-water as soon as any extra salt is added to the oceans through rivers. The process of cooling of the Earth is dynamic in nature due to the expansion of gases generated by the heat convection deep below the crust.

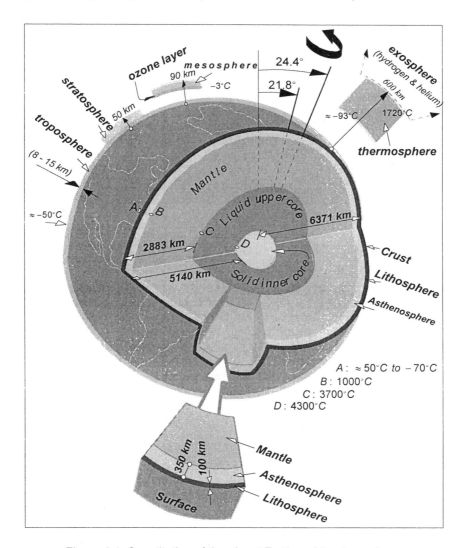

Figure 1.1: Constitution of the planet Earth and its atmosphere

---

[1] *Notwithstanding the high temperature indicated in the figure, the thermosphere would be very cold indeed due to the fact that air is so thin within this layer, so that heat cannot be transferred in any appreciable way through very few air molecules.*

The degassing mechanism in the form of volcanic activities is at the origin of the subdivision of the upper crust surface into several large areas known as plates. The dynamic activity implies that the Earth's crust is always changing through the release of magma from volcanoes, erosion activities, and the slow process of spreading, squeezing and at times melting (or recycling) of plate boundaries. This explains to a large extent why most of the geological features of the upper crust can only be traced to about 590 million years ago; that is some 4 billion years after the Earth was formed. In other words, more than 90% of the Earth geological history remains virtually unknown. The geological time scale illustrated in figure 1.2 refers to the interval between the Earth formation and 590 my ago as the *Precambrian*, which contains two Eons: the *Archean* (from 4.6 billion to 2.5 billion years ago) and the *Proterozoic* (2.5 billion to 590 million years ago).

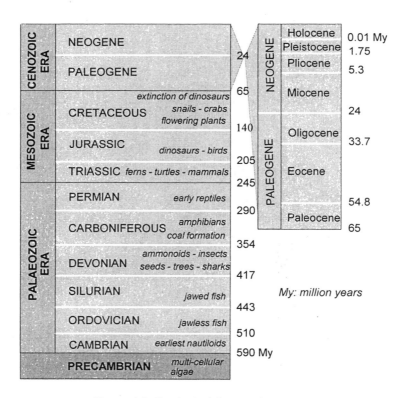

Figure 1.2: Geological time scale

The period of geological time going back to 590 my ago,   known as the *Phanerozoic* Aeon, is subdivided into the three eras of *Palaeozoic* (ancient life), *Mesozoic* (middle life) and *Cenozoic* (recent life). Although the nature of different changes and biological evolution during the Earth's geological history is outside the scope of this text, it is perhaps of interest to put Figure 1.2 in perspective, by relating different geological epochs to typical events. Some of these events are indicated in the figure up to the upper Cretaceous epoch. Typical changes that occurred during different epochs of the Cenozoic era are best summarised as follows:

- *Palaeocene:* bats
- *Eocene:* whales
- *Oligocene:* monkeys, savannahs
- *Miocene:* herbs, weeds, dolphins, apes, songbirds, snakes
- *Pliocene:* large grazers, human genus?
- *Pleistocene:* homo-erectus, Sahara desert, western hemisphere glaciation, homo-sapians (150,000 y)
- *Holocene:* extinction of large mammals, spread of agriculture little ice age (1350-1850 AD)

Another way of relating to Figure 1.2 would be to compress the geological time up to the Palaeozoic era (*i.e.* 590 million years) into one year. In which case trees and sharks would have been created in late March, dinosaurs would have been grazing in late August, only to disappear from the face of the Earth in late November; monkeys would have been climbing trees in early December, the human genus would have appeared one and half days before the New Year's Eve, and homo-sapians (the modern form of humans) would have been hunting just over two hours before midnight on New Year's Eve. Interested readers may wish to refer to the instructive texts by Stanley (1999) and Lamb & Sington (1998).

Geomorphologic and paleontologic findings allow for the relative changes in the Earth's atmosphere to be traced up to about 450 million years ago. The corresponding graph illustrated in figure 1.3 makes interesting readings. It indicates that, relative to today's climate, the Earth went through a long and severe glaciation period around 290 million years ago. This was followed some 70 million years later by a dramatic warming, the like of which occurred again towards the lower Cretaceous (some 120 million years ago). The last ice age started at the end of the Pliocene/start of the Pleistocene epoch, about 1.75 million years ago, and ended at the beginning of the Holocene circa 10,000 years ago. Though since then, the Northern Hemisphere has undergone another glaciation commonly known as the little ice age (1350-1850 AD). This glaciation and its subsequent disappearance, represent a load/unload cycle that had affected the behaviour of soils in different ways as will be explained in section 1. In fact, up to about 10,000 years ago, large areas of Eurasia and North America were covered by a thick layer of ice for long periods of geological time. The weight of the ice cap gave rise to large vertical pressures, leading to a *de facto* compaction of the soil below the ground, and increasing thus its density. Subsequent retreat of the ice cap allowed the soil to recover the elastic component of deformation; a process known as overconsolidation explained in section 5.1. Soils that underwent such a process are usually very stiff, and often have a large capacity to withstand high stress levels (refer to chapter 5).

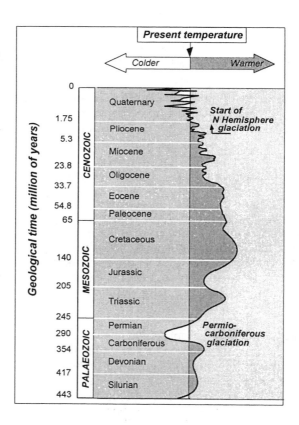

Figure 1.3: Climate change throughout geological times
(From Lamb & Sington (1988). Reproduced by permission)

1.2 Seismicity of the Earth upper crust -
Elements of earthquake theories

As was mentioned previously, the dynamic nature of the planet Earth's cooling process is at the origin of the subdivision of the upper crust surface into a dozen or so large and small plates (one may think of the cracks occurring on the shell of a boiling egg). The continuous relative slow movement of these plates generates friction and stress concentration at their boundaries.   The sudden release of stress concentration upon reaching a critical level causes earthquakes. Figure 1.4 illustrates a two dimensional view of the Earth surface, with clear delimitation of the major plates. The figure, represents a global map of earthquakes occurring between 1900 and 2001. In particular, the thick boundaries with the densest concentration of circles, known as the *ring of fire*, show the areas most prone to earthquake activities.

The seismic activity along these boundaries is entirely due to the relative movement of plates, a phenomenon at the base of the theory of *plate tectonics*. This recently developed theory was first suggested in the mid 1960's by Howard Hess and Robert Deitz, who were inspired by a previously not well received theory of continental drift developed by Alfred Lothar Wegener. In fact, as early as 1912, Wegener made an observation which can be summarised as follows: were the globe to be drawn on a piece of paper, and the continents cut separately then joined together, they would largely fit together like a rebus. Wegener then concluded that the continents were generated from what was once a single large land area he named *Pangaea*; over time, they drifted apart to reach today's geographical position. Wegener theory was initially dismissed because it did not provide an adequate answer relating to the nature of massive global forces required to move such large masses in different directions. It was not until 1938, when Arthur Holmes further developed one of Wegener's original ideas that the mantle undergoes thermal convection, that the theory of continental drift was revived. About 30 years later, detailed mapping of the ocean floor led to the discovery that the polarity of the Earth's magnetic field has reversed 170 times in the last 80 million years, though not at regular intervals. The discovery proved evidence of plates' motion, and led Hess & Deitz to suggest the new theory of plate tectonics, combining continental drift and sea-floor spreading. When considered in conjunction with figure 1.1, the theory of plate tectonics suggests that the lithosphere is fragmented into several continental and oceanic plates. These plates are in constant motion over the (plastic) asthenosphere through thermal convection. Different geological processes are induced along the plate boundaries, depending on their relative movements.   Notwithstanding the complex nature of plate movements, the three main types of plate boundaries are as illustrated in figure 1.5.

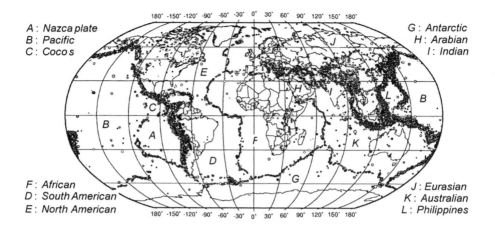

A : Nazca plate
B : Pacific
C : Cocos

G : Antarctic
H : Arabian
I : Indian

F : African
D : South American
E : North American

J : Eurasian
K : Australian
L : Philippines

Figure 1.4: Globe's seismicity map and major plates
(Courtesy of the British Geological Survey)

The figure illustrates the working of the theory of plate tectonics while providing the missing link in Wegener's continental drift theory. In fact, since its formation, the size of the planet Earth has hardly changed. Consequently, the rate at which a new crust is created along divergent plate boundaries is roughly equivalent to the rate at which the crust is destroyed along the boundaries of convergent plates. The process through which one plate sinks under another as illustrated on the right hand side of figure 1.5 is known as *subduction*. In a way, the figure, as well as the theory of plate tectonics, indicate that the Earth's crust (*i.e.* the lithosphere) is being continuously recycled.

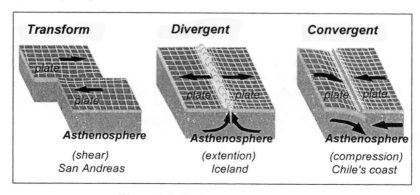

Figure 1.5: Typical plate boundaries

Iceland is　one of the best locations where the effect of divergent boundaries can be seen. The western side of Iceland is part of the North American plate, whereas the remaining eastern side belongs to the Eurasian plate, which is moving eastward relative to the North American plate. This results in Iceland being split, giving rise to volcanic activities along the plate boundaries. In fact, the divergent boundaries going through Iceland extend from the Arctic ocean to the southern tip of Africa, and constitute what is known as the mid-Atlantic ridge, spreading at an average rate of about 25 millimetres per year. As the plates spread apart, new crust is generated by magma flowing from the mantle, creating a ridge as illustrated in figure 1.5. Another example of actively divergent boundaries consists of the Arabian plate moving away from the African plate and forming the red sea in the process. Convergent boundaries on the other hand can occur between two continental plates, two oceanic plates, or between an oceanic plate and a continental one.

These three distinct types of collision engender different geological activities. In particular, the oceanic-continental convergence involves the denser oceanic plate being subducted under the lighter continental plate as illustrated in figure 1.5. The subduction process is key to plate tectonics theory, since it cancels out the effect of formation of new crust through divergent boundaries, so that the overall size of the crust surface remains largely unchanged. A well known example of this type of collision can be found off the South American coast where the oceanic Nazca plate is being subducted under the continental South American plate (figure 1.4). The movement along the converging boundaries created a trench thousands of kilometres long and up to ten kilometres deep corresponding to the deepest part of the ocean floor. The subduction process in this case has had two consequences: *a)* the uplifting of the continental South American plate and the subsequent creation of the Andes mountains, and *b)* the build-up of stresses along the deepest parts of the oceanic Nazca plate resulting in sudden energy release in the form of earthquakes every time a critical stress level is reached. Often, these two effects are combined, i.e. the occurrence of an earthquake is accompanied by an uplift of the Nazca plate boundary. The convergence of two oceanic plates results in a subduction process creating a trench. Moreover, this process often gives rise to underwater volcanic activities, leading over million of years to the formation of island arcs (*i.e.* islands with curved shape). A typical example consists of the Micronesian Mariana islands west of the Philippines, which resulted from the convergence of the pacific and Philippine plates. The trench created by the convergence of these two plates is in some parts nearly 11 kilometres deep.

The third type of convergence involving two continental plates does not induce any subduction due to the relatively low density of continental plates making them resist any downward motion. Instead, the compression at the converging boundaries induces a combination of upward and sideways movements, depending on the direction of motion of both plates. The most famous example of this type of convergence is the collision of the Indian and Eurasian plates that started circa 50 million years ago. The slow movement of these two converging plates caused, initially, in the Eurasian plate to compress and override the Indian plate, leading to the formation over the past 10 million years, of the Himalayas that include Mount Everest, the highest peak in the world at 8,854 m above sea level, and the Tibetan Plateau, which is on average 4,600 m above sea level, higher than all Alps' peaks to the exception of the Mont Blanc, the highest mountain peak in Europe at 4,807 m above sea level, and Monte Rosa (4,634 m above seal level). Transform boundaries are the result of two adjacent plates sliding horizontally along their boundaries. San Andreas fault is a typical example of this third type of boundaries. This zone, extending about 1,300 km in length, is generated by the sliding of the North American plate, moving in a south-easterly direction, and the Pacific plate moving north-westerly, over the past 10 million years at a relatively slow rate of about 50 mm/yr.

It is perhaps appropriate, at this stage, to address the question of how can the direction and rate of a plate motion be accurately determined. Prior to the advent of the Global Positioning System (GPS), consisting of 21 satellites orbiting the Earth at a height of 20,000 km, which can measure the movement of different spots with high accuracy, past rates of plate motion can be estimated from ocean floor magnetic and geological mappings. Hot spots on the other hand can be used to determine the direction of motion. A hot spot corresponds to a small geographical area that has been volcanically active for long periods of time. Hawaii is a typical example of a hot spot; however, the volcanic Hawaiian islands are situated in the interior of the pacific plate, more than 3,000 km from the nearest plate boundary. In 1963, John Tuzo Wilson surmised that such volcanic activity results from the existence of a relatively small and exceptionally hot thermal plume rising from the mantle. As a plate moves over a plume, its successive positions (*i.e.* the precise direction of its motion) are recorded in the form of a chain of volcanoes such as the Hawaiian islands as illustrated in figure 1.6. More than 40 hot spots around the globe have been identified. Typical locations include Hawaii, the Azores, Iceland, the Galápagos, the Afar in the horn of Africa, and Bermuda.

A quick glance at figure 1.4 makes one realise that the vast majority of earthquakes (90% or more) are concentrated around plate boundaries. The remaining 10% or so of quakes occur within plates along fault lines. High magnitude earthquakes, in particular, occur mainly within the narrow belt with the densest concentration of circles known as the ring of fire. This is perhaps as far as the prediction can go, since there are no (scientific) tools to pinpoint exactly where or precisely when an earthquake might occur.

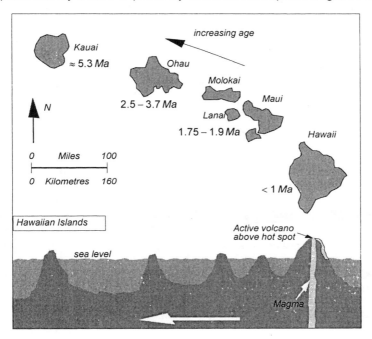

Figure 1.6: Movement of the Hawaiian Islands

None the less, the amount of data amassed in the past decades helped classify seismic zones into four categories:

- low (earthquake) activity zone where the lithosphere is so thin that it cannot store large amount of strain energy. Accordingly, quakes at this zone occur at shallow depth, and are usually associated with volcanic activity. Iceland and the Azores are typical examples.

- low activity zone, without volcanic eruption. This zone is mainly associated with transform boundary plates, where friction due to plate motion can generate large strain energies, which can be periodically released through large quakes. The San Andreas fault as well as the Anatolian fault in Northern Turkey are typical examples

- Benioff zone related to the subduction process created by the collision of oceanic and continental plates. The subducted area being an inclined plane where shallow, intermediate or deep quakes can occur, depending on the level of strain energy generated by the thrust due to subduction. The Java trench as well as the Peru-Chile trench are prime examples of a Benioff zone

- high activity zone occurring along the boundaries of continental plates, where shallow, intermediate and deep quakes can occur. The compression process generated by this type of plate boundary can be intense in some instances. this zone extends from Burma, through the Himalayas, Iran, Turkey, crossing the Mediterranean up to Gibraltar.

Earthquakes produce two types of vibrations; these are surface waves that travel along the Earth surface (causing most of the damage), and body waves which travel through the Earth surface. Body waves can be compressional or shear. Since compressional waves travel at higher velocity than shear waves, they do reach the Earth surface first, and are thence called primary waves or P-waves. In contrast, shear waves are called secondary waves or S-waves. The velocities of the two wave types are affected by the elastic properties of rocks through which the waves travel, and are calculated as follows:

- primary wave velocity:

$$V_p = \sqrt{\frac{K + \frac{4G}{3}}{\rho}} \qquad\qquad (1.1)$$

- shear wave velocity:

$$V_s = \sqrt{\frac{G}{\rho}} \qquad\qquad (1.2)$$

where K and G are the rock's bulk and shear moduli respectively, and ρ represents the rock's density. Although these parameters are explained in section 7.9 in a more rigorous way, it is worthwhile introducing unfamiliar readers to some useful definitions and relationships relating to the elasticity of materials. In fact, if a rock mass is subjected to a relatively low pressure, then it will undergo an elastic deformation. This means that as soon as the pressure is released, the rock recovers the deformation, and goes back to its original shape. This elastic behaviour only applies if the pressure does not exceed the elastic limit, known as the yield stress. Limiting our analysis for now to the elastic component of deformation, the ratio of the applied pressure increment $\delta\sigma$ to the elastic deformation increment $\delta\varepsilon^e$ is defined as the elasticity modulus of the rock (also known as Young's modulus after the British physicist Thomas Young who was first to define it):

$$E = \frac{\delta\sigma}{\delta\varepsilon^e}$$

(1.3)

The second equally important elasticity parameter is Poisson's ratio (named after the French mathematician Simon Poisson), defined as the ratio of lateral strain to axial strain, in the direction of a given uniaxial stress change as per the figure opposite:

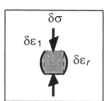

$$\nu = -\frac{\delta\varepsilon_r}{\delta\varepsilon_1}$$

(1.4)

The minus sign reflects the fact that compressive strains are conventionally defined as positive. Accordingly, $\delta\varepsilon_r$ in the figure is actually negative (extension instead of compression), hence the minus sign in equation 1.4. The reader should recall that, for some special materials such as foam, Poisson's ratio can be negative. This means that the volume of such materials can actually decrease under the effect of a compressive uniaxial stress. The bulk modulus of a rock mass is defined as the ratio of the isotropic mean stress (*i.e.* a stress that does not include any shear component) to the volumetric strain (*i.e.* the sum of all strain components). Equally, the shear modulus G corresponds to the third of the ratio of the deviatoric stress (*i.e.* the shear component of the applied pressure) to the shear strain, which in turn is defined as a fraction of the difference between the axial and radial strains. Both K and G however , are linked to the elasticity modulus E and to Poisson's ratio ν as follows (refer to sections... for a thorough mathematical analysis of these relationships):

• bulk modulus: $$K = \frac{E}{3(1 - 2\nu)}$$ (1.5)

• shear modulus: $$G = \frac{E}{2(1 + \nu)}$$ (1.6)

To complete this introduction to the theory of elasticity, the reader should know that both bulk and shear moduli can also be expressed in terms of Lamé's parameters (named after the French applied mathematician Gabriel Lamé) λ and μ, thus defined:

$$\lambda = \frac{E\nu}{(1 + \nu)(1 - 2\nu)}$$

(1.7)

$$\mu = \frac{E}{2(1 + \nu)}$$

(1.8)

The reader may wish to check that:

$$K = \lambda + \frac{2}{3}\mu, \qquad\qquad\qquad G = \mu$$

On substitution for the bulk and shear moduli from equations 1.5 & 1.6, into the primary and shear wave velocities equations 1.1 & 1.2, the reader may wish to check that the following expression of Poisson's ratio can be established:

$$\nu = \frac{r^2 - 2}{2(r^2 - 1)} \qquad\qquad\qquad (1.9)$$

with $\qquad\qquad r = \dfrac{V_p}{V_s} \qquad\qquad\qquad\qquad (1.10)$

So that, not only can Poisson's ratio be determined from a uniaxial compression test in terms of strain ratio via equation 1.4, but also from a geophysics test in terms of wave velocities ratio, using equation 1.9. Notice that, when the shear wave velocity V_s is zero, equation 1.9 yields a Poisson's ratio $\nu = 0.5$. Equally, when the material maintains a constant volume regardless of the magnitude of the applied stress, its volumetric strain $\varepsilon_v = \varepsilon_1 + 2\varepsilon_r$ is zero, which implies $\varepsilon_1 = -2\varepsilon_r$. Under these conditions, equation 1.4 also yields a Poisson's ratio $\nu = 0.5$. Consequently, a value $\nu \approx 0.5$ is indicative of, either a gas reservoir (gas cannot transmit any shear waves), or an incompressible material. Most rocks of interest to engineers have Poisson's ratios between 0.23 and 0.32 as indicated in table 7.5.

Example 1.1

Consider the case of a wave travelling through a thick layer of intact basalt having a density $\rho = 2.9\,Mg/m^3$ (that is mega-grammes per cubic metre), an elasticity modulus $E = 9 \times 10^4\,MN/m^2$ (mega Newton per square metre), and a Poisson's ratio $\nu = 0.25$. Both bulk and shear moduli are calculated from equations 1.5 & 1.6.

- bulk modulus: $\qquad K = \dfrac{E}{3(1 - 2\nu)} = \dfrac{9 \times 10^4}{3 \times (1 - 2 \times 0.25)} = 6 \times 10^4\,MN/m^2$

- shear modulus: $\qquad G = \dfrac{E}{2(1 + \nu)} = \dfrac{9 \times 10^4}{2 \times (1 + 0.25)} \approx 3.6 \times 10^4\,MN/m^2$

Knowing that $1\,MN = 10^3\,Mg\dfrac{m}{s^2}$, it follows that the P-wave velocity is:

$$V_p = \left(\frac{6 \times 10^7 + \frac{4}{3} \times 3.6 \times 10^7}{2.9} \right)^{1/2} = 6.10 \times 10^3\,m/s$$

and the S-wave velocity:

$$V_s = \left(\frac{3.6 \times 10^7}{2.9}\right)^{1/2} = 3.52 \times 10^3 \, m/s$$

Notice in this instance the P-wave velocity is about 1.73 times higher than the S-wave velocity. This ratio is representative of most cases in practice, and can be used to calculate Poisson's ratio as per equation 1.9:

$$\nu = \frac{1.73^2 - 2}{2(1.73^2 - 1)} \approx 0.25$$

An earthquake is characterised by a *focal depth*, which is the depth from the Earth surface to the hypocentre or *focus* of the quake. Deep quakes have focal depths than can exceed 700 km. Quakes with focal depths between 70 and 300 km are referred to as intermediate, and those for which the focal depth does not exceed 70 km are classified as shallow. The *epicentre* of a quake is the point on the Earth surface resulting from the vertical projection of the focus as illustrated in figure 1.7.

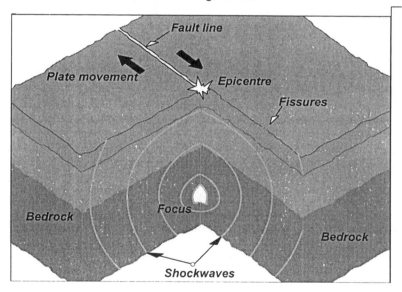

Figure 1.7: Propagation of a shockwave generated by an earthquake

Any vibration resulting from an earthquake can be detected and recorded by a *seismograph* (an instrument) in the form of *seismogram* (see figure 1.9). A network of seismographs installed in strategic locations all over the globe provides a comprehensive coverage of the Earth surface. The *magnitude* of a quake, which is a measure of its energy release, is determined from a seismogram. *The Richter scales* (named after its inventor Charles Francis Richter) were developed in 1935 to measure the magnitude of earthquakes based on seismograms, and are illustrated in figure 1.8. The local scale is used when the distance D from the seismograph location to the epicentre is less than about 700 km. Alternatively, the magnitude can be calculated using the following relationship:

$$M_l = \log A + 2.76 \log D - 2.48 \qquad (1.11)$$

For larger distances (*i.e.* $D > 700\,km$), the magnitude is estimated from either the global scale in figure 1.7, or the following equation:

$$M_s = \log A + 1.66 \log D + 2 \qquad (1.12)$$

where, in both equations, the amplitude A, expressed in millimetres, is read from the seismogram (refer to the sketch in figure 1.8), and the distance D from the instrument location to the epicentre is measured in kilometres. In practice, the accurate recording of an earthquake waves at a seismic station requires at least three separate seismographs measuring the waves motion in three directions: east-west, north-south, and vertical. Moreover, the exact location of the epicentre of an earthquake is usually determined by triangulation using seismogram measurements at 3 different seismic stations.

Example 1.2

The Kobe earthquake that shook the south-western part of Japan in 1995 caused significant loss of life, due to the fact that the area was a major population centre. Seismograms of the tremor were recorded at three seismic stations situated at Pusan (south-east of South Korea), Akita (north of Japan) and Tokyo. The three seismograms illustrated in figure 1.9, are characterised by the following amplitudes and P-S time intervals:

Table 1.1: Measured amplitude and P-S time for Kobe earthquake, Japan

	amplitude (mm)	Δt (s)	D (km)
Tokyo	170	45	440
Pusan	90	56	548
Akita	30	71	694

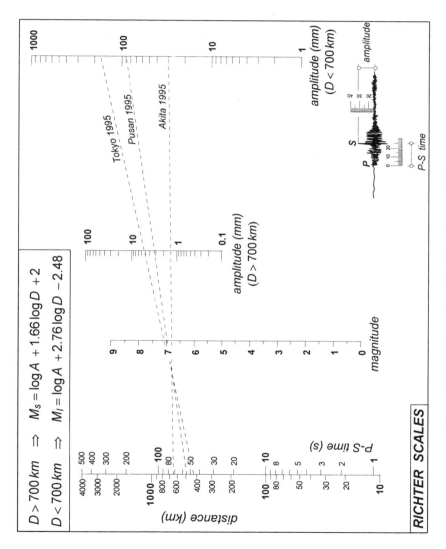

Figure 1.8: Richter scales of earthquake magnitude

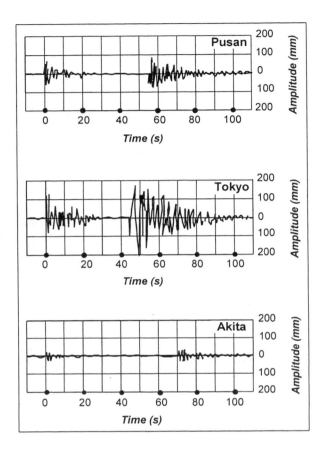

Figure 1.9: Seismograms of the Kobe earthquake (Japan, 1995)

Note that the location of the epicentre requires converting Δt into distances using the following approximate linear relationship:

$$D = 9.78\,\Delta t \qquad\qquad\qquad (1.13)$$

where D is the distance in kilometres from the seismic station to the epicentre, and Δt the P-S time lag in seconds. Next, for each geographical location, a circle with a radius equal to the distance calculated above, and a centre at the corresponding seismic station can be drawn to scale on a map of the region. The point at which the three circles intersect corresponds to the epicentre. It is left to the reader to show graphically that such a procedure leads to Kobe as the epicentre of the earthquake. Referring to the figures listed in the table above, it is of interest to point out that, as the distance from the seismic station to the epicentre increases, the *P-S* time lag increases, while the amplitude of the shear waves decreases. Finally, the magnitude can be estimated from figure 1.8, or from equation 1.11, which yields in this case 3 estimates for the three stations:

Tokyo:	$M = \log 170 + 2.76 \log 440 - 2.48 \approx 7$
Pusan:	$M = \log 90 + 2.76 \log 548 - 2.48 \approx 7$
Akita:	$M = \log 30 + 2.76 \log 694 - 2.48 \approx 6.8$

Hence an average magnitude of ≈ 6.9. The slight discrepancy in the calculated magnitudes is due to the fact that the seismogram measurements are affected by the nature of rocks through which the waves travel. This may result in the three circles not intersecting at a precise point, in which case a slight correction may be needed.

The *energy* released by a quake is a more representative measure of a tremor since it corresponds to a physical quantity, as opposed to the magnitude. The energy can be related to the magnitude through the following Gutenberg-Richter relationship developed in 1956:

$$\log E = 4.8 + 1.5M \qquad\qquad (1.14)$$

in which the energy E is expressed in Joule ($1J = 1Nm$)

Due to the logarithmic nature of equations 1.11, 1.12 & 1.14, the reader may wish to establish that for a fixed epicentre (*i.e. D* constant), an increase in magnitude from M_0 to M_1 corresponds to an increase in amplitude from A_o to:

$$A_1 = 10^{(M_1 - M_0)} A_o$$

The corresponding seismic energy, on the other hand, increases more significantly from E_o to:

$$E_1 = 10^{1.5(M_1 - M_0)} E_o$$

On that basis, it is easy to see that were the magnitude of the same earthquake to rise from say, 4.8 to 7.6, the amplitude will increase by a factor:

$$10^{(7.6-4.8)} = 10^{2.8} = 630.95$$

while the energy release will augment by a staggering factor:

$$10^{(1.5 \times 2.8)} = 10^{4.2} \approx 15,849.$$

The energy is also linked to the inertial matter's mass through Einstein's equation:

$$E = m.c^2 \qquad\qquad (1.15)$$

where E is the energy in Joule, m represents the inertial matter's mass in kg and c is the speed of light ($c \approx 3 \times 10^8 m/s$).

Example 1.3

The west coast of Sumatra is one of the most geologically active regions in the world, where the Indian-Australian plate is being subducted under the Burma plate at a rate of $\approx 7\,cm/year$ (see figure 1.4). On the 26th of December 2004, the plates movement generated an earth quake with a magnitude $M = 9.3$ on the Richter scales (refer to Figure 1.8). The epicentre of the quake was situated offshore between the Sunda trench and the Sumatra fault, and its focus (or hypocentre) was some $10\,km$ below sea bed. The combination of the very high magnitude and shallow depth of focus generated -high waves (Tsunami) that killed an estimated 300,000 people around the Indian Ocean. The energy released by the quake can be calculated from the Gutenberg-Richter equation 1.14:

$$E = 10^{(4.8+9.3)} = 5.6234 \times 10^{18}\ Joules$$

In relative terms, the energy released from the Hiroshima nuclear bomb is estimated at $E \approx 6.3 \times 10^{13}\ Joules$. The reader may wish to check that in terms of energy release, the 2004 Indian Ocean quake is equivalent to 89,260 Hiroshima atom bombs. On the other hand, according to Einstein equation 1.15, the inertial matter 's mass used in Hiroshima bomb is:

$$m = \frac{E}{c^2} = \frac{6.3 \times 10^{13}}{9 \times 10^{16}} = 0.7 \times 10^{-3} kg$$

compared to an inertial matter's mass used in the 2004 Indian Ocean quake:

$$m = \frac{5.6234 \times 10^{18}}{9 \times 10^{16}} = 62.482 \times 10^{-3}\ kg.$$

Notice finally that, although the scales in figure 1.8 are open-ended, the maximum ever recorded magnitude of a quake is around 9.5. The following table 1.2 provides an *aperçu* of the level of damage induced by varying magnitude levels on the Richter scale and their corresponding accelerations.

Table 1.2: Seismic intensity relating to the Richter scale

Magnitude	acceleration (m/s^2)	Severity
0 - 4.3	0 - 0.05	mild
4.3 - 4.8	0.05 - 0.10	moderate
4.8 - 6.2	0.10 - 1.0	intermediate
6.2 - 7.3	1.0 - 7.5	severe
7.3 - 8.1	7.5 - 9.8	disastrous
> 8.1	> g	catastrophic

1.3 Plate tectonics and deformation of the Earth upper crust

The relative plates movement introduced earlier, not only generate a seismic activity along the edges of plates, but can also engender very large compressive pressures on the sides of each plate. This in turn leads to the structure of the plate undergoing a slow process of plastic deformation. Accordingly, for a plate made of layers of different rocks through geological processes explained in the following section, the overall deformation will have different local effects. Figure 1.10 illustrates the extent to which the compressive pressure can deform a layered rock mass. In particular, notice the extent of folding as the pressure increases. Eventually, on reaching the yield pressure (that is the maximum pressure a rock can withstand), failure ensues, and a fault develops. These faults are similar in principle to those occurring along plate boundaries, except that they can occur well within a plate. This type of deformation can be seen on any exposed side of a cliff made of different rock layers. Thin rock layers in particular, can undergo an extraordinarily high degree of folding due to their intrinsic elasto-plastic properties compared to thicker rock layers. The overall deformation affects different rock layers in dissimilar ways. Locally, the high compressive pressure to which each rock layer is subjected causes fractures to develop. Although these fractures   develop in nearly all rocks, they have different sizes and are classified according to their density (*i.e.* spacing):

- *micro-fissures*: with an average spacing from 1 *mm* to 1 *cm*
- *joints*: 1 cm to 1 *m*
- *faults*: >1 *m*

The fractures play a primary role in the eventual disintegration of the rock structure, a process known as weathering, introduced in section 1.4. Indeed, water percolating through fractures will eventually react chemically with the rock minerals, leading eventually to the decomposition of the rock. In the specific case of soluble rocks such as limestone, marble, dolomite and gypsum, water can literally dissolve the rock (see section 1.4.4).

Equally, rock fractures constitute a key parameter affecting the (shear) strength of the rock mass, as will be explained in chapter 5.   On the other hand, the percentage per volume of pore space within a rock mass, corresponding mainly to the percentage per volume of the void space created by the fractures, is defined as *porosity*. This important physical property reflects the capacity of a rock mass to store water. Furthermore, the ease with which water can flow through the interconnected fractures in a rock mass is defined as the rock *permeability*, which is proportional to the porosity. Both permeability and porosity are key to any exploitation of groundwater resources, and though the physical properties of rocks are discussed in the following sections, it is clear that porosity depends on the type as well as on the state of rocks.

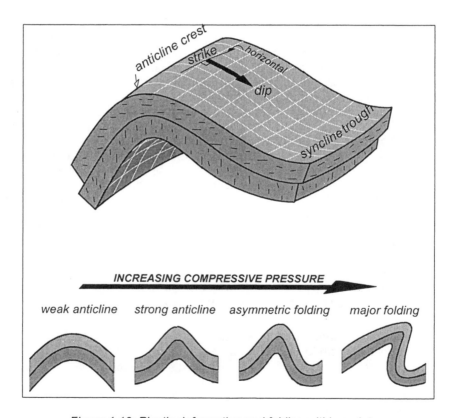

Figure 1.10: Plastic deformation and folding within a plate

1.4 Cycle of rock formation

1.4.1 Introduction

Plate tectonics theory provides a satisfactory explanation to the dynamic nature of the Earth crust. Central to the theory is the idea that the rate at which a new crust is created along divergent plate boundaries is roughly equivalent to the rate at which the crust is destroyed through subduction. Accordingly, the crust is being continuously recycled at a rate (slow as it may appear considering that the fastest rate of plate movement is about 15 cm per year), such that the vast majority of geological features of the upper crust cannot be traced beyond 590 million years ago. Subduction however, is not the only way in which old crust material is destroyed; erosion occurring through millions of years contributes to the process of recycling. While the previous section elaborated partly on the link between plate movements and seismo-volcanic activities, this section is concerned with the entire cycle of formation/destruction of crust material. This cycle, sketched in figure 1.11, contains the themes to be developed shortly, including the process of magma/lava flows, aspects of rock mineralogy, type of rocks and their eventual weathering, and the formation of fine-grained soils through sediment transport and deposition.

Magma is defined as the molten rock material that arises from within the upper mantle. Once magma reaches the Earth surface through volcanic eruption, it becomes known as lava. Magma is mainly composed of silicon, oxygen, iron, magnesium, aluminium, titanium, calcium, sodium, potassium and manganese. The precise chemical composition varies markedly, depending on the environment in which magma flow occurs. The chemical make up, combined with the rate of cooling, lead to the formation of the first type of rocks known as *igneous rocks*. Moreover, the rise of magma from within the mantle towards the surface radiates heat to the extent that existing rocks in the vicinity can undergo a metamorphism process. This process can alter the texture and mineralogy of existing rocks, thus generating the second type of rocks known as *metamorphic*. Subject to changing climatic conditions (rain, heat, freeze-thaw cycles, wind) over millions of years, both igneous and metamorphic rocks can weather into fragments of different sizes. Fragments can be transported by wind, ice or water. Those transported by streams and rivers, are often deposited under water in horizontal layers as the water velocity becomes slower. The transported material may contain, not only rock fragments, but also organic material such as dead plants and animal remains. As the thickness of the deposited material increases, so does the pressure due to self weight, generating a compaction process, which over millions of years can alter the mineral composition of the material; a process known as lithification. This process is at the origin of the third type of rocks referred to as *sedimentary*.

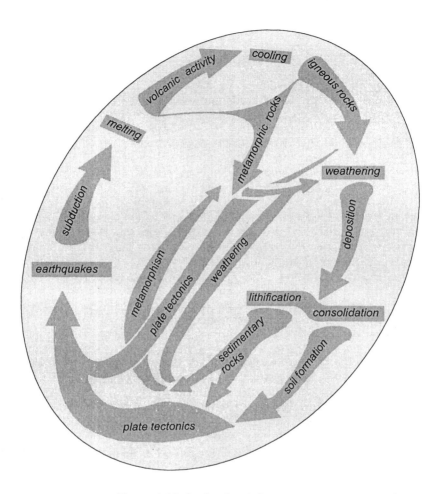

Figure 1.11: Cycle of rock formation

Prior to analysing the engineering properties of the three types of rocks, and the weathering process that leads to the formation of fine-grained soils, it is appropriate to tackle the mineral composition of such materials. Although rocks are classified according to the way they were formed, their engineering properties are dependent on their mineral constitution. Prior knowledge of the mineral composition of rocks is therefore key to understanding their behaviour in terms of strength, deformation and chemical reactions.

1.4.2 Rock minerals

A mineral is an inorganic substance occurring naturally, which has a unique chemical composition; a rock in contrast, is a collection of one or more minerals. Minerals are classified into groups according to their chemical composition. The physical properties of minerals are best described in terms of colour, cleavage relative density and hardness. A cleavage plane corresponds to the crystallographic direction relating to a plane of weakness in the atomic structure (one may think of the slate rock, which has one cleavage plane, along which it can be perfectly split into thin sheets). Some minerals such as quartz display no cleavage; others such as feldspars have more than one cleavage plane as will be introduced shortly. Relative density (also referred to as specific gravity G_s in section 2.1 of chapter 2) corresponds to the ratio of the density of the mineral ρ relative to the reference density of water $\rho_w = 1 g/cm^3$:

$$G_s = \rho/\rho_w \hspace{3cm} (1.16)$$

Most common rock minerals have low relative density ranging between 2.2 and 4.0. Metallic ores have a medium relative density between 4.5 and 7.5. With the exception of diamond which has a low relative density $G_s = 3.52$, rare minerals are characterised by very high specific gravity, and are unlikely to be encountered at shallow depth within the Earth's crust. Osmium (an element of the platinum group) is the heaviest known metal with $G_s = 22.8$. Other typical examples include pure platinum with $G_s = 21.5$, gold with a specific gravity $G_s = 19.3$, and pure silver for which $G_s = 12$. Hardness, on the other hand, is a relative term that can be defined using a relative scale, developed by Frederick Mohs in 1879, and made of ten standard minerals. The original scale, illustrated in figure 1.12, is expressed in degrees, and ranges between 1 for talc (the softest mineral) and 10 for diamond (the hardest mineral). Notice that, based on this scale, a fingernail can make an indentation on minerals with hardness of up to 4, a penny can indent a mineral with a hardness of 5, whereas a penknife is needed to indent a mineral with a hardness of 6 on the scale. Most importantly perhaps, the scale in figure 1.12 is not linear: whereas minerals with hardness between 1 and 9 have relatively small differences in "scratchability", an increase from 9 to 10 corresponds to a 40-time increase in indentation resistance.

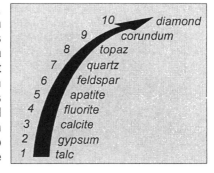

Figure 1.12: Original Mohs' scale of hardness

Some of the major mineral groups and a select few of their best known minerals are introduced below.

- Carbonates group: includes calcite, nitrates and borate

Calcite is arguably one of the best known minerals in this group. Calcite, which is a calcium carbonate ($CaCO_3$), derives its name from *chalix,* a Greek word for lime. It is one of the most common minerals making some 4% (by weight) of the Earth's crust. As such, calcite is a major constituent of different rock types that will be introduced shortly (examples include limestone, sandstone, shale, and marbles). Moreover, calcite constitutes the primary mineral relating to the formation of caves. Cave explorers would have came across stalactites and stalagmites, which result from the precipitation of pure calcite. The process originates from the dissolution (over thousands of years) of overlying calcite rich layers of limestone and marble. This results in the calcite enriched water seeping into the (dry) caves. Precipitates of pure calcite are formed as the water evaporates. Stalactites correspond to the deposits resembling an icicle hanging from the roof or sides of caves; whereas stalagmites are calcite precipitates formed on the cave floor by the drip of calcareous water (note that stalactite is spelt with *"c"* as in *"ceiling"*, whereas stalagmite is spelt with *"g"* as in *"ground"*). Sometimes, stalactites and stalagmites are slightly coloured due to the presence of very small impurities such as iron traces. *Kents Cavern* in Torquay, South West of England is a typical example where the life cycle of calcite formation can be seen. This exceedingly slow cycle (calcite forms at a rate of about 1.5 *cm* per thousand years) includes the formation of a small cylindrical *straw* at the cave's ceiling, building up to a cone shaped *stalactite*. With time, stalactites form a hanging *curtain* resembling the shape of shark 's fins. There are (rare) instances when calcite crystals grow sideways and upwards, resulting in very beautiful formations known as *helictites. Stalagmites* are formed from water falling to the cave's floor. Over time, calcite accumulation results in an upright candle shape or beehive shape formation. When stalactites and stalagmites join together, they form *columns*. Perhaps the most artistic formation is that of a *flowstone*, where calcite deposits are spread over large areas down the cave walls, creating beautiful candle dripping effects. Calcite is characterised by 3 cleavage planes, a hardness of 3 (can be scratched by a fingernail), and an average specific gravity of 2.7. Calcite colour on the other hand can vary appreciably.

Dolomite or calcium magnesium carbonate $CaMg(CO_3)_2$, is another well known mineral of the group carbonates. Its name is derived from the French mineralogist *Dèodat de Dolomieu*. It is a common mineral found in the sedimentary rock known appropriately as dolomite, introduced in the next section. Dolomite usually has a pinkish colour, 3 cleavage planes, a hardness of about 4 and an average specific gravity of 2.85.

- **Sulfates group**: contains sulfides, selenates, selenites and chromates

Gypsum or hydrated calcium sulfate $CaSO_4 - 2(H_2O)$, is a common mineral that contributes to the process of formation of sedimentary rocks. Gypsum is formed from precipitation out of highly saline waters, and is constituted of different varieties such as selenite, which is a colourless and transparent variety, and alabaster in the form of a fine grained material used in fine carving. Gypsum is usually white in colour, has one good plane of cleavage, a hardness of 2, and a specific gravity of 2.3. Pyrite or iron sulphide FeS_2, is another mineral in this group that has a rather peculiar reputation. In fact, because of its shiny yellow colour, it is most often mistaken for gold. This mineral is common in the Earth upper crust. Pyrite has a yellow (brassy) colour, no cleavage planes, a hardness of 6.3 and a specific gravity of 5.1.

- **Halides group**: composed of fluorite, halite and chlorides

Fluorite (calcium fluoride CaF_2) is the most dazzling mineral in this group due to its wide range of colours, as well as to its fluorescent nature. In fact the word fluorescence is derived from the word fluorite, whose origin comes from the use of fluorite as a flux in steel processing. Fluorite which is sometimes referred to as fluorospar, has a widely variable (intense) range of colours. Its 4 cleavage planes make it perfect for forming octahedrons. It has a hardness of 4 and a specific gravity of 3.1
Halite (sodium chloride $NaCl$), commonly known as rock salt, is the product of evaporite deposits. As such, halites are water soluble soft minerals. Halite is often clear or white in colour, has a perfect 3-plane cleavage, a hardness of 2 and a specific gravity of 2.1

- **Oxides and hydroxides group:** comprises soft to hard minerals that include metallic ores (but not metallic elements), which are found in a variety of rocks. Hematite (iron oxide Fe_2O_3) is an example of an iron ore mineral belonging to this group. Hematite has a silver or grey colour, no cleavage planes, a hardness of 5.5 and a specific gravity of 5.3.

- **Silicates group:** includes feldspars, quartz, micas, garnet.

Silicates are by far the most dominant mineral group in rocks. The feldspars are the most common group of minerals in Earth's crust. Feldspars constitute a large group made of nearly 20 minerals, half of which are well known. Generally, feldspars have similar structure and hence similar characteristics. Table 1.1 contains the physical properties of the following four (selected) minerals of the feldspars group:
- albite (sodium aluminium silicate $NaAlSi_3O_8$): a plagioclase feldspar that contains more than 90% sodium
- anorthite (calcium aluminium silicate $CaAl_2Si_2O_8$): a plagioclase

feldspar that contains more than 90% calcium
- orthoclase (potassium aluminium silicate $KAlSi_3O_8$): the most common potassium (or alkali) feldspar
- sanidine (potassium aluminium silicate): has the same chemical composition as orthoclase but has different crystal structure.

While feldspars constitute the most common group of minerals, quartz (silicon dioxide SiO_2) is by far the most common mineral in the Earth's crust. Quartz is (often the primary) constitutive mineral in almost all types of rocks. Its physical characteristics are included in table 1.3. Quartz is most varied in terms of colour and also in terms of crystallography. Varieties include semiprecious stones such as onyx, sard, carnelian, flint and jasper. Garnets, like feldspars, represent another group of (relatively) common minerals in the formation of igneous and metamorphic rocks (refer to section..). Garnets are variable in colour, usually hard (a degree of 7 on the hardness scale), and have no cleavage. The physical properties of the following (three) selected minerals in the garnets group are summarised in table 1.3:
- almandine: iron aluminium silicate $Fe_3Al_2(SiO_4)_3$
- andradite: calcium iron silicate $Ca_3Fe_2(SiO_4)_3$
- pyrope: magnesium aluminium silicate $Mg_3Al_2(SiO_4)_3$

A third equally important group of silicate minerals is represented by the mica group. Often, the term mica is used abusively as if it were a mineral when it actually refers to a group consisting of more than 30 minerals. The physical properties of the following three most common (true) mica minerals are included in table 1.3:
- muscovite (potassium aluminium silicate hydroxide fluoride $KAl_2(AlSi_3O_{10})(F, OH)_2$): a constituent of the three main types of rocks as will be introduced shortly.
- biotite (potassium iron magnesium aluminium silicate hydroxide fluoride $K(Fe, Mg)_3AlSi_3O_{10}(F, OH)_2$): especially present in metamorphic rocks (refer to section...)
- lepidolite (potassium lithium aluminium silicate hydroxide fluoride $KLi_2Al(Al, Si)_3O_{10}(F, OH)_2$): a less common mineral found in granitic masses.

The clay minerals group is closely associated to the mica group of minerals due to their similar structure and common properties. The clay minerals however contain a variable percentage of water trapped between silicate sheets, thus affecting their behaviour. Clays can be plastic, can shrink or expand, depending on the ability of their minerals to react to water. This in turn affects their specific gravity which can vary markedly. The actual process of clay formation is presented in detail in section 1.5. However, the four major clay mineral groups are summarised below:

- The kaolinite group (aluminium silicate hydroxide $Al_4Si_4O_{10}(OH)_8$): The structure of this mineral group consists of silicate sheets Si_4O_{10} tightly bonded to aluminium hydroxide layers $Al_4(OH)_8$ known as gibbsite layers. These tight bonds make kaolinite minerals stable *vis à vis* water. China clay used in ceramics is a good example of this type of minerals.
- The montmorillonite/smectite group: the main mineral in this group is also known by the same name (montmorillonite or smectite). The word montmorillonite is derived from the name of the commune of Montmorillon in western France where this mineral was first discovered. The mineral is a hydrated sodium calcium aluminium magnesium silicate hydroxide: $(Na, Ca)(Al, Mg)_6(Si_4O_{10})_3(OH)_6 - nH_2O$. Typically, it forms microscopic crystals that tend to swell to several times their initial volume by absorbing water. Montmorillonite is the main constituent of the mud bentonite, often used during drilling to support the walls of the borehole, to cool the drilling bits and to prevent any ingress of water towards the borehole (refer to section , chapter)
- The illite group: illite is the only mineral in this group. It consists essentially of hydrated muscovite (potassium aluminium silicate hydroxide $KAl_4Si_7O_{20}(OH)_4$. Illite has a white colour and represents the dominant type of clay minerals, with a maximum crystal size. It is a common mineral in shales.
- The chloride group: this group of minerals is often considered not to be part of clay minerals.

Other silicate minerals include:

- Olivine (magnesium iron silicate $(Mg, Fe)_2SiO_4$): a mineral found in igneous rocks with high iron and magnesium content, whose physical properties are summarised in table 1.3.
- Serpentine (another magnesium iron silicate hydroxide $(Mg, Fe)_3Si_2O_5(OH)_4$): a major rock forming mineral found in metamorphic as well as igneous rocks. Table 1.3 gives the main physical characteristic of this mineral
- Talc (magnesium silicate hydroxide $Mg_3Si_4O_{10}(OH)_2$): popularly known as the primary ingredient of talcum powder. The mineral talc has the lowest hardness on the Mohs scale in figure 1.12.

Table 1.3: Physical properties of some silicate minerals

	Mineral	Colour	Cleavage	Specific	Hardness
feldspars	Albite	white	one	2.6	6.5
feldspars	Anorthite	white, gray	one	2.75	6.5
feldspars	Orthoclase	yellow	two	2.55	6.0
feldspars	Sanidine	yellow	two	2.55	6.0
garnet	Almandine	reddish	none	4.3	7.0
garnet	Andradite	variable	none	3.8	7.0
garnet	Pyrope	(dark) red	none	3.6	7.0
mica	Muscovite	variable	one	2.8	2.5
mica	Biotite	variable	one	3.1	2.5
mica	Lepidolite	variable	one	2.8	2.5
	Quartz	variable	none	2.65	7.0
	Olivine	green	none	3.2	6.75
	Serpentine	variable	none	2.4	4.0
	Talc	variable	one	2.75	1.0

1.4.3 Igneous rocks

Rocks are classified by origin, texture and mineralogy. The reader should recall that igneous rocks are formed from the cooling of molten rock either below the surface (case of magma), or at the Earth surface (case of lava). Depending on their origin, igneous rocks are known as:

- *intrusive* or *plutonic* if they have crystallised from magma within the crust,
- *extrusive* or *volcanic* if they have crystallised from lava on the surface.

Igneous intrusions, also called plutons, are classified according to their sizes and shapes. Thus, *sills* are tubular or sheet-like plutons that form within the Earth's crust in between layers of pre-existing rock (referred to as country rock). *Dykes* on the other hand, are tubes or sheet intrusions formed from magma flowing into fissures within the country rock masses. Dykes are known as discordant intrusions because they cut through pre-existing rocks, whereas sills represent concordant intrusions since they form parallel to the bedding of the country rock. Batholiths are massive discordant protuberant intrusions typically between 5 and 50 *km* in diameter, and mostly formed of granitic magma that can cause the country rock to melt or metamorphose. Because of the slow cooling rate of magma below the surface, large crystals can form from individual minerals. Thus, intrusive igneous rocks are characterised by a coarse-grained (or *phaneritic*) texture, with grain size > 1 *mm*. They include granite, diorite and gabbro.

Dartmoor in the Southwest of England is a typical example where differential weathering over million of years exposed the large granitic intrusions, unravelling in some instances dramatic rocky outcrops of granite known as *tors*. Also, Dartmoor has a distinctive barren landscape due to the acid nature of its soil that can only allow very few plants like heathers and gorses to grow. The weathering of granite generates a large amount of quartz, which then accumulate over millions of years to form a sandy soil. The Mont Blanc in the Chamonix valley (the highest peak in the European Alps with a summit at 4,807 *m*), is another example of a very large mass of granite, which has been relentlessly shaped over millions of years by the relative movement of glaciers. Granite is an ideal building rock, since it has a large compressive strength (between 100 and 200 MN/m^2), and can be easily quarried, carved or cut to different shapes. Many early churches, houses and bridges were built of granite. Some of the granite used to build London bridge was quarried in Hay tor in Dartmoor. The giant faces (circa 18 *m* from chin to forehead) of George Washington, Thomas Jefferson, Abraham Lincoln and Theodore Roosevelt were carved (by Joha Borglum and his son) in the massive granite intrusion of Mount Rushmore in Dakota.

Extrusive igneous rocks are formed from basaltic molten rock erupting from within the Earth's crust through volcanoes or fissures, then cooling at the surface. Although the specific type of rocks thus formed depends on the nature of eruption, the fast cooling rate of extrusive rocks does not allow for the formation of large mineral crystals. Consequently, most extrusive or volcanic rocks are characterised by fine-grained (or *aphanitic*) texture, with grain size < 1 *mm*. All magmas contain dissolved gases, and upon reaching the surface, the confining pressure decreases and the dissolved gases escape either quietly (case of low viscosity lava), or explosively if the lava is characterised by high viscosity. In the latter case, the level of explosion depends on the pressure built up within the lava before the gas can escape. In the case of low-viscosity basaltic lava, the flow occurs mainly quietly through fissures on the flanks of a volcano cone. An instantaneous cooling leads to the formation of obsidian, a volcanic igneous rock with a glassy texture (also known as volcanic glass). A quick cooling rate on the other hand may yield extrusive rocks with aphanitic texture such as basalt, rhyolite and andesite. The Giant's Causeway in Northern Ireland is a remarkable example of basaltic rocks, generated by violent volcanic eruptions some 50 million years ago. Up to 40,000 vertical columns, with near perfect hexagonal cross-sectional areas, with circumscribed circles of about 45 *cm* diameter were formed. The hexagonal shape resulted from the contraction of molten lava as it cooled. Patterns of hexagonal cracks were first generated at the surface, and as the cooling penetrated through the lava mass, the contraction became three dimensional in nature, resulting in a network of near vertical basaltic columns. Fingal's Cave in the small Scottish Hibridean island of Staffa is another fine example of prism shaped, long columns basaltic formations, resulting from the slow cooling of lava. The cliff wall partly eroded under the constant effects of sea waves, forming an 18 *m* high, 60 *m* deep cave [1].

The eruption of high-viscosity lava is always explosive in nature. The violent separation of gases from lava results in volcanic fragments being thrown into the atmosphere. These fragments, known as pyroclasts (meaning fire fragments) weld together upon falling to the surface to form different types of extrusive rocks, depending on the size of pyroclasts. Thus, the extrusive rock *tuff* is formed from heat-bonded volcanic ash, which is the smallest size pyroclast. Similarly, volcanic breccia is a rock formed from larger size pyroclasts. In some instances, the separation of gas from lava may produce rocks with frothy texture. This is the case when lava solidifies rapidly before the gas escapes from within the lava matrix. This process leads to the formation of vesicular rocks characterised by high porosity (a Swiss cheese like surface) and low density. Typical examples include pumice, an extrusive rock with a structure containing abundant cavities making the rock so light that it floats on water.

Igneous rocks are also classified into three groups according to their mineral composition:

• *felsic* or *sialic* igneous rocks are rich in silicon and aluminium (*Si-Al*). These rocks, found on continental crust, are formed from high-viscosity magma or lava, and their minerals commonly include albite, orthoclase, quartz and biotite. Granite and rhyolite are typical examples

• *intermediate* or *andesitic* rocks having average composition in silicon, magnesium and iron. Examples include andesite and diorite, whose mineral composition contains plagioclase feldspar, biotite, pyroxene and quartz

• *mafic* or *basaltic* rocks are rich in magnesium and iron silicates, and are characteristically found on oceanic crust (also found on the surface of the Moon, Venus and Mars). They form from low-viscosity lava, and their mineral composition include anorthite, olivine and pyroxene. Typical examples include basalt and gabbro.

---

[1] *The echoes of the sounds made by the inflow and outflow of seawater into the cave are known to have inspired Felix Mendelssohn to compose the Scottish symphony, that includes the famous Hebrides overture, also called "the Fingals cave".*

1.4.4 Sedimentary rocks

As the name infers, sedimentary rocks are formed from sediments resulting essentially from the fragmentation of parent rocks of different types. Sediments of different sizes and shapes, at times including organic material, can become sedimentary rocks through lithification (refer to the sketch in figure 1.11). This process involves (geological) time, compaction cementation and re-crystallization. However, prior to their formation, sedimentary rocks require sediments, mainly composed of rock fragments generated from the weathering process of parent rocks. Weathering is also at the origin of the formation of soils such as gravel, sand , silt and clay; a subject that will be duly explored in section 1.5. Weathering, which is the process of decomposition and disintegration of rocks at the Earth surface can be of two types:

• Mechanical weathering generated by:

  • pressure release in the rock mass due to the exposure of deep intrusive or metamorphic rocks by erosion (over thousands or millions of years) of the overlying softer material. The unloading process generates an expansion of the exposed rock mass, which leads to the spread of cracks especially along weak cleavage planes
  • abrasion of rock surfaces generated by water, wind or ice
  • cycles of thermal expansion and contraction as water in cracks of rocks expands when it freezes, exerting more pressure on the cracks' surface

• Chemical weathering due to the dissolution of minerals through hydrolysis (reaction with water) or oxidation (reaction with oxygen in the atmosphere).

Pressure and cementation are central to the lithification process that leads to the formation of sedimentary rocks. Compactive pressure is generally generated by the self-weight of sediments as they accumulate and increase in thickness. Cementation however requires the presence within the sediments' matrix of a cement such as calcite, silica or iron oxide. Once these requirements are met, lithification can take place over a geological time span that can be measured in tens of thousands or even millions of years. Depending on the nature of sediments, the type of cement and the level of pressure, three types of sedimentary rocks can be generated:

a- clastic sedimentary rocks

Formed from different size clasts (rock fragments), and classified according to the texture of the clasts as illustrated in figure 1.13.

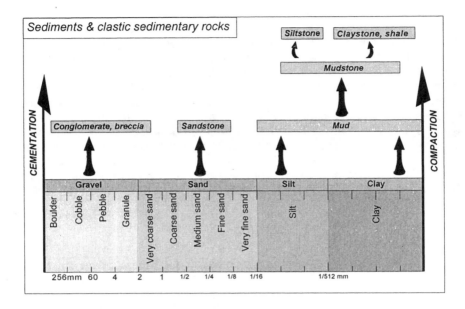

Figure 1.13: Sediments and clastic sedimentary rocks

Clastic sedimentary rocks include:

- *conglomerate*: a clastic coarse grained sedimentary rock containing rounded clasts with sizes > 2 mm
- *breccia*: similar to conglomerate except the clasts in this case are angular
- *sandstone*: a clastic medium grained sedimentary rock which can be dominated by quartz or feldspar grains, with typical grain sizes between 1/16 *mm* and 2 *mm*
- *siltstone*: a clastic argellaceous fine grained sedimentary rock with grain sizes typically between 1/512 *mm* and 1/16 *mm*
- *shale*: a fissile clastic argellaceous sedimentary rock composed of clay particles with grain size less than 1/512 *mm*
- *claystone*: similar to shale but not fissile.
- *mudstone*: a clastic argellaceous sedimentary rock, containing both silt and clay particles (a mud is technically a mixture of silt and clay)

The ancient city of Petra[2] in Jordan, considered to be the eighth wonder of the world, is carved in sandstone. Uluru rock[3] (also known as Ayers rock) in central Australia is a famous landmark, consisting of a very large arkostic sandstone rich in feldspar. Other examples include the Grand Canyon site carved by the Colorado river, exposing several sandstone layers, some of which are estimated to be in excess of 2 billion years old. Also, the four gigantic statues guarding the Abu Simbel Temple (built by Ramses II around 1260 BC), were originally carved deep into a sandstone cliff.

b- chemical and biogenic sedimentary rocks

Formed by deposition under seawater, essentially through a combination of chemical (dissolution in seawater) and biological (shell growth) processes. Examples include:

1- several types of **limestone** such as:
- *limestone*: a very fine grained calcite-rich carbonate rock, made essentially of tiny shells.
- *tufa* (not to be confused with the extrusive igneous rock *tuff*), is a soft porous banded calcite formed by precipitation in flowing water.
- *white chalk* is a weak, friable bioclastic limestone made of very fine grained shells and skeletal debris.

Limestone, in particular, constitutes an ideal building material due to its workability (easy to carve) and strength (weather resistant). The Pyramids in Gisa were built of limestone blocks. More recently, the gothic building of the Palace of Westminster in London was built of limestone extracted from Bolsover Moor in Derbyshire, whereas St Paul's cathedral was built of Portland limestone (extracted from the island of Portland as the mane infers). On the other hand, the large body of chalk making the white cliffs of Dover in England, and those along the Normandy coast in France, was formed in the upper Cretaceous period, some 70 millions years ago.

2- **calcite** (which is also a mineral) is a carbonate sedimentary rock that forms mainly in caves (stalactites & stalagmites) from the evaporation of calcite rich water
3- **dolostone**: a carbonate sedimentary rock rich in dolomite
4- **gypsum:** a chemical sedimentary rock formed from the evaporation of seawater or other natural water

---

[2] *The city was established by the Nabatean Arabs in the 6th century BC. The sandstone in which it was carved is characterised by a wide range of colours from white or pale yellow, through rich red, to dark brown.*

[3] *The rock, thought to be a tip of a mountain, is 3.4 km long, 2 km wide, and 345 m high. This roughly oval shaped rock is characterised by a distinctive pinky red colour (due to the presence of feldspar mineral), and is particularly renowned for the spectacular way in which its colour changes, especially at sunrise and sunset.*

5- ***chert & flint***: cryptocrystalline silica; in other words these are chemical sedimentary rocks, consisting of extremely small quartz crystals that have been precipitated from watery solutions. Impurities may give chert a grey, brown or black colour. Black chert in particular has the highest proportion of silica. ***Flint*** is the name commonly used to refer to black chert as well as to the chert that occurs in chalk formations. Expressed otherwise, flint is a type of chert (not the other way around).

c- organic sedimentary rocks

Composed principally of organic matter. They include peat (which is an organic material with very large porosity), lignite and bituminous coal. Actual coal is technically classified as a metamorphic rock.

1.4.5 Metamorphic rocks

Metamorphism describes the change in texture and in mineralogy of a rock mass under the effects of heat, pressure, or chemical fluids. The threshold at which this process is triggered corresponds to a temperature of around $200\,°C$ and a pressure higher than 300 *MPa*. Higher temperatures can be generated through:
> • *geothermal gradient*: the temperature below the ground surface increases with depth, initially at a rate of some 25 to $30°C$ per kilometre. Notice however that the temperature-depth relationship is non-linear in nature.
> • *igneous intrusions*

Higher pressure on the other hand results from:
> • *overburden*: the pressure due to self-weight of the rock mass increases with depth. As will be shown shortly, the overburden pressure can easily be calculated at any depth, provided the density of the material is known
> • *plate tectonics*: subduction and continental collisions result in higher pressures applied to a rock mass
> • *transform plate boundaries*

Finally chemical fluid effects are related to hydrothermal solutions (mineral dissolution in hot water).

Although the interaction between pressure and temperature is a rather complex process, metamorphism can be classified into three types as illustrated in figure 1.14.
• *Dynamic metamorphism*: largely due to shear deformation generated along fault zones (transform plate boundary in figure 1.5). The sliding generates enough heat and pressure to cause ductile flow of rocks along the boundaries. This type of metamorphism is usually restricted to a narrow zone and is not very common.

- *Regional metamorphism*: usually occurs at depths of between 5 and 40 km (see figure 1.14), and is generated by an increase in heat and pressure.

- *Contact metamorphism*: associated with contact of a parent rock with magma (below the ground surface) or lava (at the surface). This may occur in a restricted zone surrounding an igneous intrusion, known as a metamorphic aureole. It may also occur as lava flowing from a volcano comes into contact with a parent rock. Contact metamorphism usually occurs at high temperature and low pressures (see figure 1.14) and produces rocks known as *hornfels*.

Metamorphism causes a rock to change its texture and mineralogy. In particular, the change in texture occurs when the rock undergoes an extremely slow process of compaction and re-crystallization. The process, induces higher density and smaller porosity, and engenders the growth of new crystals from the minerals existing within the rock mass. In many cases, a preferred orientation of minerals termed *foliation* develops within the rock structure, reflecting especially the alignment of sheet silicate minerals (biotite, muscovite, chlorite, talc and serpentine), depending on the *metamorphic grade*, in other words the level of heat and the magnitude of pressure. Consider for instance the metamorphism of shale (a fissile clastic sedimentary rock composed of clay minerals and quartz as per figure 1.13). At low grade metamorphism (at temperatures between $200°C$ and $320°C$ and relatively low pressure), shale is metamorphosed to *slate*, a very fine grained rock characterised by a slaty cleavage foliation as shown schematically in figure 1.15a. The preferred orientation of sheet silicates causes the rock to break effortlessly along these planes, which always develop normal to the maximum applied pressure.

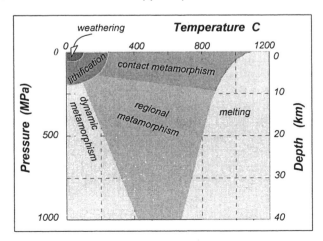

Figure 1.14: Types of metamorphism

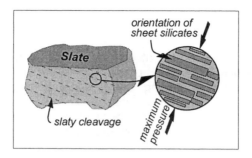

Figure 1.15a: Slaty cleavage foliation

At intermediate grade metamorphism (temperature as high as 500°C), *shist* is formed from shale. In this case, quartz and feldspar grains show no preferred orientation; however, the sheet silicates (mainly biotite and muscovite) eventually develop an irregular planar foliation known as schistosity (see figure 1.15b).

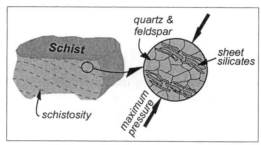

Figure 1.15b: Schistosity foliation

At high grade metamorphism (temperatures between 500C and 800 C), shale is metamorphosed to *Gneiss*. Under high temperature, the sheet silicates become unstable, leading to the growth of dark coloured minerals such as pyroxene, which eventually become segregated in bands, forming a gneiss banding foliation as shown in figure 1.15c.

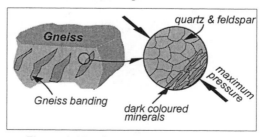

Figure 1.15c: Gneiss banding foliation

Hornfels are non-foliated metamorphic rocks, characterised by a mosaic structure formed by almost equidimentional grains such as quartz and calcite (as opposed to elongated sheet silicates), with no preferred orientation. Varieties include *marble* (a homogeneous granular metamorphic rock formed from pure limestone, *quartzite* (another homogeneous granular rock corresponding to a metamorphosed sandstone), and *greenstone* (a low grade metamorphism of basalt). Marble is a widely used building material due to its strength and the beauty of its finished surface. The famous marble made in Cararra, Italy is quarried from the surrounding Tuscan mountains, which are made of solid marble. The same quarries were used by Michelangelo to select marble for his works. Taj Mahal[4] in Agra, India is built entirely of white marble.

1.5 Weathering and soil formation

1.5.1 Natural process of sinkhole formation

The process of cave formation was discussed earlier in section 1.4.2. The discussion dealt primarily with the precipitation of pure calcite, due to the dissolution of overlaying layers of limestone and marble, and the formation of stalactites, stalagmites, and (on rare occasions) helictites. However, the dissolution process of biogenic sedimentary rocks such as limestone, marble, dolomite and gypsum, not only generates caves, but also causes the ground surface to subside, forming sinkholes in the process as depicted in figure 1.16; the corresponding topography being known as *karst terrain*. Sinkholes can also result from the collapse of the roof of a cave formed within the soluble bedrock. In either case, sinkholes are engendered by the slow process of biogenic rock dissolution. When rainwater percolates the top soil layer, it becomes slightly acidic due to presence of carbon dioxide in the soil generated from decaying organic matter.

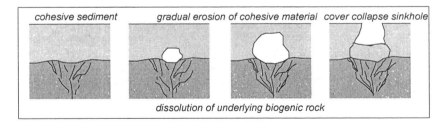

Figure 1.16: Cover collapse sinkhole

---

[4] *Taj Mahal was built by the Mughal emperor Shah Jahan in memory of his wife Mumtaz Mahal, and completed in 1648.*

Upon contact with a rock such as limestone, the acidic water starts to dissolve the calcium carbonate as it flows downward through the interconnected pores and fractures. As the dissolution proceeds, the flow path is gradually enlarged, allowing for more water to flow, thus accelerating the dissolution process. This in turn results in the formation of pipes permeating deep through the limestone mass. If the limestone layer is exposed at the ground surface, then the surface flow of water results in the dissolution of the limestone around the pipes, resulting in a bowl shaped depression. The gradual accumulation of soil residue generated from any insoluble minerals may eventually prevent any water from seeping through, leading to the formation of a sinkhole lake. With time, more sediments can be deposited, resulting eventually in the formation of a layer of fine grained soil such as silt or clay. This relatively young material being unconsolidated, its structure allows for precipitation to percolate through, seeping down to the impermeable limestone surface. Water then migrates to the edge of the sinkhole, and toward the solution pipes, then deep into the limestone. The sediment directly above the pipes would gradually erode, and is thus transported by water flowing through the pipes. The process generates a cavity in the soil, whose size keeps increasing with time. Eventually, the roof of the cavity becomes too thin to sustain its own weight, and collapse ensues, resulting in a new larger sinkhole as depicted in figure 1.16. Notice finally that sinkholes can also result from the collapse of void generated by underground mining activity, or the lowering of the water table.

1.5.2 Type of soil deposits

A quick reference to figure 1.11 shows that soils as well as sedimentary rocks are formed by the deposition of sediments generated from the weathering of different types of rocks. The formation of sedimentary rocks through lithification is an exceedingly slow process that involves large pressures, cementation and recrystallization. Soils, on the other hand, constitute the very upper crust layers, and are thus subjected to lower levels of pressure due to self-weigh. Over time, increasing self-weight effectively compacts the soil, leading to an increase in density, and a reduction in porosity. The implication of such a consolidation process in terms of engineering properties and design requirements are the subject of chapter 4. Soils are clastic in nature since they are made of rock fragments of different sizes. They are classified into three types, according to the size of their solid particles (see figure 1.13):

- ***Clastic coarse grained soils*** (commonly known as gravel) have fragments larger than 2 *mm* in size. They include:

  • granule (2 *mm* to 4 *mm*),
  • pebble (4 *mm* to 8 *mm*),

- cobble (60 *mm* to 256 *mm*),
- boulder (> 256 *mm*)

- *Clastic medium grained soils* consisting of all varieties of sand, which are subdivided into:
  - very fine sand (1/16 *mm* to 1/8 *mm*),
  - fine sand (1/8 *mm* to 1/4 *mm*),
  - medium sand (1/4 *mm* to 1/2 *mm*),
  - coarse sand (1/2 *mm* to 1 *mm*),
  - very coarse sand (1 *mm* to 2 *mm*)

- *Clastic fine grained soils*, which include:
  - silt with grain sizes between 1/512 *mm* and 1/16 *mm*,
  - clay with grain size < 1/512 *mm*.

The formation of soils is a process that involves natural selection of clastic sediments according to their size. Soils consist of a mixture of sediments that can range from boulders to clay particles, and are commonly classified according to the way they were deposited. Hence, if the present location of a soil is (in the vicinity of) that in which the original weathering of the parent rock occurred, the soil is known as *residual.* If it is not the case, the soil is referred to as *transported.* The process by which a soil is transported from one location to another can be due to gravity, wind, ice or water.

A• *Gravity deposits*

These are deposits resulting generally from rock weathering at the face of a cliff that causes rock fragments to fall to the foot of the cliff, thus forming a pile of rock deposit, greatly varying in size, known as *talus.* The final position of each fragment is entirely due to gravitational forces, and no other transporting agent is involved in this process depicted in figure 1.17.

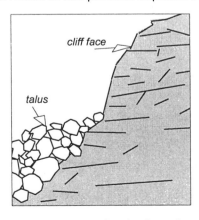

Figure 1.17: Gravity deposit

B. Wind deposits

Wind is a powerful transport agent, capable of moving not only small solid particles through suspension in the air, but also larger sediments through a process known as *saltation*; a process referring to short jumps of solid particles dislodged from the ground by the wind as depicted in figure 1.18.

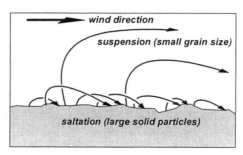

Figure 1.18: Wind deposit through saltation and suspension.

Winds are generated if there is enough (solar) energy to heat the air near the surface. As the lighter warm air rises into the atmosphere and towards the poles, a low pressure area is then engendered, into which cooler denser air rushes, resulting in winds. Storm winds (*i.e.* winds with an average speed of $\approx 95 \, km/h$) are known to cause saltation of solid particles up to 100 *mm* in size. Wind speeds, classified according to the Beaufort scale (named after Francis Beaufort, 1805) are presented in the useful table 1.4. Depending on its velocity, wind can cause erosion either by *deflation* or through *abrasion*. Deflation is generated by the removal through wind of fine-grained solid particles so that eventually, the ground surface consists only of variable size coarse fragments that cannot be transported by wind. Abrasion on the other hand is the shaping of a rock surface caused by the exposure to wind-blown sediments. The smooth abraded surface thus produced is known as *ventifact* as illustrated in figure 1.19.

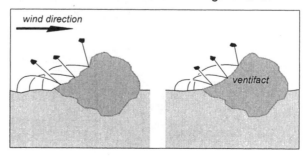

Figure 1.19: Rock abrasion by wind effect.

Table 1.4: Beaufort scale

Beaufort number	Description	Wind speed 10 m above ground		
		Mph	knots	km/h
0	calm	0 - 1	0 - 1	0 - 1.6
1	light air	1 - 3	1 - 3	1.6 - 5
2	light breeze	4 - 7	4 - 6	6.5 - 11
3	gentle breeze	8 - 12	7 - 10	13 - 20
4	moderate breeze	13 - 18	11 - 16	21 - 29
5	fresh breeze	19 - 24	17 -21	30 - 39
6	strong breeze	25 - 31	22 - 27	40 - 50
7	near gale	32 - 38	28 - 33	51 - 61
8	gale	39 - 46	34 - 40	63 - 74
9	severe gale	47 - 54	41 - 47	76 - 87
10	storm	55 -63	48 - 55	88 - 101
11	violent storm	64 -72	56 - 63	103 - 116
12	hurricane	73 +	64 +	118 +

Wind transport through saltation and suspension is most common in arid regions such as deserts. These are technically defined as being areas where evaporation exceeds precipitation, so that no water can be retained within the soil. Different topological features can thus be generated, depending on the grain size and wind speed as well as direction. Thus, sand ripples are created as small sized solid particles are transported through suspension, leaving larger grains to form ripples, in curves perpendicular to wind direction. Sand dunes, on the other hand, are formed when solid particles, transported by wind encounter an obstacle (such as a rock mass or a vegetation). The obstacle causes a slowdown in the wind, resulting in the solid particles being deposited to form, initially a mound, which then becomes a dune as the accumulation of sand grains increases. Sand dunes can reach heights of more than 500 m, and can cover large areas. They are asymmetrical in shape, consisting of a gentle upwind slope, and a steeper slip face on the downwind side. Perhaps some of the most relevant wind deposits in geotechnical engineering consists of dust deposit known as *loess*. This is a loose, metastable soil, whose open structure is liable to collapse as will be discussed in section 2.7. Loess is formed from large deposits of dust made from silt and clay particles. Because of the very small size of these dry solid particles (predominantly $20\,\mu m$ to $63\,\mu m$), they can be suspended in air and transported over large distances. Volcanic ash is a typical example in which large quantities of dust-sized tephra can be ejected high in the atmosphere. It then becomes wind-suspended, and can thus be carried over long distances, depending on the speed and direction of the wind. When it is eventually deposited, it can form thick layers of wind-deposited material, with poor engineering properties. *Collapsible soil deposits* are widely spread notably across South East Asia, China and North America, and are estimated to cover about 10% of the Earth's surface. Some of these deposits are so thick and so far away from any known (active or extinct) volcanoes that they are thought to have been formed through depositions of ash generated by super volcanoes. The corresponding volcanic eruption is thought to have been so powerful that the ash was ejected high into the upper stratosphere, and transported by wind for thousands of kilometres before being deposited.

C• *Glacial deposits*

Glacial deposits were formed throughout the glaciation that started approximately at the beginning of the Pleistocene epoch, circa 1.75 million years ago (refer to figure 1.3). The flow of large ice masses was such that it caused soils at the interface to be eroded and rocks to be crushed, scraped off or ground down. The debris thus transported, known as glacial drift, is formed of soil particles and rock fragments of various sizes and shapes, and is buried at what was the bottom of glaciers, forming in the process what is known as *glacial till* which may contain very large boulders called *erratics*. These boulders were carried by the glacier as it advanced. On retreat of the glacier, these erratics are then left behind among the much smaller size rock fragments and solid particles that constitute the *ground moraine*. The moraine, which is the glacial till at the glacier base, formed as the ice melted away, can be unstructured and unstratified. In some instances, however, ground moraine can form a compact layer of relatively impervious basal till, consisting of sediments derived from weathered rocks. The self weight of a glacier generates large frictional forces at the ice-ground interface, capable of scraping off and grinding down the bedrock. In the process, rock fragments of different sizes adhere to the bottom of the glacier as it flows downward with increasing friction. This in turn causes ice at the bottom of the glacier to melt, and a water flow to take place. Small fragments as well as rock flour (the fine powder produced by abrasion of the bedrock) are then carried by streams of meltwater, whereby large size particles are deposited first, while smaller size particles are transported further downstream.

D• *Water deposits*

These soils are formed when sediments of varying sizes are transported by water and deposited as the water velocity gradually decreases. During the process, a natural selection occurs in that the heavier clasts are deposited first, while the lighter ones travel further downstream and are deposited through sedimentation. Soils thus formed are often characterised by a layered structure, and are commonly classified into three categories: *alluvial deposits* when sediments are deposited along a stream of running water, *lacustrine soils* corresponding to sediment deposition in lakes, and *marine deposits* for soils formed through deposition in the sea. The nature of alluvial deposits in particular depends on water velocity. Figure 1.20, shows a largely empirical relationship between solid particle dimensions (*i.e.* weight) and water velocity. Notwithstanding its unrefined nature, the figure gives a clear indication on how and where an alluvium can be formed. For instance, it is seen that a medium sized sand grain with a dimension of about 0.3 *mm* is transported when the water velocity v is roughly $0.06\,m/s \le v \le 0.2\,m/s$. For a water velocity smaller than the lower limit of 0.6 *m/s*, sand grains are deposited. Above the upper limit of 0.2 *m/s*, water flow causes the sand to erode.

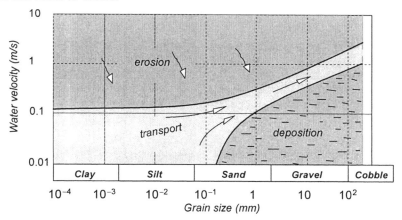

Figure 1.20: Water velocity - sediment transport relationship
(From Waltham (1994), by permission)

The engineering properties of soils are largely dependent on the size, therefore the type, of solid particles within the soil matrix. This in turn is related to the entire process of weathering, sediment transport and deposition. For example, a soil formed from decomposed granite would be sandy, since the decomposition in this case releases quartz (sand grains), and feldspar, which converts to clay that would eventually be washed away. The weathering of basalt on the other hand produces clay-rich soils because no quartz would be generated. Soils can therefore be classified according to their content in terms of sand, silt, or clay particles as illustrated in the empirically generated figure 1.21.

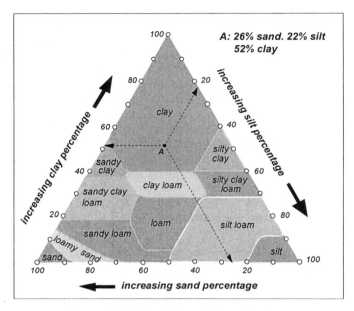

Figure 1.21: Alternative soil classification

Problems

1.1   Explain the physical phenomenon representing the engine that drives the dozen or so plates, into which the Earth upper crust is subdivided, relative to one another.

1.2   Write an essay explaining how does the subduction process fit within plate tectonics theory, and why the planet Earth's geological history can only be traced back to circa 590 my (million years) ago

1.3   Refer to figure 1.2 then compress the geological times elapsed since the Palaeozoic Era into one year, and write an essay linking the evolution of life on the planet Earth to climatic changes illustrated in figure 1.3.

1.4   Discuss the geological processes leading to the formation of the Andes in South America, the Himalayas and the Tibet plateau north of the Indian subcontinent, and the Alps in Europe.

1.5   Explain the process of storage of strain energy along plate boundaries. Discuss how the stored energy is released in the form of earthquakes.

1.6   Define the following terms, and explain how are they used in practice:
- seismograph and seismogram,
- focal depth, epicentre and magnitude of an earthquake.

1.7   Write an essay detailing the different seismic zones around the globe surface

1.8   Explain the main difference between a surface wave and a body wave in earthquake engineering.

1.9   Discuss why the velocity of a shear wave is smaller than that of a compressive primary wave travelling through the same medium.

1.10   A deep earthquake produced a body wave that was transmitted through a substantially thick layer of granite. The rock is characterised by a relative density of 2.7, a modulus of elasticity $E = 7.5 \times 10^4 MN/m^2$, and a bulk modulus $K = 4.8 \times 10^4 MN/m^2$. Estimate both primary and shear wave velocities

Ans: $V_p = 5.719 \times 10^3 \, m/s,$ $V_s = 3.347 \times 10^3 \, m/s$

1.11   Using the *Gutenberg-Richter* relationship, compare the energy released by a quake of magnitude $M_1 = 4.2$ with that of a magnitude $M_2 = 6.95$.

1.12   Discuss how hot spots are formed, and how the precise velocity and movement direction of a plate could be determined, prior to the use of satellite technology.

1.13   Define the following terms: weathering, consolidation, lithification, metamorphism

1.14   Explain the difference between a mineral and a rock, then define cleavage, relative density and hardness of rock minerals. Also, discuss why are rare minerals unlikely to be encountered at shallow depth.

References

Holes, A. (1938) *Principles of Physical Geology.*
        Thomas Nelson & Sons, Edinburgh
Lamb, S. and Sington, D. (1998) *Earth story: the shaping of our world.*
        BBC Book, London.
Stanley, S. M. (1999) *Earth system history.* W. H. Freeman & company,

New York.

Waltham, A.C. (1994) *Foundations of Engineering Geology.* Blackie Academic & Professional, New York.

Wegener, L.A. (1966) *The origins of continents and oceans.* Dover Publications, New York

CHAPTER 2

Engineering properties of soils

2.1 Physical properties of soils

On the basis of the grains size of different soils given in table 2.1 (see also figure 1.13), one would expect, for instance, a clay with solid particles of a size smaller than $2 \times 10^{-3}\, mm$ to be much more compressible than a sand; similarly, a gravel would be much more permeable than a silt. These logical conclusions are closely related to the soil composition, whose behaviour is dependent on the type and size of solid particles and their volumetric proportion with respect to water and air, as well as on the soil stress history (*i.e.* the way in which it was deposited and its subsequent loading-unloading cycles).

Table 2.1: Grain size corresponding to different types of soils

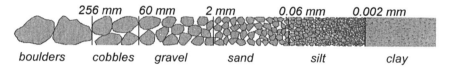

| 256 mm | 60 mm | 2 mm | 0.06 mm | 0.002 mm |

| boulders | cobbles | gravel | sand | silt | clay |

Consider the volume of soil depicted in figure 2.1a. Assume that a microscopic analysis revealed that water is not filling all the voids between solid particles and that some pockets of air exist within the soil matrix. Now imagine that the volume *V* of this *unsaturated soil* is rearranged in a (theoretical) way such that all solid particles are squeezed together so that no gap is left for water or air to fill (figure 2.1b). The remainder of the volume is therefore constituted of water and air, hence :

$$V = V_s + V_w + V_a \qquad\qquad (2.1)$$

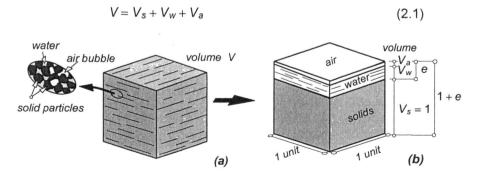

Figure 2.1 (a) Elementary volume of soil, (b) soil composition.

The volume V_s in the above equation is that of solid particles and the quantity $V_w + V_a$ corresponds to the *volume of voids* V_v. Notice that the total volume of soil V in figure 2.1*b* is selected so that V_s corresponds to one unit. This does not affect in any way the general aspect of the ensuing formulation. The following basic soil properties can thus be defined in a straightforward way: specific gravity: $G_s = \dfrac{M_s}{V_s P_w}$

- *the void ratio:*

$$e = \frac{V_v}{V_s} \tag{2.2}$$

- *the specific volume:*

$$V = V_s + V_v = V_s\left(1 + \frac{V_v}{V_s}\right)$$
$$= V_s(1 + e) \tag{2.3}$$

- *the degree of saturation:*

$$S = \frac{V_w}{V_v} \tag{2.4}$$

- *the water content:*

$$w = \frac{M_w}{M_s} \tag{2.5a}$$

or

$$w = \frac{V_w}{V_s}\frac{1}{G_s} \tag{2.5b}$$

and

$$G_s = \frac{\rho_s}{\rho_w} \tag{2.6}$$

The dimensionless parameter G_s in equation 2.6 refers to the *specific gravity* and represents the relative density of solid particles with respect to water. Typical values of G_s for soils are in the range 2.65 (sands) to 2.75 (clays). M_s and M_w correspond to the mass of solids and that of water respectively, and ρ_w refers to the density of water ($\rho_w = 1 Mg/m^3$). Equation 2.4 indicates that a *fully saturated soil* has a volume of water identical to that of voids because no air is contained within the soil matrix, in which case the degree of saturation is $S = 100\%$. On the other hand, a totally dry soil contains no water and therefore its degree of saturation according to equation 2.4, is $S = 0\%$. In practice, the water content is calculated from equation 2.5a in which the quantities M_w and M_s are measured in the laboratory in a very simple way. For a given volume of soil, the operator needs to determine the mass of soil in its natural state M_t, then its mass M_s after being thoroughly dried in an oven at 105°C for long enough (usually 24 h) to ensure that all but the chemically bonded water has evaporated; the mass of water M_w is therefore $M_t - M_s$. Also, it is easy to show that, by substituting for V_v and V_s from equations 2.4 and 2.5b respectively, into equation 2.2, the following expression for water content can be established:

$$w = \frac{e\,S}{G_s} \tag{2.7}$$

so that for a fully saturated soil (*i.e.* $S = 100\%$), the latter equation reduces to $e = wG_s$. However, for a totally dry soil, equation 2.7 cannot be used to calculate the void ratio since, in this case, both w and S are zero. *Typical values* for the void ratio range from 0.5 to 0.8 for sands and between 0.7 and 1.3 for clays. Another useful property related to the void ratio and known as *porosity* is defined as the proportion of the volume of voids (that is air *and* water) with respect to the total volume (refer to figure 2.1*b*):

$$n = \frac{V_v}{V} = \frac{e}{1 + e} \tag{2.8}$$

The air content in a soil mass corresponds to the ratio of the volume of air to the total volume and, referring to figure 2.1*b*, it can be seen that:

$$A = \frac{V_a}{V} = \frac{V_v - V_w}{V} = \frac{V_v}{V}\left[1 - \frac{V_w}{V_v}\right] = \frac{e}{1 + e}(1 - S) \tag{2.9a}$$

Substituting for S from equation 2.7, it follows that:

$$A = \frac{e - wG_s}{1 + e} \tag{2.9b}$$

A relationship between the degree of saturation S of a soil and its air content A can easily be found were the void ratio in the above equation to be replaced by its value from equation 2.7, in which case:

$$S = \frac{1 - A}{1 + A/wG_s} \tag{2.10}$$

Equation 2.10 is markedly non-linear when the air content is larger than zero.

The soil *density* is defined as the ratio of the soil mass to its volume. Accordingly, the following relationships which will be most useful for soil compaction calculations (see section 2.6) are easily established using equations 2.2 to 2.6:

- the *bulk density*: $\qquad \rho = \dfrac{M_s + M_w}{V} = \dfrac{G_s(1 + w)}{1 + e}\rho_w \tag{2.11}$

- the *dry density* (*zero water content:* $w = 0$): $\qquad \rho_d = \dfrac{G_s}{1 + e}\rho_w \tag{2.12}$

- the *saturated density* ($w = e/G_s$, equation 2.7 with $S = 100\%$):

$$\rho_{sat} = \frac{G_s + e}{1 + e}\rho_w \tag{2.13}$$

A combination of equations 2.11 and 2.12 yields the relationship between the bulk and dry densities of a soil:

$$\rho_d = \rho/(1+w) \tag{2.14}$$

Furthermore, it is most helpful during a compaction process (which will be explained shortly) to relate the dry density to the air content of the soil. Thus, rearranging equation 2.1:

$$\frac{V_s}{V} + \frac{V_w}{V} + \frac{V_a}{V} = 1 \tag{2.15}$$

Making use of equations 2.3 and 2.12, it follows that:

$$\frac{V_s}{V} = \frac{1}{1+e} = \frac{\rho_d}{\rho_w}\frac{1}{G_s}$$

On the other hand, both equations 2.2 and 2.4 can be exploited:

$$\frac{V_w}{V} = \frac{V_w}{V_v(1+V_s/V_v)} = S\frac{1}{1+1/e}$$

Hence, substituting for the degree of saturation S from equation 2.7 and rearranging:

$$\frac{V_w}{V} = \frac{wG_s}{1+e} = \frac{w\rho_d}{\rho_w}$$

The last ratio in equation 2.15 corresponds to the air content (equation 2.9a). From whence, a straightforward substitution for the different ratios into equation 2.15 yields:

$$\frac{\rho_d}{\rho_w}\frac{1}{G_s} + w\frac{\rho_d}{\rho_w} + A = 1$$

or

$$\rho_d = \frac{G_s(1-A)}{1+wG_s}\rho_w \tag{2.16}$$

As will be seen later, the calculation of stresses are undertaken using the appropriate soil *unit weight* instead of the density, the two being related through the acceleration due to gravity $g = 9.81\,m/s^2$. Accordingly, the *bulk unit weight* of a soil is established from equation 2.11:

$$\gamma = \rho g = \frac{G_s(1+w)}{1+e}\gamma_w \tag{2.17}$$

γ_w being the unit weight of water $(\gamma_w = 9.81\,kN/m^3)$.

Both the *dry* and the *saturated unit weights* are obtained in a similar way from equations 2.12 and 2.13 respectively:

$$\gamma_d = \rho_d g = \frac{G_s}{1+e}\gamma_w \qquad (2.18)$$

$$\gamma_{sat} = \rho_{sat} g = \frac{G_s+e}{1+e}\gamma_w \qquad (2.19)$$

When a soil is fully saturated (or submerged), its solid particles are subjected to a buoyancy due to the water in accordance with *Archimedes'* principle. In that case, the *effective unit weight* of the soil corresponds to the difference between its saturated unit weight and the unit weight of water:

$$\gamma' = \gamma_{sat} - \gamma_w = \frac{G_s-1}{1+e}\gamma_w \qquad (2.20)$$

Example 2.1

A sample of sand occupying a total volume $V = 1000\,cm^3$ has a total mass $M = 1960\,g$. Once dried in the oven, the mass of the sample was reduced to $M_s = 1710\,g$. Assuming the specific gravity of the solid particles is $G_s = 2.65$, let us evaluate the different following quantities:

• *the water content:* using equation 2.5a, it is seen that:

$$w = \frac{M_w}{M_s} = \frac{1960-1710}{1710} = 14.6\,\%$$

• *the void ratio:* equation 2.2 yields $e = \frac{V_v}{V_s}$, where the volume of solids is calculated from equation 2.6:

$$V_s = \frac{M_s}{G_s\rho_w} = \frac{1710}{2.65\times1} = 645\,cm^3$$

Hence the volume of voids: $V_v = V - V_s = 1000 - 645 = 355\,cm^3$, and therefore the void ratio:

$$e = \frac{355}{645} = 0.55$$

• *the degree of saturation:* equation 2.4 is now used, and as $\rho_w = 1\,g/cm^3$, it follows that:

$$S = \frac{V_w}{V_v} = \frac{1960-1710}{355} = 70.4\,\%$$

- *the bulk density:* calculated from equation 2.11:

$$\rho = \frac{M}{V} = \frac{1960}{1000} = 1.96\,Mg/m^3$$

- *the air content:* found from equation 2.9a:

$$A = \frac{V_a}{V} = \frac{V_v - V_w}{V} = \frac{355 - 250}{1000} = 10.5\%$$

If the sample of sand were saturated, then obviously the air content would be reduced to zero, implying that the volume of voids is equal to that of water: $V_v = V_w$. Accordingly, the mass of water becomes:

$$M_w = V_v \rho_w = 355 \times 1 = 355\,g$$

thus yielding a water content (for the saturated sand) of:

$$w = \frac{355}{1710} = 20.8\%$$

The void ratio is defined as the ratio of the volume of voids to that of solids, both of which are unchanged, and hence, the void ratio remains constant. Knowing that the degree of saturation is in this case $S = 100\%$, equation 2.7 then yields:

$$e = wG_s = 0.208 \times 2.65 = 0.55$$

which is the same value as the one calculated previously. The density of the sand, however, increases to reflect the saturation and is calculated from equation 2.11 in which the total mass is now:

$$M = M_s + M_w = 1710 + 355 = 2065\,g$$

Therefore: $\rho_{sat} = \frac{2065}{1000} = 2.065\,Mg/m^3$

Example 2.2

A sample of compacted clay with a total volume $V = 7.85 \times 10^{-4}m^3$ has a moisture content $w = 15\%$, an air content $A = 8\%$, and a specific gravity $G_s = 2.7$. Required are: the degree of saturation, void ratio, porosity, and bulk, dry and saturated densities.
The volume of air is 8% of the total volume and thus :

$$V_a = 0.08 \times 7.85 \times 10^{-4} = 0.628 \times 10^{-4}m^3$$

Moreover, the volume of water as a proportion of the volume of solids can easily be calculated from equation 2.5b:

$$V_w = wG_s V_s = 0.15 \times 2.7 V_s = 0.405 V_s$$

Since the total volume is $V = V_a + V_w + V_s$, it follows that:

$$V = 0.08V + 1.405 V_s$$

Hence:

$$V_s = \frac{0.92}{1.405} V = 5.14 \times 10^{-4} m^3$$

and

$$V_w = 0.405 V_s = 2.08 \times 10^{-4} m^3$$

The degree of saturation is evaluated from equation 2.4:

$$S = \frac{V_w}{V_a + V_w} = \frac{2.08}{0.628 + 2.08} = 77\%$$

the void ratio and the porosity being calculated from equations 2.7 and 2.8 respectively:

$$e = \frac{wG_s}{S} = \frac{0.15 \times 2.7}{0.77} = 0.53, \qquad n = \frac{e}{1+e} \approx 0.35$$

Finally the bulk, dry and saturated densities are determined from equations 2.11, 2.12 and 2.13 respectively, in which the density of water is taken as $\rho_w = 1 Mg/m^3$:

$$\rho = G_s \frac{(1+w)}{1+e} \rho_w = \frac{2.7 \times 1.15}{1.53} = 2.03 \, Mg/m^3$$

$$\rho_d = \frac{G_s}{1+e} \rho_w = \frac{2.7}{1.53} = 1.77 \, Mg/m^3$$

$$\rho_{sat} = \frac{G_s + e}{1+e} \rho_w = \frac{2.7 + 0.53}{1.53} = 2.11 \, Mg/m^3$$

2.2 Particle size analysis

The mechanical behaviour of a given soil depends on the size of its solid particles, on the minerals it contains, as well as on its stress history. In particular, the resistance of a soil to any applied load or the ease with which water can flow through its matrix is governed by its *granulometry* (i.e. the range of solid particles it contains). Soils can be classified either as *granular* or as *fine-grained*.

• **Granular soils** such as sands and gravel have individual solid particles, most of which can be identified by sight. The strength of such materials results from the interlocking of solid particles which provides resistance through friction. Accordingly, the range of particle size present within the soil matrix and the way these particles interact are a key element to predicting the soil behaviour. The grain size distribution can be determined with the help of a technique known as *sieving*. This old technique, which applies to granular soils (*i.e.* soils that do not contain silt or clay), has the advantage of being simple and cheap. During the standard procedure (a detailed description of which can be found in any standard laboratory testing manual), the soil is sifted through progressively finer woven-wire sieves, down to a mesh size of 63 μm. The percentage *by weight* of material passing through each sieve is then plotted on a chart representing the particle size distribution such as the one depicted in figure 2.3. The shape of the curve thus obtained gives an indication of the distribution by weight of different sizes of solid particles within the soil. However, the graph in question does not correspond to the *true* weight distribution since the material retained in any sieve yields the weight of solid particles with an individual size exceeding that of the sieve mesh, including those (elongated) particles with only one dimension larger than the mesh size. Accordingly, the outcome of such a test depends on the time and method of operation: the longer it takes to undertake the test, the more likely that some (or in some instances all) elongated solid particles will fall through the sieve because of a change in orientation.

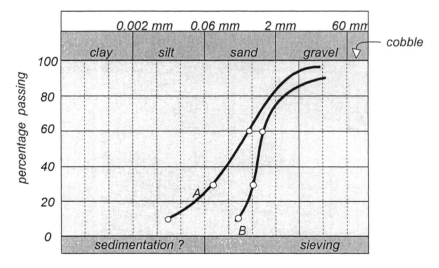

Figure 2.3: Particle size distribution for granular soils.

Assuming that these shortcomings are acceptable, then the two typical curves in figure 2.3 are indicative of different soil grading: the soil corresponding to curve A is referred to as *well graded* because the graph reflects relatively similar proportions of different particle sizes. For curve B, however, although there is no disproportion between the solid particles' size distribution, the graph is more compact than in case A, and the corresponding soil is known as *uniformly graded*. Moreover, if d_{10}, d_{30} and d_{60} are the solid particle sizes corresponding to 10%, 30% and 60% respectively of percentage passing, then it is useful to calculate the two following coefficients:

- *the uniformity coefficient*: $$C_u = \frac{d_{60}}{d_{10}} \qquad (2.21)$$

- *the coefficient of gradation*: $$C_g = \frac{d_{30}^2}{d_{10}d_{60}} \qquad (2.22)$$

The higher the value of C_u, the larger the range of particle sizes contained within the soil matrix. Also, the coefficient of gradation of a well graded sand is usually in the range $1 \le C_g \le 3$.

Example 2.3

Calculate the coefficients of uniformity and gradation of the soils corresponding to graphs A and B in figure 2.3.

For soil A, it is seen that: $d_{10} \approx 0.01\,mm$, $d_{30} \approx 0.09\,mm$, $d_{60} \approx 0.55\,mm$.

Hence: $C_u = \dfrac{0.55}{0.01} = 55$, $C_g = \dfrac{0.09^2}{0.55 \times 0.01} = 1.47$.

For soil B : $d_{10} \approx 0.35\,mm$, $d_{30} \approx 0.6\,mm$, $d_{60} \approx 1.1\,mm$, and

$$C_u = \frac{1.1}{0.35} = 3.1, \qquad C_g = \frac{0.6^2}{1.1 \times 0.35} = 0.94.$$

Soil A contains a wide range of particle sizes, from gravel to silt (hence the large value of C_u), none of which is predominant. This is reflected in the value of the coefficient of gradation C_g. Soil B on the other hand has a uniform grading indicated by a grading coefficient value of slightly smaller than one.

- **Fine-grained soils** have solid particles with a size smaller than $0.063\,mm$, making the sieving technique impractical. Instead, the grain size distribution of such soils can be determined using other techniques such as *sedimentation*. This traditional method, which is only (realistically) applicable to grain sizes in the range 2 to $50\,\mu m$, is based on Stokes' law relating the terminal velocity v of a solid particle with an equivalent sphere diameter D_s, falling in water of dynamic viscosity η, to its weight (read diameter D_s):

$$v = \frac{(\rho_s - \rho_w)}{18\eta} gD_s^2 \qquad (2.23)$$

where g is the acceleration due to gravity, ρ_s and ρ_w are the densities of solid particles and of water respectively, and $\eta = 1.005 \times 10^{-6}$ $Mg/m.s$ is the water dynamic viscosity at a standard temperature of $20°C$. Equation 2.3 can therefore be used in a straightforward way to calculate the settling time.

Example 2.4

Estimate the time t that will take a solid particle with an equivalent diameter $D_s = 1\,\mu m$ and a density $\rho_s = 2.5\,Mg/m^3$ to settle a distance $h = 1\,cm$ in water at $20°C$. Rearranging equation 2.23, it follows that:

$$v = \frac{h}{t} = \frac{(\rho_s - \rho_w)}{18\eta} g.D_s^2 \;\Rightarrow\; t = \frac{18\eta h}{(\rho_s - \rho_w)gD_s^2}$$

therefore:

$$t = \frac{18 \times 10^{-2}}{(2.5 - 1) \times 10^6 \times 9.81 \times 10^{-12}} \approx 12,200\,s$$

The time needed for this particle to settle a mere 1 *cm* (about 3.4 *hours*) is an indication that sedimentation of very fine particles is an exceedingly slow process. Knowing that Stokes' law uses an equivalent diameter D_s which assumes that the solid particle has a regular compact spherical shape, one therefore expects an irregularly shaped normal particle to have a larger surface area than its equivalent sphere, thus causing the settling to be even slower because of the increased drag. Consequently, the time calculated using equation 2.23 is likely to deviate substantially from the actual settling time. Furthermore, theoretical and experimental evidence indicate that for particles smaller than $2\,\mu m$ in size, the gravitational settling calculated from Stokes' law is markedly affected by the Brownian movement (*i.e.* the irregular oscillations of particles suspended in water) which can induce an error of more than 20%. On the other hand, Stokes' law is no longer applicable for particles larger than $50\,\mu m$ in size, the settling being turbulent. Therefore the range 2 to $50\,\mu m$ mentioned earlier within which equation 2.23 can be applied under a strict temperature control since the water viscosity η is a temperature dependent parameter (it is useful to remember that a $1°C$ change in temperature will induce a 2% change in water viscosity). To offset these shortcomings, other sophisticated techniques have been developed and are slowly being adopted in soil mechanics laboratories, although their use was restricted until recently to the fields of clay mineralogy and sedimentology. These techniques include *photon correlation specstroscopy* which can be applied to measure particle sizes in the range $1\,nm$ to $1\,\mu m$ (that is $10^{-9}\,m$ to $10^{-6}\,m$). Because of their small size, these particles known as *colloids* are subjected mainly to a Brownian motion that scatters light. The principle of the method consists of relating the diffusion of particles to the auto-correlation function of the scattered light, and more details can be found in MacCave and Syvitski (1991) and Weiner (1984). *Laser diffraction spectroscopy* is another reliable technique that can be applied to measure particle sizes in the range $0.1\,\mu m$ to $2\,mm$. The method is based on the fact that the light diffraction angle is inversely proportional to particle size. The technique itself consists of passing a laser beam through a suspension and focusing the diffracted light on to a ring detector which senses the angular distribution of scattered light intensity. This distribution is then related to the size distribution of the suspension through an appropriate mathematical expression, the details of which can be found in Weiner (1979) and Agrawal and Riley (1984).

2.3 Statistical analysis of the grain size distribution: the Φ-method

The statistical analysis of the grain size distribution of a granular soil can be undertaken using several methods such as *a)* the arithmetic method of moments, *b)* the geometric method of moments, *c)* the logarithmic method of moments, *d)* the logarithmic (original) Folk and Ward graphical measures, *d)* the geometric (modified) Folk and Ward graphical measures. Details of these methods can be found in the paper by Blott & Pye (2001) for instance. In what follows however, only the logarithmic (original) Folk and Ward (1957) graphical measures method is developed due to its practical usefulness. The method consists of plotting the *"percentage sediment coarser than"* against *phi* (Φ) *units*:

$$\Phi = -\log_2 d \qquad\qquad (2.24)$$

where d is the grain diameter in millimetres, and $\log_2$ is logarithm to the base 2. The graph is then used in conjunction with size scale table 2.3 compiled by Friedman and Sanders (1978) to determine the precise composition of the soil in terms of percentage as well as type of grains. More importantly, the statistical analysis of the grain size distribution can be undertaken using the logarithmic Folk and Ward graphical measures method in accordance with tables 2.2. The statistical analysis consists of calculating:
- the average grain size through *the mean,*
- the spread of size around the average through *the standard deviation,*
- the degree of grain concentration relative to a normal distribution through the *kurtosis,*
- the preferential spread to one side of the average through *the skewness.*

Table 2.2a: Logarithmic (original) Folk and Ward (1957) graphical measures skewness and kurtosis calculations

Skewness		Kurtosis	
$S = \dfrac{\Phi_{16} + \Phi_{84} - 2\Phi_{50}}{2(\Phi_{84} - \Phi_{16})} + \dfrac{\Phi_5 + \Phi_{95} - 2\Phi_{50}}{2(\Phi_{95} - \Phi_5)}$		$K = \dfrac{\Phi_{95} - \Phi_5}{2.44(\Phi_{75} - \Phi_{25})}$	
Skewness	S	Kurtosis	K
very fine skewed	+ 0.3 to + 1	very platykurtic	< 0.67
fine skewed	+ 0.1 to + 0.3	platykurtic	0.67 to 0.90
symmetrical	+ 0.1 to - 0.1	mesokurtic	0.90 to 1.11
coarse skewed	- 0.1 to - 0.3	leptokurtic	1.11 to 1.50
very coarse skewed	- 0.3 to -1.0	very leptokurtic	1.50 to 3.0
		extremely leptokurtic	> 3.0

Table 2.2b: Logarithmic (original) Folk and Ward (1957) graphical measures mean and standard deviation calculations

Mean	Standard deviation
$M = \dfrac{\Phi_{16} + \Phi_{50} + \Phi_{84}}{3}$	$\sigma = \dfrac{\Phi_{84} - \Phi_{16}}{4} + \dfrac{\Phi_{95} - \Phi_5}{6.6}$
Sorting	(σ)
very well sorted	< 0.35
well sorted	0.35 to 0.50
moderately well sorted	0.50 to 0.70
moderately sorted	0.70 to 1.00
poorly sorted	1.00 to 2.00
very poorly sorted	2.00 to 4.00
extremely poorly sorted	> 4.00

It is useful to point out that in relation to the terminology used in conjunction with the kurtosis, the word mesokurtic describes a normal *S*-shaped graph, platykurtic describes a flat *S*-shape, and leptokurtic is used to describe an elongated *S*-shape.

Table 2.3: Friedman & Sanders (1978) size scale

Grain size		Type of soil	
phi	**d**		
-11	2048 mm		very large
-10	1024 mm	**Boulders**	large
-9	512 mm		medium
-8	256 mm		small
-7	128 mm	**Cobbles**	large
			small
-6	64 mm		
-5	32 mm		very coarse
-4	16 mm		coarse
-3	8 mm	**Pebbles**	medium
-2	4 mm	**Gravel**	fine
-1	2 mm		very fine
0	1 mm		very coarse
1	500 μm		coarse
2	250 μm	**Sand**	medium
3	125 μm		fine
4	63 μm		very fine
5	31 μm		very coarse
6	16 μm		coarse
7	8 μm	**Silt**	medium
8	4 μm		fine
9	2 μm		very fine
		Clay	

Example 2.5

Consider the soil in figure 2.4 in which the "percentage coarser than" is plotted against phi (Φ) units according to Folk and Ward "log-normal method". According to the size scale table 2.3, the sample consists of 24% gravel (2/3 of which is very fine), 24% very coarse sand, 16% coarse sand, 12% medium sand, 7% fine sand, 5% very fine sand, and the remaining 12% silt and clay.

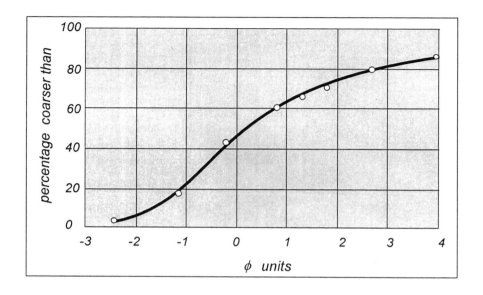

Figure 2.4: Folk & Ward Particle size analysis method.

The statistical analysis corresponding to the same figure 2.4, based on the "log-normal" method in tables 2.2 yields the following parameters:

- the mean:

$$M = \frac{\phi_{16} + \phi_{50} + \phi_{84}}{3} = \frac{-1.4 + 0.2 + 3.2}{3} = 0.66$$

- the standard deviation:

$$\sigma = \frac{\phi_{84} - \phi_{16}}{4} + \frac{\phi_{95} - \phi_{5}}{6.6} = \frac{3.2 + 1.4}{4} + \frac{7 + 2.3}{6.6} = 2.56$$

- the kurtosis:

$$K = \frac{\phi_{95} - \phi_{5}}{2.44.(\phi_{75} - \phi_{25})} = \frac{7 + 2.3}{2.44 \times (1.8 + 0.9)} = 1.41$$

- the skewness:

$$S = \frac{\phi_{16} + \phi_{84} - 2\phi_{50}}{2(\phi_{84} - \phi_{16})} + \frac{\phi_{5} + \phi_{95} - 2\phi_{50}}{2(\phi_{95} - \phi_{5})}$$

$$= \frac{-1.4 + 3.2 - 2 \times 0.2}{2 \times (3.2 + 1.4)} + \frac{-2.3 + 7 - 2 \times 0.2}{2 \times (7 + 2.3)} = 0.383$$

Referring to tables 2.2, these results correspond to a very poorly sorted ($\sigma = 2.56$), leptokurtic ($K = 1.41$), very fine skewed soil ($S = +0.383$).

Example 2.6

Figure 2.5 corresponds to the grain size distribution of two fine grained soil samples, extracted from two sites of mining waste in the South West of England. The results, measured using laser diffraction spectroscopy, can be analysed quantitatively with the help of the size scale table 2.3. Accordingly, sample *A* consists of some 12% fine sand, 36% very fine sand, 47% silt and 5% clay. Sample *B* on the other hand is made of 9% very fine sand, 86% silt and 5% clay. As such, sample *A* is classified as a mixture of silt and sand, whereas sample *B* is sandy silt.

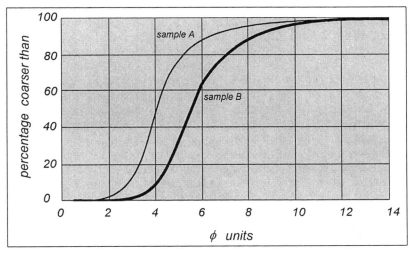

Figure 2.5: Particle size distribution measured through laser diffraction spectroscopy.

Both samples can now be analysed statistically using tables 2.2 as per the previous example, so that :

- the mean

$$M_A = \frac{3.1 + 4.05 + 5.2}{3} = 4.1 \text{ (sample } A), \quad M_B = \frac{4.2 + 5.3 + 7.2}{3} = 5.6 \text{ (sample } B)$$

- the standard deviation:

$$\sigma_A = \frac{5.2 - 3.1}{4} + \frac{7.85 - 2.2}{6.6} = 1.38, \qquad \sigma_B = \frac{7.2 - 4.2}{4} + \frac{9 - 3.9}{6.6} = 1.52$$

- the kurtosis:

$$K_A = \frac{7.85 - 2.2}{2.44 \times (4.9 - 3.3)} = 1.45, \qquad K_B = \frac{9 - 3.9}{2.44 \times (6.6 - 4.7)} = 1.1$$

- the skewness:

$$S_A = \frac{3.1 + 5.2 - 2 \times 4.05}{2 \times (5.2 - 3.1)} + \frac{2.2 + 7.85 - 2 \times 4.05}{2 \times (7.85 - 2.2)} = 0.22 \quad \text{(sample } A\text{)}$$

$$S_B = \frac{4.2 + 7.2 - 2 \times 5.3}{2 \times (7.2 - 4.2)} + \frac{3.9 + 9 - 2 \times 5.3}{2 \times (9 - 3.9)} = 0.36 \quad \text{(sample } B\text{)}$$

Accordingly, sample A is technically classified as a fine skewed, leptokurtic poorly sorted soil, whereas sample B corresponds to a very fine skewed, mesokurtic poorly sorted sandy silt. Clearly, this description sounds somewhat mechanical, and in order to relate these figures to the actual physical behaviour, the results in figure 2.5 are re-plotted in figure 2.6 as a non-cumulative percentage (coarser than) versus phi units, and at first glance, both graphs have the shape of a normal distribution. Referring to the statistical quantities calculated above, both samples are characterised by a positive skew, which translates in both graphs in figure 2.6 being elongated to the right hand side. This implies that both samples contain a larger proportion of solid particles with a size smaller than the mean particle size. Consequently, a grain size distribution graph with a negative skew (i.e. a graph such as either of the two illustrated in figure 2.6 elongated to the left) indicates that the soil in question contains a larger proportion of solid particles with a size larger than the mean particle size. The kurtosis on the other hand is an indication of the proportion of solid particles with a size similar to the mean particle size. This is indicated by the peak of each graph in figure 2.6: the higher the kurtosis, the sharper the peak. Thus a mesokurtic soil sample such as B has a kurtosis close to 1, and is characterised by a graph with a shape akin to a normal distribution, whereas a leptokurtic sample such as A in figure 2.6 has a larger kurtosis resulting in a higher peak than in the case of sample B.

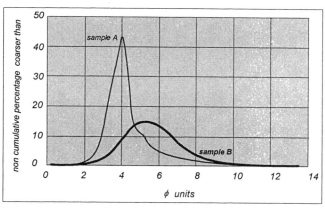

Figure 2.6: Particle size distribution plotted as non cumulative percentage retained versus phi units.

2.4 Design of soil filters

Soil filters are used to drain water seeping out of a given soil surface in a controlled way so as to prevent the erosion of the natural soil. Examples include seepage through an earth dam, behind a retaining wall or around a pumping well. To fulfil these requirements, the grain size distribution of the filter material, relative to that of the soil it supports, must include enough large particles to ensure free drainage of water, and an adequate proportion of small particles to preclude the migration of the natural soil's finer material. Also, to prevent any gaps in the grading of the filter material, it is suggested that the shape of its grain size distribution curve should be similar to that of the natural soil against which the filter is applied. Extensive experimental studies led to the establishment of empirical rules satisfying the previously mentioned requirements. In what follows, the design rules suggested by the *Hong Kong Geotechnical Engineering Office* (1993) are adopted, other rules suggested by different authors being marginally different. Note that subscripts *f* and *s* refer to the *filter* and to the natural *soil* respectively.

1• to prevent the migration of the natural soil's fine particles through the filter:

$$d_{15f} \leq 5 \times d_{85s}$$

2• to ensure that the filter is more permeable than the soil:

$$d_{15f} \geq 5 \times d_{15s}$$

3• to ensure a good performance of the filter:

$$4 \leq d_{60f}/d_{10f} \leq 20 \quad \text{and}$$

$$d_{maxf} \leq 50\,mm, \;(d_{maxf} \text{ being the maximum particle size of the filter material)}$$

These design criteria can be extended to include the suggestions by Somerville (1986):

4• to ensure an adequate drainage of water:

$$d_{5f} \geq 0.0750\,mm$$

5• to prevent any segregation of the filter material:

$$d_{50f} \leq 25 \times d_{50s}$$

6• were the filter to be placed against a screen mesh (the case of a well for instance),

d_{85f} should not be less than *twice* the mesh size,

7• the grading curve of the natural soil should be limited to a maximum particle size:

$$d_{maxs} \leq 19\,mm$$

Example 2.7

Consider a well whose lining has maximum mesh size of 0.75 *mm*. Assuming that the soil in which the well is dug has a grading represented by curve *A* in figure 2.7, it is seen that:

$$d_{15s} = 0.07\,mm, \quad d_{50s} = 0.15\,mm, \quad d_{85s} = 0.5\,mm, \quad d_{maxs} = 2\,mm.$$

Applying the above rules to design the soil filter to be placed around the lining, the following limiting values are easily computed:

1. $d_{15f} = 5 \times d_{85s} = 5 \times 0.5 = 2.5\,mm,$
2. $d_{15f} = 5d_{15s} = 5 \times 0.07 = 0.35\,mm,$
3. $d_{maxf} = 50\,mm,$
4. $d_{5f} = 0.075\,mm,$
5. $d_{50f} = 25 \times d_{50s} = 25 \times 0.15 = 3.75\,mm,$
6. $d_{85f} = 2 \times mesh\ size = 2 \times 0.75 = 1.5\,mm,$
7. $d_{maxs} = 19\,mm.$

These values are then plotted in the same figure yielding the shaded area within which should lie the grain size distribution curve of the filter material. Although any graph within the shaded area meets the filter design requirements, the one shown in bold represents a good compromise because: (*a*) it has no grading gaps, (*b*) its shape is somewhat similar to curve *A*, and more importantly (*c*) it meets the design requirement represented by rule 3. In fact, taking the bold curve as that of the filter material, it follows that:

$$\frac{d_{60f}}{d_{10f}} = \frac{2.5}{0.5} = 5$$

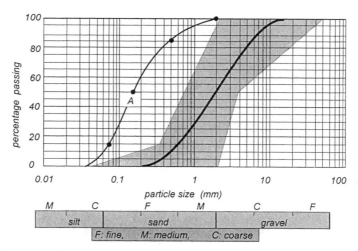

Figure 2.7: *Grain size distribution graphs for natural soil and filter material.*

2.5 Classification of fine-grained soils

Given the small size of its solid particles, a clay soil is characterised by a large *specific surface* (*i.e.* the surface area per volume of solid particles) and extremely small pores in comparison with sand. In fact, taking the sand pores as a reference, the clay pores in figure 2.6 (depicting the arrangement of perfectly spherical solid particles for identical volumes of sand and clay) are in reality at least twenty five times smaller than the ones shown in the figure. Accordingly, clays have a high *surface tension* which results in a high *capillary rise* as will be explained in details in chapter 3; most importantly, the velocity with which water can seep through the pores, known as *permeability* is much lower for clays than for sands. Furthermore, the behaviour of a clay can be markedly affected by the types of mineral that it contains and their reaction to porewater. Of the three main clay minerals introduced earlier, kaolinite is the most stable *vis à vis* water so that practically no volume change occurs if water content changes.

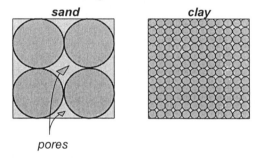

Figure 2.6: Theoretical arrangement of solid particles for sands and clays.

On the other hand, illite has a moderate reaction to water in that the changes in volume due to a variation in water content can result in modest swelling or shrinkage. However, montmorillonite is well known for its swelling and shrinkage properties so that a clay containing this mineral is bound to be subject to large volume changes in the event of water content variation. The water content of clay soils has therefore an effect on their mechanical behaviour, so much so that the empirical system of classification, based exclusively on the moisture content and known as the consistency limits is widely used to classify the type of fine-grained soil. Hence, the *liquid limit* w_L corresponds to the moisture content of the soil as it changes from a plastic state to a slurry type material. The *plastic limit* w_P on the other hand is the water content when the soil changes from plastic to friable state as per figure 2.7. In practice, both liquid and plastic limits can be determined using a cone penetrometer test. The apparatus sketched in figure 2.8, consists of a 35 *mm* long, 30° cone of stainless steel. The standard test corresponds to a cone and a sliding shaft with a combined mass of 80 grams. The actual test consists of lowering the cone so that it just touches the surface of the soil (contained in a 55 mm diameter, 40 mm deep cup), locking it in its support, then releasing it for a period of 5 s, and recording its depth of penetration. The procedure is repeated four to five times, using the same sample but increasing its moisture content each time. The (logarithm of) penetration is thereafter plotted against the moisture content, and the liquid limit w_L corresponds to the moisture content at a penetration of 20 mm as illustrated in figure 2.8.

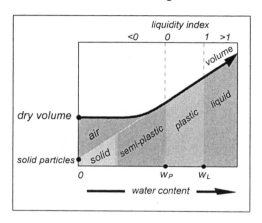

Figure 2.7: Consistency limits for fine-grained soils.

The plastic limit w_P on the other hand, can be determined from a second test using a 240 grams cone (i.e. a cone three times heavier than the standard one). The idea stems from Skempton's finding that the shear strength of a soil at the liquid limit is about 100 times smaller than that at the plastic limit. However, there is a strong experimental evidence showing that, for any of the two tests, the penetration under the liquid limit is about 3 times higher than that under the plastic limit. Hence the slope of the 80 g cone line in figure 2.8 :

$$\tan \alpha = \frac{w_L - w_P}{\log (20/d_o)} \approx \frac{w_L - w_P}{\log 3} \qquad (2.25a)$$

Equally, results measured from 10 different fine grained soils indicate that under identical moisture content, the ratio of penetration of two cones with masses $m_2 = 240\,g$ and $m_1 = 80\,g$ is proportional to the square root of the ratio m_2/m_1. Therefore the slope of the two parallel lines in figure 2.8 is:

$$\tan \alpha = \frac{\Delta w}{\log (20/d_1)} \approx \frac{\Delta w}{\log \sqrt{m_2/m_1}} = \frac{\Delta w}{\log \sqrt{3}} \qquad (2.25b)$$

Equating equations 2.25 (which are identical) and rearranging, it follows that:

$$w_p = w_L - \frac{\log 3}{\log \sqrt{3}} \Delta w = w_L - 2\Delta w \qquad (2.26)$$

Notice that these limits are measured using a sample of soil whose fabric has been totally destroyed.

These limits are most useful when applied in conjunction with the plasticity chart (due to *Casagrande*) represented in terms of variation of the liquid limit of the soil versus its *plasticity index* defined as:

$$I_P = w_L - w_p \qquad (2.27)$$

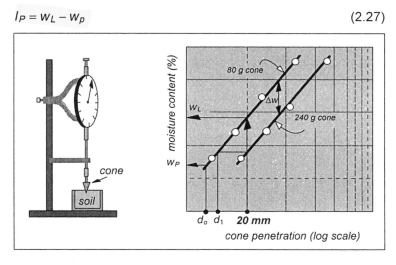

Figure 2.8: Cone penetration test.

The chart, shown in figure 2.9, provides a quick useful way of classification according to the moisture content of the soil and its plasticity index. The skewed line in the figure separates clays from silts so that, for instance, a soil with a liquid limit $w_L = 40\%$, a plastic limit $w_P = 20\%$ corresponds to a *clay of intermediate plasticity* (point B on the chart). Similarly, a soil with $w_L = 30\%$, $w_P = 4\%$ is a *silt of low plasticity* (point C on the chart). Highly plastic silts with liquid limits $w_L > 50\%$ are *organic soils* whose natural moisture content at a saturated state can be as high as 1000% (bog peat for instance) corresponding therefore to void ratios in excess of 10.

Another useful relationship between the natural *in situ* moisture content w of a soil and its plasticity index I_P is given by the *liquidity index* I_L:

$$I_L = \frac{w - w_P}{I_P} = \frac{w - w_P}{w_L - w_P} \qquad (2.28)$$

Equation 2.28, as well as figure 2.7 clearly imply that:
$$I_L < 0 \quad \Rightarrow \quad \text{soil is in a non-plastic state,}$$
$$0 \leq I_L \leq 1 \quad \Rightarrow \quad \text{soil is in a plastic state,}$$
$$I_L > 1 \quad \Rightarrow \quad \text{soil is in a liquid state.}$$

Finally, the *activity* of a soil, defined as:

$$A = \frac{I_P}{\% \, clay \, particles \, (< 2 \, \mu m)} \qquad (2.29)$$

reflects the *degree of plasticity* of the soil. Fine clay mineral particles with dimensions $< 2 \, \mu m$ carry a negative surface charge, which makes them interact with polar water molecules. As a result, clays are characterised by very slow seepage rates as will be explained in chapter 3. Also, because the liquid limit is proportional to the surface area, it follows that the greater the liquid limit, the higher the clay content, and the more compressible the soil. Typical A values for the three main clay minerals are as follows:
- kaolinite $A = 0.5$
- illite $0.5 \leq A \leq 1$
- montmorillonite $A > 1.25$.

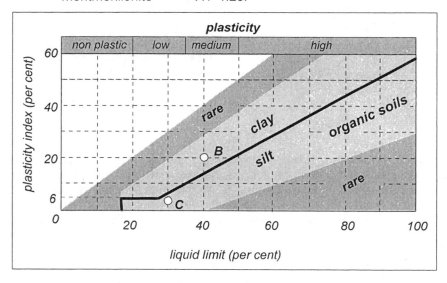

Figure 2.9: Empirical plasticity charts for soils.

From a mechanical point of view, undisturbed clays with low plasticity are characterised by small deformations when subjected to external loading. Once disturbed, a clay can potentially exhibit a marked decrease in its resistance or *shear strength,* depending on its structure. Microscopic studies of such soils, though not conclusive, tend to link the structure of natural clays to the way in which they were formed; thus a glacial till does not have the same structure as a lacustrine clay. Accordingly, once disturbed or *remoulded*, through excavation for instance, part of the natural structure will be destroyed. The effect that this structural dislocation has on the resistance of the clay can be measured by the *sensitivity*, defined as:

$$Sensitivity = \frac{strength\ of\ undisturbed\ soil}{strength\ of\ remoulded\ soil}$$

Hence, clays with a sensitivity larger than 16 are referred to as *quick clays*, and extra-sensitive clays are known to have a sensitivity in excess of 100. The structure in this case is liable to total collapse, leading to a transformation of the clay from a plastic material to a viscous liquid almost instantaneously. Quick clays can be activated by any type of shock such as vibration or earthquake activities, and are spread especially throughout Scandinavia and Canada. Bjerrum's (1954) empirical scale, illustrated in figure 2.10a can be used as a guide to clay sensitivity:

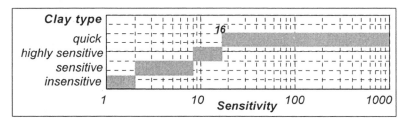

Figure 2.10a: Bjerrum's sensitivity scale

Bjerrum suggested that the sensitivity of the post-glacial Scandinavian clays (*i.e.* 10,000 to 15,000 years old clays) is related to the salt content of their pores. This suggestion is supported by the graph in figure 2.10b showing a dramatic increase in sensitivity when the salt content becomes smaller than 10 g/l. One has to bear in mind, however, that Bjerrum's suggestion is not universal; in fact Sangrey (1972)

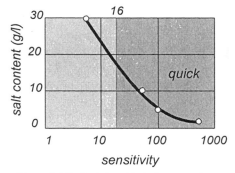

Figure 2.10b: Relationship between salt content and sensitivity for Norwegian post-glacial clays (Bjerrum, 1954, by permission of the ICE London)

reported that some of the highly sensitive post-glacial Canadian clays were deposited in fresh water.

2.6 Soil compaction

The process of compaction applies to *remoulded unsaturated soils*, and consists of increasing mechanically the *density* by reducing the volume of air contained within the soil matrix, without any significant change in the moisture content. This process is generally used in conjunction with fill materials behind retaining structures or during the construction of roads, embankments and earth dams. The increase in density, generated by a reduction in the void ratio, results in a substantial increase in *shear strength* of the soil and a marked decrease in its *compressibility* as well as *permeability*. The compaction is usually measured in terms of dry density ρ_d , whose value depends on the level of compacting energy, the soil type and its natural moisture content. Accordingly, the maximum dry density ρ_{dmax} that can be achieved for a given soil increases with increasing level of compacting energy. The maximum dry density is measured in the laboratory using compaction tests. The *standard* test is undertaken on a completely remoulded soil sample with a moisture content well below its natural value (often the sample is dried prior to testing). The test itself is conducted in stages, the first of which consists of mixing the dry soil sample with a small amount of water so that it becomes damp. An extended mould is then filled with moist soil in three equal layers, each one being compacted using 27 evenly distributed blows from a rammer weighing 2.5 *kg* and falling freely from a height of 305 *mm*. Once compaction is completed, the mould extension is then removed and the soil at the top of the mould is levelled off so that the remaining volume of compacted soil is precisely 1000 cm^3 (1 *litre*). The bulk density ρ of the soil is then calculated by weighing the known volume of the sample. A small quantity of soil is then taken randomly from within the mould and placed in an oven for drying so that the moisture content w can be calculated. Knowing ρ and w, the corresponding dry density ρ_d is thence determined from equation 2.14:

$$\rho_d = \rho/(1 + w)$$

The sample is next removed from the mould, mixed with the remainder of the original soil to which an increment of water is added to increase its moisture content. The compaction procedure is then repeated in precisely the same way as described previously. Usually five to six points are enough to yield a compaction graph such as the ones depicted in figure 2.11, corresponding to a clay with a specific gravity $G_s = 2.7$. The figure represents the variation of moisture content with the dry density at different energy levels:

- graph *EFG* corresponds to a standard compaction energy,
- graph *BCD* represents a higher compaction energy.

In both cases, the *maximum dry density* ρ_{dmax} is achieved at a water content known as the *optimum moisture content* w_{op}, and in the case of figure 2.11, it can be seen that:

- along *EFG* : $\rho_{dmax} \approx 1.72 \, Mg/m^3$, $w_{op} \approx 15.7\,\%$,
- along *BCD* : $\rho_{dmax} \approx 1.845 \, Mg/m^3$, $w_{op} \approx 13\,\%$,
  where $\rho_w = 1 \, Mg/m^3$.

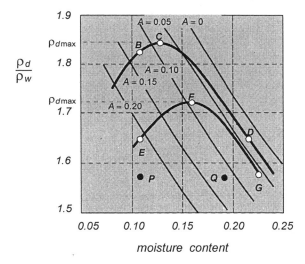

Figure 2.11: Effects of the energy of compaction
on the relative dry density of a soil.

Both graphs, which are similar in shape, indicate that initially the test yields a comparatively small dry density, because at a low moisture level the relatively dry soil tends to form in lumps that have to be crushed before any significant reduction in void ratio takes place. As the moisture content increases, so does the soil workability and energy efficiency, leading thus to a gradual decrease in void ratio and a steady increase in dry density until ρ_{dmax} is reached at the optimum moisture content w_{op}. Beyond the value w_{op}, the build-up of porewater pressure within the soil matrix starts in earnest, increasing in the process the void ratio, thus decreasing the dry density of the soil.   On the other hand, the maximum dry density equation can be expressed as follows:

$$\rho_{dmax} = \rho/(1 + w_{op}) \tag{2.30}$$

and so figure 2.11 together with equation 2.30 show clearly that the higher the compaction energy, the higher the maximum dry density, and the lower the optimum moisture content.

Example 2.7

The graphs in figure 2.11, corresponding to laboratory measurements, contain valuable information for a site engineer in charge of building an embankment, for instance, using the same material. Under such circumstances, the engineer has to make a decision as to what maximum dry density (and hence what compaction energy level) is required to minimise post-construction problems related to settlement and shear strength. If, for example, the material used corresponds to point *P* on the figure with a natural moisture content $w = 11\%$, the choice consists of either increasing the moisture content of the soil by about 5% and using a standard compaction energy to achieve a maximum dry density similar to that of the graph *EFG*, or increasing the moisture content by 3% and using a high compaction energy leading to a maximum dry density comparable to that of the curve *BCD*. If, on the other hand, the material used has a natural moisture content $w = 19\%$ (point *Q* on the figure), the decision is more straightforward since either level of compaction energy used on site would lead to similar values of $\rho_{d\max}$, the difference being marginal. The graphs corresponding to different air contents in the figure are calculated from equation 2.16:

$$\rho_d = \frac{G_s(1-A)}{1+wG_s}\rho_w$$

On the basis of these graphs, the air content relating to both points *C* and *F* where both optimum moisture contents occur can be estimated, then the corresponding degrees of saturation can be determined from equation 2.10:

$$S = \frac{1-A}{1+A/wG_s}$$

According to figure 2.11, point *C* with an optimum moisture content $w_{op} = 13\%$ corresponds to an air content $A \approx 8\%$. Similarly in the case of curve *EFG*, the air content corresponding to point *F* with an optimum moisture content $w = 15.7\%$ is $A \approx 9\%$. Therefore the degrees of saturation at *C* and at *F* are respectively:

$$S_C = \frac{1-A}{1+A/w_{op}G_s} = \frac{1-0.08}{1+\frac{0.08}{0.13\times2.7}} = 75\%$$

$$S_F = \frac{1-0.09}{1+\frac{0.09}{0.157\times2.7}} = 75\%$$

These simple calculations indicate that the optimum moisture content corresponds approximately to a constant degree of saturation, usually between 75% and 80%, regardless of the level of energy used for compaction.

2.7 Practical aspects of soil compaction

Because of the random shape of solid particles, it is not physically possible to remove all the air from within a volume of an *unsaturated soil*. In other words, it is not possible to achieve full saturation through compaction. Accordingly, the graph in figure 2.11 corresponding to $A = 0$ is just a theoretical limit. Moreover, experience shows that the *maximum dry density* achieved in ideal laboratory conditions is difficult to reproduce under field conditions and so, in practice, one rather aims at achieving a *minimum* dry density *in situ* through the use of the *relative compaction* defined as follows:

$$RC = \frac{\rho_{d(field)}}{\rho_{d\,max}} \times 100\% \tag{2.31}$$

where a value $RC = 95\%$ or thereabouts is deemed acceptable. (*Note that* $RC = 95\%$ *does not imply an air content* $A = 5\%$). Now consider what effect the notion of relative compaction has on the *in situ* compaction of soils. If the compacted fill were cohesive, then specifying a relative compaction of, say, 98% as is the case in figure 2.12 does not constitute the only criterion for compaction. The reason is depicted in the figure, in that an $RC = 98\%$ can be achieved at two different values of moisture content ($w_1 \approx 12\%$, $w_2 \approx 18.5\%$) on each side of the optimum value $w_{op} = 15.7\%$.

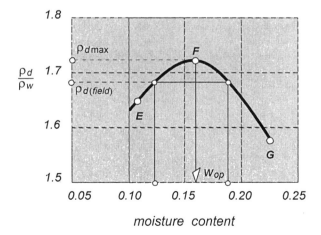

Figure 2.12: Effects of moisture content on the in situ dry density.

Consequently, the moisture content becomes a criterion for compaction and has to be specified together with the relative compaction. This effect is illustrated in figure 2.13*b* corresponding to the compaction of a layer of clay, whose natural moisture content is higher than its optimum moisture content. However, in the case of granular soils, ample experimental evidence indicates that the moisture content is not as important a criterion, and that the choice of the compaction equipment has more impact on the dry density to be achieved. On the practical side, the fill material is usually compacted in the field in layers about 0.2 *m* thick, using as many passes as needed to achieve the required density which must be checked randomly through *in situ* tests. Figure 2.13*a* shows that the compaction energy required to achieve a maximum dry density for a soil under the same moisture content increases proportionally to the increase of the thickness of the compacted layer. The type of equipment used for compaction depends on the nature of fill and the energy level required to achieve a given relative compaction. Considering that an average family car exerts an average pressure through its tyres of around $200\,kN/m^2$, it should come as no surprise that all compaction equipment used for road building generates pressures well in excess of this value. Thus, for example, a *smooth wheel roller* produces a contact pressure of $400\,kN/m^2$ and can be used in conjunction with all types of soils with the exception of boulder clays. When used on sands, the wheels may be vibrated to create the conditions whereby the solid particles are rearranged in an optimal way that minimises the voids, much in the way that fresh concrete is vibrated to increase its density. A *pneumatic roller* that has two or more rows of narrow tyres, whose position is alternated between consecutive rows, can generate pressures of up to $700\,kN/m^2$ and can be used to compact sand or clay fills. *Sheepsfoot rollers* on the other hand are only used for clays and can produce pressures ranging from $1.5\,MN/m^2$ to $7\,MN/m^2$.

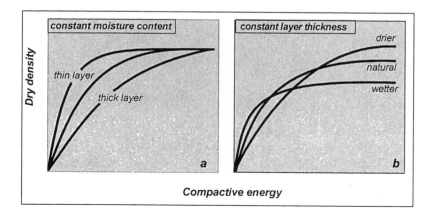

Figure 2.13 : Practical aspects of field compaction

Example 2.8

A road embankment is constructed of clay fill compacted to a bulk density $\rho = 2\,Mg/m^3$ at a water content $w = 20\%$. With an assumed specific gravity of the solid particles $G_s = 2.7$, the following quantities can be calculated:
- *the clay porosity:* it is seen that the use of equation 2.8 necessitates the knowledge of the void ratio, which, in turn, can be evaluated from equation 2.11:

$$e = G_s(1 + w)\frac{\rho_w}{\rho} - 1 = \frac{2.7 \times 1.2}{2} - 1 = 0.62$$

Therefore:

$$n = \frac{e}{1 + e} = \frac{0.62}{1.62} = 0.38$$

- *the degree of saturation:* using equation 2.7:

$$S = \frac{wG_s}{e} = \frac{0.2 \times 2.7}{0.62} = 87\%$$

- *the air content:* clearly, a combination of equations 2.7 and 2.9*b* yields:

$$A = n(1 - S) = 0.38 \times (1 - 0.87) = 4.9\%$$

- *the fill dry density:* either equations 2.12 or 2.14 yield $\rho_d = 1.67\,Mg/m^3$.

Example 2.9

A laboratory compaction test undertaken on a clay soil resulted in a maximum dry density $\rho_{dmax} = 1.65\,Mg/m^3$. The same soil, which is characterised by a specific gravity $G_s = 2.7$, was then used *in situ* to build a 7 m high embankment for a highway, where it was subjected to a relative compaction of $RC = 95\%$. Assuming that the (*in situ*) compacted clay has a bulk density $\rho_f = 1.8\,Mg/m^3$, then its optimum moisture content w_{op} can be estimated from equation 2.14:

$$\rho_f = \rho_{df}(1 + w_{op})$$

where the field dry density is calculated as follows:

$$\rho_{df} = 0.95\rho_{dmax} = 1.57\,Mg/m^3$$

Hence: $w_{op} = \dfrac{1.8 - 1.57}{1.57} = 14.6\%$

The air content of the embankment soil can be determined from equation 2.16:

$$\rho_{df} = \frac{G_s(1 - A)}{1 + w_{op}G_s}\rho_w \quad \Rightarrow \quad A = \frac{2.7 - 1.57 \times (1 + 0.146 \times 2.7)}{2.7} = 18.9\%$$

Now the void ratio and degree of saturation are found from equations 2.9*b* and 2.10 respectively:

$$e = \frac{A + w_{op}G_s}{1 - A} = \frac{0.189 + 0.146 \times 2.7}{1 - 0.189} \approx 0.72$$

$$S = \frac{1 - A}{1 + A/w_{op}G_s} = \frac{1 - 0.189}{1 + \frac{0.189}{0.146 \times 2.7}} = 55\%$$

2.8 Collapsible soils

Collapsible soils are naturally occurring materials, consisting predominantly of $20\mu m$ to $60\mu m$ silt and fine sand particles, loosely deposited through wind transport. In a dry state, such soils are characterised by a relatively high apparent strength, a low density, and a high porosity due to the large amount of voids between solid particles. Upon wetting however, the soil structure can potentially undergo a collapse mechanism known as *hydro-collapse*, inducing large deformations. The extent of collapse is linked to the degree of wetting, the depth of loose deposit, and the magnitude of overburden pressure. Collapsible soils deposits are widely spread across the world.

Loess, also known as yellow soil, is a typical example found in some parts of Asia, such as north-eastern Thailand, where top soils consist often of loose deposits of sandstone and siltstone fine sediments, exhibiting the characteristics of collapsible soils. Typically, loess is predominantly made of quartz, with some feldspar, bonded in a metastable open structure by clay and carbonate particles. In a dry state, loess is characterised by a low dry density, while exhibiting high shear strength. Once saturated, the bonding between solid particles degenerates, causing the open structure to collapse. The hydro-collapse as it is known, results in a denser rearrangement of solid particles, at the expense of large, sudden, and potentially dangerous settlement deformation as illustrated typically in figure 2.14. The sudden increase in moisture content (*i.e.* wetting) of such soils can be typically engendered by water retention structures such as reservoirs, or poor surface drainage. Although the hydro-collapse mechanism is complex in nature, it is somewhat similar to the structural collapse of frozen soils upon *adfreeze* disintegration. Adfreeze represents the strong ice bonds between solid particles generated by the freezing of the porewater within a soil matrix. A warming up of the soil from say $-2°C$ to $-1°C$ can potentially halve the soil shear strength and upon complete thaw, the soil structure can undergo large settlements, similar to the behaviour exhibited by loess once wetting occurs. The collapse potential refers to the magnitude of deformation ε_1 generated upon wetting of the soil as indicated in figure 2.14. This potential is typically summarised in the following table 2.4:

Table 2.4: Hydro-collapse potential magnitude

collapse potential (%)	1 - 3	3 - 5	> 5
Severity	low	moderate	high

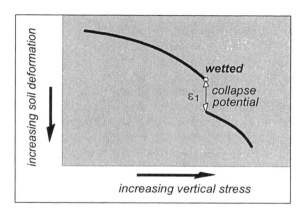

Figure 2.14: Hydro-collapse potential

The behaviour of a collapsible soil is difficult to analyse, let alone predict. The main problems arise from the disturbance affecting the soil matrix during sampling, the degree of wetting, and the magnitude of loading. None the less, the collapse process leads to a marked increase in the soil dry density as illustrated ideally in figure 2.15a. The sharp increase is due to the rearrangement of solid particles, which has an effect of natural compaction as it were. Figure 2.15b on the other hand illustrates a typical delimitation of the area within which a soil structure is liable to collapse.

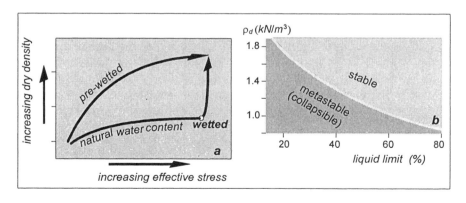

Figure 2.15: Typical relationships between dry density, stress level and liquid limit.

The effects of soil collapse can be prevented or limited using various engineering solutions, depending on *in situ* conditions. These solutions include causing the soil to collapse, so as to increase its density, prior to founding any structure. Alternatively, collapsible soils can be compacted *in situ* using a wide range of techniques presented in the following section.

2.9 Methods of deep compaction

The use of surface rollers for field compaction is essentially suitable for fill material placed in layers of controlled thickness. However, the effect of this type of equipment on an existing layer of soil is usually confined to a few metres below the surface, at best. Thus, in order to densify natural deep deposits of granular soils or soft clays, other techniques are used. These techniques rely on more sophisticated equipment, and are therefore more versatile, in that they can be used on sites of varied complexities, and can increase soil compaction at a deeper level. They include:

- *Dynamic compaction*

The method consists basically of dropping repeatedly a heavy weight of several tonnes from varying heights onto the soil. This results in compacting the soil throughout the impact area as well as in its vicinity. Experimental evidence indicates that such a technique can improve the compaction of loose granular materials up to a depth of 10 m below the ground surface.

- *Vibro-floatation*

The technique uses a *vibrofloat* (a large probe) made of a cylindrical tube with water jets, housing eccentrically rotating weights to produce horizontal vibratory motion. The probe is (usually) 400 mm in diameter, 2 m in length, weighing about 2 tonnes. The vibrofloat is allowed to penetrate the soil under its own weight, and on reaching the desired depth, water flow is reduced, and the vibrofloat is withdrawn in small lifts while feeding sand or gravel into the hole formed at the surface. The compacted zone around the probe can extend to a radius of up to 3m, and this technique is particularly effective in loose sands or granular fills.

- *Vibro-placement*

Corresponds to the same technique and procedure of vibro-floatation without water. This technique is used exclusively in conjunction with soft clays and inorganic fills. Charges of well graded gravel of granular size between 100 mm and 80 mm are added while withdrawing the probe, creating *stone columns*. The vibrofloat is repeatedly withdrawn and reinserted to ensure a uniform density. With each charge of gravel, the vibrofloat displaces the backfill horizontally into the existing soil, while at the same time compacting underneath its bottom edge. Repetition of the procedure produces an irregular cylindrical gravel column, with a diameter ranging from 0.6 *m* to 1 *m*, depending on the strength of the existing soil. Stone columns are usually installed in a square or a triangular grid pattern, with a centre-to-centre spacing of between 1 *m* and 3 *m*.

- *Grouting techniques*

Though all grouting techniques are based on the same principle of injecting a grout into the native soil, so as to improve its physical properties (such as strength and permeability), there are several variations on this theme. Thus, *chemical grouting* is a technique used essentially to control seepage, and hence increase the soil strength. This technique consists of injecting a chemical solution (usually sodium or acrylic solutions) into the pre-existing fine fissures within the soil mass through a *tube à manchettes* by inducing a hydrofracture (also known as *claquage*). The cost effectiveness and efficiency of the *tube à manchettes* tube system makes it one of the most widely used grouting techniques for foundations and underground excavations. The method consists of a PVC or a steel pipe with small holes perforated around the circumference at regular intervals along its length. Each set of holes is covered by a rubber sleeve or a *manchette* as illustrated in figure 2.16, so that when a grout is injected under pressure, the manchette expands allowing the grout to flow out of the pipe.

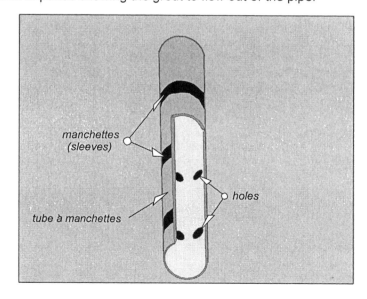

Figure 2.16: Tube à manchettes.

Once grout injection is complete, the *manchette* collapses onto the pipe, thus preventing any flow into the pipe, making the holes act as one way valves in the process. The grouting process *per se* consists of the following three steps:

- insertion of the *tube à manchettes* into a pre-drilled borehole of a larger diameter,
- use of a light sleeve grout so as to seal the *tube à manchettes* into the borehole, thus preventing any high pressure grout from flowing up the tube/borehole interface,
- proceeding from the bottom of the borehole up, each set of holes is isolated by two inflatable packers which are operated from within the *tube à manchettes* pipe and inflated so that they straddle the set of holes. The *manchette* around the isolated holes is then expanded by pumping water under pressure through the holes, causing thus a *claquage* (hydrofracture) in the soil around the sleeve. Grout is then injected under the maximum design pressure (or volume) to fill the fissures created within the soil matrix in the vicinity of the manchette.

The process is repeated by moving the packers upward and isolating the next set of holes.

Compaction grouting on the other hand is based on the same principle, in that a low viscosity silicate-based grout (circa 20% bentonite/cement grout) is injected into the native soil under controlled pressure (just above the overburden pressure) using the same technique. The grout consistency is such that it causes the native soil to compress, thus increasing its density. This technique is particularly effective when used on loose granular soils or soft clays. When this technique is used with the specific aim to, either counteract the effects of active settlements, or to compensate for the deformation of the native soil due to past settlements, it becomes known as *compensation grouting*. Finally, *jet grouting* is one of the most successful techniques, developed in Italy in the 1970s, particularly effective for seepage control, underpinning, and in situ foundation construction. This technique consists of mixing *in situ* native soil with a cement grout jetted radially under high pressure (between 30 *MPa* and 60 *MPa*; that is 300 to 600 bars). The jet may consist of a single fluid (cement grout), a double fluid (cement grout and air), or a triple fluid (cement grout, air and water). The air pressure used in conjunction with double and triple jets is usually between 700 *kPa* and 1.2 *MPa*. The high pressure enables the grout to mix with the destroyed native soil fabric, resulting in the formation of a homogeneous structural element as illustrated in figure 2.17. The size, shape and composition of the formed column depends on the rotation and lifting rates of the jet rod. Jet grouting can be applied to different soil types ranging from poorly graded granular soils to plastic clays.

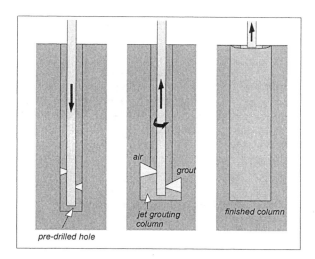

Figure 2.17: Double fluid jet grouting technique

• *soil mixing*

In some special cases of sites with restricted access, a simple technique of soil mixing can be very effective. This technique is suitable for soils with very poor engineering properties, and consists of stabilising the soil by using a double auger to break up the soil before adding a special binder (such as dry lime) and re-compacting to form a column. This is particularly effective for the stabilisation of slopes and embankments.

Problems

2.1 A thick layer of clay has an average void ratio $e = 0.75$ and a specific gravity $G_s = 2.7$, the water level being 2 *m* below the ground surface.

(a) Calculate the water content of the (saturated) clay below the water level.
(b) If the clay above the water table has an air content $A = 0.04$, determine its water content and degree of saturation.
(c) Calculate both bulk and saturated unit weights of the clay.

Ans: (a) $w = 28\%$, (b) $w = 25.2\%$, $S = 90.6\%$, (c) $\gamma = 18.9\,kN/m^3$, (d) $\gamma_{sat} = 19.3\,kN/m^3$.

2.2 Calculate the ratio γ_{sat}/γ between saturated and bulk unit weights of a clay having a void ratio $e = 1.0$, a water content $w = 25\%$, and a specific gravity $G_s = 2.7$.

Ans: $\gamma_{sat}/\gamma = 1.1$.

2.3   A cylindrical soil sample with a diameter of 100 *mm* and a height of 100 *mm* was extracted from within a thick layer of a stiff clay. The sample has a weight of 1320 *g*, and after being thoroughly dried, its weight has reduced to 1075 *g*.
Assuming the clay has a specific gravity $G_s = 2.7$, determine its:
(*a*) water content,
(*b*) void ratio,
(*c*) degree of saturation,
(*d*) air content,
(*e*) bulk and dry densities.

Ans: (*a*) $w = 22.8\%$,   (*b*) $e = 0.97$,   (*c*) $S = 63.3\%$,   (*d*) $A = 18\%$,
(*e*) $\rho = 1.68\,Mg/m^3$, $\rho_d = 1.37\,Mg/m^3$.

2.4   Refer to the graph in figure *p*2.4 obtained in the laboratory from a test on a soil in which a well is being dug.
(*a*) Determine the coefficients of curvature and grading.
(*b*) Give an estimate of the soil permeability.
(*c*) Using the criteria given in section 2.4, design a soil filter to be placed around the well lining whose maximum mesh size is 2 *mm*.

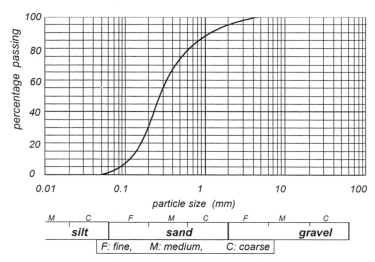

Figure p2.4

Ans: (*a*) $C_u \approx 3$, $C_g \approx 1.2$, (*b*) $k \approx 1.1 \times 10^{-4}\,m/s$.

2.5   A soil with 23% of clay content has an activity $A = 0.72$ and a
plastic limit $w_p = 16\%$.
(a) Calculate its liquid limit, then use the plasticity chart in
section 2.5 to classify the soil.
(b) In its natural state, the soil is characterised by a liquidity index
$I_L = 0.75$. Determine its natural moisture content.

Ans: (a) $w_L = 32.5\%$, $I_P = 16.6\%$, $\Rightarrow$ clay of low plasticity.
(b) $w = 28.4\%$.

2.6   A compaction test undertaken on a sample of clay with a specific
gravity $G_s = 2.7$ yielded an air content $A = 3\%$ and a maximum
dry density $\rho_{dmax} = 1.65\,Mg/m^3$. Calculate the corresponding
optimum moisture content.

Ans: $w_{op} \approx 22\%$.

2.7   A laboratory compaction test undertaken on clay yielded the
following results:

Moisture content (%)	11	13	16	21
Bulk density (Mg/m^3)	17.75	18.92	19.84	19.48

(a) Plot the variation of the dry density with the moisture content,
then determine the maximum dry density and the optimum
moisture content.
The same clay was then used for the construction of an
embankment, where it was subjected to a relative compaction
$RC = 95\%$ at the optimum moisture content.
(b) Calculate the bulk density of the compacted fill.
(c) Assuming the clay fill has a specific gravity $G_s = 2.7$,
determine its air content, degree of saturation and porosity.

Ans: (a) $\rho_{dmax} = 1.71\,Mg/m^3$, $w_{op} = 16\%$.   (b) $\rho = 1.88\,Mg/m^3$,
(c) $A \approx 13.8\%$, $S = 65.2\%$, $n \approx 0.40$.

References

Agrawal, Y. C. and Riley, J. B. (1984) *Optical Particle Sizing for Hydrodynamic
Based on Near-forward Scattering.* Society of Photo-Optical
Instrumentation Engineers (489), pp. 68–76.
Bell, F. G. (1993) *Engineering Geology.* Blackwell Science, London.
Bjerrum, L. (1954) *Geotechnical properties of Norwegian marine clays.*
Géotechnique, Vol. 4 (2), pp. 49–69.
Friedman, G.M. and Saunders, J.E. (1978). *Principles of Sedimentology.*
Wiley, New York
Folk, R.L. and Ward, W.C. (1957). *Brazos river bar: a study in the significance*

of grain size parameters. Journal of Sedimentary Petrology. **27**pp. 3-26
Hong Kong Geotechnical Engineering Office. (1993) *Review of Granular and Geotextile Filters.*
Lamb, S. and Sington, D. (1998) *Earth story: the shaping of our world.* BBc Book, London.
MacCave, I. N. and Syvitski, J. P. M. (1991) *Principles and Methods of Particle Size Analysis.* Cambridge University Press.
Sangrey, D. A. (1972) *Naturally cemented sensitive soils.* Géotechnique, 22, pp. 139–152.
Simon, J. B. and Kenneth, P. (2001). *GRADISTAT: A grain size distribution and statistics package for the analysis of unconolidated sediments.* Earth Surface Processes and Landforms, 26. pp. 1237-1248
Somerville, S. H. (1986) *Control of Groundwater for Temporary Works.* CIRIA Report 113, Construction Industry Research and Information Association, London.
Stanley, S. M. (1999) *Earth system history.* W. H. Freeman & company, New York.
Waltham, A.C. (1994) *Foundations of Engineering Geology.* Chapman & Hall, London.
Weiner, B. B. (1979) *Particle and Spray Sizing Using Laser Diffraction.* Society of Photo-Optical Instrumentation Engineers (170), pp. 53–56.
Weiner, B. B. (1984) *Particle Sizing Using Photon Correlation Spectroscopy.* Modern Methods of Particle Size Analysis, Edited by H.G. Barth, Wiley, New York, pp. 93–116.

CHAPTER 3

Stress distribution within a soil mass

3.1 Effective stress principle

Consider the case of figure 3.1 where a *fully saturated* soil (*i.e.* all voids are filled with water) is subjected at its surface to a given load (which can be of any type). Thus, under *static water conditions*, the overall *total weight W* of a selected volume *V* of soil, generates a *total stress* $\sigma = W/A$, where *A* represents the cross-sectional area. The weight *W* is in fact the sum of a component due to the solid particles and one due to water:

$$W = W_s + W_w$$
$$= g(\rho_s V_s + \rho_w V_w) \tag{3.1}$$

where g is the acceleration due to gravity, ρ_s is the density of solid particles, ρ_w that of water, and V_s, V_w are the volumes of solids and water respectively.

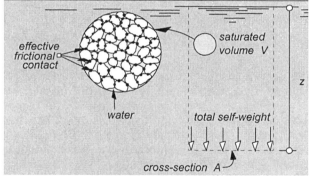

Figure 3.1: Pressure due to a loaded volume of saturated soil.

Since the total volume is $V = V_s + V_w = A z$, it is easy to derive the expression of the total stress:

$$\sigma = \frac{V_s}{A} g(\rho_s - \rho_w) + \frac{V}{A} g \rho_w \tag{3.2}$$

A combination of equations 2.6 & 2.13 established earlier in section 2.1 yields the following:

$$(\rho_s - \rho_w) = (\rho_{sat} - \rho_w)(1 + e) \tag{3.3}$$

where ρ_{sat} represents the density of the saturated soil, as opposed to ρ_s which is the density of solid particles. Thus, substituting for $(\rho_s - \rho_w)$ from equation 3.3 into equation 3.2:

$$\sigma = \frac{V_s(1+e)}{A}g(\rho_{sat} - \rho_w) + \frac{V}{A}g\rho_w \qquad (3.4)$$

Referring once more to equation 2.3 in section 2.1, the total volume can be expressed in terms of the volume of solid particles as follows:

$$V = V_s(1+e) \qquad (3.5)$$

Knowing that $V/A = z$, $g\rho_w = \gamma_w$ (unit weight of water), $\gamma_{sat} = g\rho_{sat}$ (saturated unit weight of soil), equation 3.4 then reduces to:

$$\sigma = z(\gamma_{sat} - \gamma_w) + z\gamma_w \qquad (3.6)$$

Equation 3.6, known as *the effective stress principle,* was established by Karl Terzaghi (1936) and constitutes one of the most fundamental relationships that governs soil behaviour, the effect of which will become clearer in the following chapters. Because the quantity $z\gamma_w = u$ represents the pressure exerted by a column of water of a height z, equation 3.3 is usually written as follows:

$$\sigma = \sigma' + u \qquad (3.7)$$

where u is referred to as the *porewater pressure* and σ' represents the *effective stress.* Accordingly, the effective stress principle stipulates that the total stress existing at a depth z is the sum of the component of normal stress applied to the soil skeleton through contact between solid particles, and a porewater pressure induced in the water filling the voids. Since water cannot sustain any shear stress, both volume changes and shear strength of the soil are controlled by the effective stress. The *actual* effective stress corresponds to the *average* normal stress generated through contact between solid particles on a given plane within the soil mass (see Mitchell (1993), for instance). However, experimental evidence indicates that equation 3.6 is highly reliable, provided that the solid particles are relatively incompressible and the overall intergranular contact area is small compared with the cross-sectional area of the corresponding volume of soil. Both requirements are fulfilled for most saturated soils.

3.2 Stresses due to self weight

As has already been established in the previous chapter, in the absence of any external loading, the stresses generated within a soil mass can be calculated using the soil unit weight γ, whose value can be estimated using any of the three equations 2.17 to 2.19, depending on the soil's degree of saturation.

Under *static water conditions*, the overall *total stresses* due to self weight, for a *fully saturated* soil, are calculated at any depth z as follows (see figure 3.2):

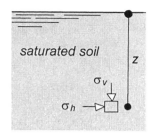

Figure 3.2: Total stress due to self weight.

$$\sigma_v = \gamma_{sat}\, z \qquad\qquad (3.8a)$$

$$\sigma_h = K_o\, \sigma_v \qquad\qquad (3.8b)$$

where σ_v and σ_h are the vertical and horizontal stresses respectively, K_o, known as the coefficient of earth pressure at rest, is a constant that reflects the mode of soil deposition and its stress history, and will be discussed thoroughly in section 10.2, and γ_{sat} is the saturated unit weight of soil. Because of the linear nature of equation 2.8b, the following derivations will deal exclusively with the vertical stress component σ_v, for which the corresponding effective stress is found by using the general equation 3.7:

$$\sigma_v' = \sigma_v - u \qquad\qquad (3.9)$$

Accordingly, the *effective vertical stress* due to the self weight of soil at a given depth depends on the porewater pressure, in other words on the level of the groundwater. Consider the general case of figure 3.3 depicting a homogeneous soil with the groundwater at a depth z_w below the ground surface. Below water, the fully saturated soil has a *saturated unit weight* γ_{sat} that can be calculated from equation 2.18; however, above the water level depicted in the figure, a *bulk unit weight* $\gamma < \gamma_{sat}$ applies since the soil is only partially saturated.

The presence of moisture above the water level is due to *capillary rise* (much in the way water rises against gravity from the root of a tree to the branches which can be as high as 30 m or more), which in turn depends on the size of voids between solid particles, and therefore on the type of soil.

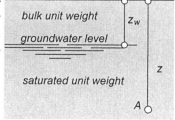

Figure 3.3: Effect of water on the unit weight of soils.

The voids between solid particles within a soil matrix are interconnected, thus forming a complex network of channels that can be thought of as capillary tubes. According to (the enlarged) figure 3.4, the capillary rise h_c of water inside a channel is proportional to the ratio of the *surface tension force T* to the "effective" channel diameter d. Hence, at equilibrium, the following equation applies:

$$T\pi d = \frac{\pi d^2}{4} u_w \qquad\qquad (3.10)$$

where $u_w = h_c \gamma_w$ is the *water suction* (*i.e.* the negative water pressure), and T represents the surface tension of the water/air interface ($T = 0.073\,N/m$ at $10°C$). Hence, substituting for u_w into equation 3.10, then rearranging:

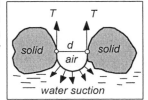

$$h_c = \frac{4T}{d\gamma_w} \qquad\qquad (3.11)$$

Figure 3.4: Surface tension and water suction within a soil matrix.

Equation 3.11 indicates that, in theory, a clay having an average voids size of, say, $d = 10^{-6}\,m$ will have a capillary rise of just under 30 m. In practice however, the nature of the connection of voids within a soil matrix has a limiting effect on the theoretical value of h_c calculated using the above equation. Terzaghi and Peck (1967) suggested relating the capillary rise within a soil to its effective size d_{10} (mm) [refer to section 2.2] and void ratio e as follows:

$$h_c \approx \frac{C}{e\,d_{10}} \qquad\qquad (3.12)$$

C having a value between 10 mm^2 and 50 mm^2.
While equation 3.12 yields a maximum capillary rise h_c, the actual level of capillary saturation h_s can be estimated from the relationship:

$$h_s \approx h_c \frac{d_{10}}{d_{60}} \qquad\qquad (3.13)$$

d_{60} being the particle size as defined in section 2.2.

Example 3.1

Consider the case of the two following soils:
   (a) a clay with the parameters: $e = 1.0$, $d_{10} = 0.7\,\mu m$, $d_{60} = 3\,\mu m$,
   (b) a sand having : $e = 0.8$, $d_{10} = 0.2\,mm$, $d_{60} = 0.7\,mm$.

Assuming that both soils are characterised by the same parameter $C = 10 \, mm^2$, then equations 3.12 and 3.13 yield:

- *for the clay:*

$$h_c = \frac{10^{-5}}{1 \times 7 \times 10^{-7}} = 14.28 \, m \quad \Rightarrow \quad h_s = 14.28 \times \frac{0.7}{3} = 3.33 \, m$$

- *for the sand:*

$$h_c = \frac{10^{-5}}{0.8 \times 2 \times 10^{-4}} = 62.5 \times 10^{-3} \, m \quad \Rightarrow \quad h_s = 62.5 \times \frac{0.2}{0.7} = 17.9 \times 10^{-3} \, m$$

The corresponding water suction (*i.e.* the *negative* porewater pressure) in each case is:

$u = h_c \gamma_w = -14.28 \times 10 = -142.8 \, kN/m^2$ for the clay, as opposed to $u = -0.62 \, kN/m^2$ for sand.

This simple example shows that cohesive soils such as silts and clays are characterised by capillary saturation levels that are much higher than those corresponding to granular soils.

A *partially saturated soil* occurs naturally above the groundwater level which, in a temperate climate, does not extend to any great depth. Thus, with reference to figure 3.5, the suction generated above the groundwater level can be ignored, and a unique *bulk unit weight γ* (equation 2.17) can be assumed to apply from the ground surface down to the static water level situated at a depth z_w.

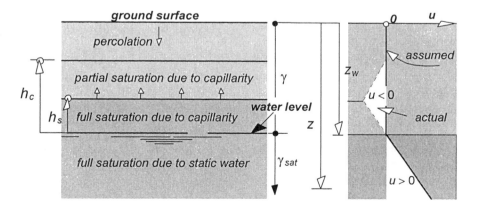

Figure 3.5: Assumption related to the use of bulk unit weight.

Therefore, the *total vertical stress* at any given depth z, as depicted in figure 3.5, is calculated in the following way:

$$\sigma_v = \gamma\, z_w + \gamma_{sat}(z - z_w) \tag{3.14}$$

the porewater pressure at the same point being:

$$u = \gamma_w(z - z_w) \tag{3.15}$$

so that the *effective vertical stress* is:

$$\begin{aligned}\sigma'_v &= \sigma_v - u \\ &= \gamma\, z_w + (z - z_w)(\gamma_{sat} - \gamma_w)\end{aligned} \tag{3.16}$$

Equations 3.14 to 3.16 imply that for a dry soil, $z_w = z$ and both *effective* and *total vertical stresses* are identical since the porewater pressure u is reduced to zero. On the other hand, when the soil is fully saturated, then $z_w = 0$ and equation 3.16 reduces to equation 3.9. These conclusions are further illustrated in figure 3.6. In practice, the difference between saturated and bulk unit weights is typically of the order of 1 to $2\, kN/m^3$; also, the unit weight of water can be taken as $\gamma_w \approx 10\, kN/m^3$.

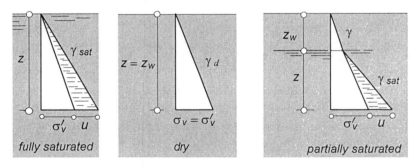

Figure 3.6 : Effects of groundwater on the stress due to self weight of a soil.

Example 3.2

A thick clay layer has a bulk unit weight $\gamma = 19\, kN/m^3$ and a saturated unit weight $\gamma = 19.5\, kN/m^3$; the unit weight of water being $\gamma_w \approx 10\, kN/m^3$. Knowing that the groundwater level is at a depth of 4 m below the surface, then the depth z_1 at which the *vertical effective stress* has a value $\sigma'_{z1} = 120\, kN/m^2$ is such that:

$$120 = 4 \times 19 + (z_1 - 4)(19.5 - 10) \quad \Rightarrow \quad z_1 = \frac{120 - 76}{9.5} + 4 = 8.63\, m$$

After the exceptional occurrence of two wet seasons, the groundwater has risen to a new level, so that its depth has dramatically reduced from the original 4 m to z_w as depicted in figure 3.7. Assuming this rise in the water level caused the effective stress (estimated at the same depth z_1 calculated above), to decrease to $\sigma'_{z1} = 90\,kN/m^2$, then the corresponding depth z_w is:

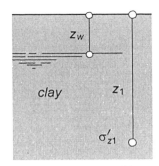

Figure 3.7: Soil conditions.

$$90 = z_w \times 19 + (8.63 - z_w)(19.5 - 10) \quad \Rightarrow \quad z_w = \frac{90 - 82}{9.5} = 0.83\,m$$

The variation with depth (up to $z_1 = 8.63\,m$) of the effective vertical stress σ'_v, the porewater pressure u and the total stress $\sigma = \sigma'_v + u$ is depicted in figure 3.8. Originally, when the groundwater level was 4 m deep, σ'_v increased linearly from $\sigma'_{v1} = 19 \times 4 = 76\,kN/m^2$ at 4 m depth, to:

$$\sigma'_{v2} = 76 + (8.63 - 4)(19.5 - 10) = 120\,kN/m^2 \quad \text{at 8.63 } m \text{ depth}$$

The porewater pressure on the other hand varied between $u_1 = 0$ at 4 m, to: $u_2 = (8.63 - 4) \times 10 = 46.3\,kN/m^2$ at 8.63 m depth.

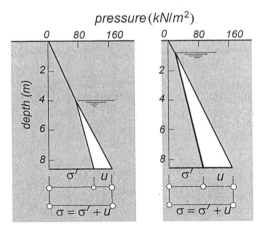

Figure 3.8: Pressure distribution with depth.

After the depth of the groundwater level has reduced to 0.83 m, the variation of the effective stress then reduced from:

$\sigma'_v = 0.83 \times 19 = 15.8\,kN/m^2$ at 0.83 m,

to: $\sigma'_v = 15.8 + (8.63 - 0.83)(19.5 - 10) = 89.9\,kN/m^2$

while the porewater pressure increased from:

$u = 0$ at 0.83 m, to $u = (8.63 - 0.83) \times 10 = 78\,kN/m^2$ at 8.63 m

In this case, while the rise of the groundwater level has caused the porewater pressure to increase and the effective stress to decrease, the total stress (at any depth) remained virtually constant. For instance, at the depth 8.63 m, it is seen that:
- groundwater level 4 m deep: $\sigma = \sigma'_v + u = 120 + 46.3 = 166.3\,kN/m^2$,

- groundwater level 0.83 m deep: $\sigma = \sigma'_v + u = 89.9 + 78 = 167.9\,kN/m^2$.

The marginal difference reflects the difference between bulk and saturated unit weights of the soil. This result however, is very significant in that, as stated earlier, the *shear strength* of the soil is controlled by the *effective stress*. Accordingly, any increase in the porewater pressure will induce a decrease in the effective stress and therefore a decrease in the soil strength.

Example 3.3

Following a prolonged period of heavy rain, a saturated thick layer of clay was subjected to flood water as depicted in figure 3.9a. At its peak, the water level above the ground surface reached 1 m, and the corresponding pressure diagram shown in the figure indicates clearly that the water above the ground causes a uniform increase of the porewater pressure with depth. The stresses can be evaluated at any depth in a straightforward manner. For example at a depth of 4 m, assuming a saturated unit weight of the clay $\gamma_{sat} = 20\,kN/m^3$ and a unit weight of water $\gamma_w = 10\,kN/m^3$, it follows that:

- *the porewater pressure:* $u = 5 \times 10 = 50\,kN/m^2$,
- *the total stress:* $\sigma = 1 \times 10 + 4 \times 20 = 90\,kN/m^2$,
- *the effective stress:* $\sigma' = \sigma - u = 40\,kN/m^2$.

Once the flood water is drained away leaving a fully saturated clay layer, the pressure diagram remains remarkably similar to that of figure 3.9a except for the porewater pressure due to the water above the ground which will then disappear as depicted in figure 3.9b. This means that the effective stress remains constant because the drainage of flood water decreases both the total stress and the porewater pressure in the same proportion, leaving unchanged the effective stress in the process.

Accordingly at a depth of 4 *m*, it is seen from figure 3.9*b* that:
- *the porewater pressure:* $u = 4 \times 10 = 40 \, kN/m^2$,
- *the total stress:* $\sigma = 4 \times 20 = 80 \, kN/m^2$,
- *the effective stress:* $\sigma' = \sigma - u = 40 \, kN/m^2$.

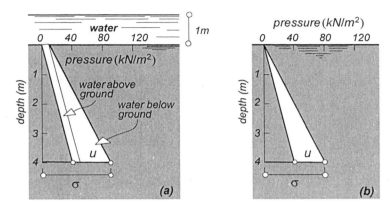

Figure 3.9: Pressure diagrams:(a) at the peak of the flood,
(b) after drainage of flood water

3.3 Effective stresses related to unsaturated soils

There are instances in which the void space within a soil matrix is in part filled with air or any other gas, the remaining volume of voids being filled with water. Such an *unsaturated soil* occurs naturally in a hot arid climate where the groundwater level can be situated at a great depth. Also, soils used for the construction of embankments and earth dams are usually compacted and, as such, are unsaturated. A third group is composed of marine deposits within which the decomposition of organic sediments leads to the formation of bubbles of methane gas. Naturally, the behaviour of such soils depends on the proportion of air or gas contained within the voids, in other words on the degree of saturation. In most cases of interest in civil engineering practice, unsaturated cohesive soils have an intermediate degree of saturation (*i.e.* $S < 0.85$). Figure 3.10 depicts the surface tension force T generated at the water/gas interface at a typical voids channel between two solid particles of an unsaturated soil. The relationship between the pore water pressure u_w, the pore gas pressure u_g and T is as follows:

$$(u_g - u_w)\frac{\pi d^2}{4} = T\pi d$$

or

$$(u_g - u_w) = \frac{4T}{d} \tag{3.17}$$

Conclusive evidence (see Jennings and Burland (1962), for example) indicates that the behaviour of such unsaturated cohesive soils (*i.e.* with a degree of saturation $S < 85\%$), *cannot* be represented by a single effective stress variable as in the equation suggested by Bishop and Donald (1961), which is still being (unjustifiably?) advocated in some quarters for this particular type of soil.

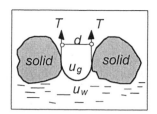

Figure 3.10: Surface tension for an unsaturated soil.

Rather, the shear strength and the void ratio are related to two stress variables, namely:
- the effective stress : $\sigma' = \sigma - u_g$,
- the soil matrix suction as per equation 3.17: $(u_g - u_w)$.

The variation of the void ratio **e** with these two stress variables yields a warped surface as depicted in figure 3.11, which is only used for illustration purposes. Clearly, as the suction $(u_g - u_w)$ decreases (in other words as the degree of saturation increases), the soil behaves differently depending on the magnitude of the net stress $(\sigma - u_g)$. A soil (volume) expansion occurs under low values of $(\sigma - u_g)$ (stress path *CD* in figure 3.11), as opposed to a contraction under high $(\sigma - u_g)$ values (stress path *AB*).

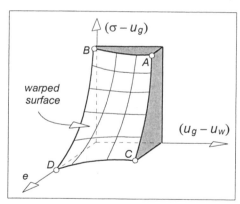

Figure 3.11: Stress–void ratio relationship for unsaturated cohesive soils (S<0.85).

The shear strength of such soils is also related to the two stress variables used in figure 3.11, and reference should be made to the paper by Fredlund (1979) in which appropriate expressions relating the void ratio and the shear strength to the above two stress variables are discussed. For unsaturated cohesive soils with a degree of saturation limited to

$0.85 \leq S \leq 1$, the presence of gas leads to the formation of gas bubbles. If the size of these bubbles is smaller than the void space between solid particles as depicted in figure 3.12, then the behaviour can be described by the Bishop and Donald (1961) equation :

$$\sigma' = (\sigma - u_g) + \chi\,(u_g - u_w) \qquad\qquad (3.18)$$

where χ represents a constant ($0 \leq \chi \leq 1$) that depends on the degree of saturation, u_g and u_w being as defined previously. Because of the presence of gas bubbles, the porewater becomes compressible, so that a positive porewater pressure will cause the bubbles to dissolve, decreasing in the meantime the volume of water. A negative porewater pressure on the other hand will lead to the expansion of the gas bubbles and an increase in the volume of water. Accordingly, depending on the soil stress history and the level of loading applied at its surface, a positive porewater pressure will generate almost immediately a decrease in the volume of water and an increase in the intergranular stresses, and therefore an increase (in the short term) of the soil strength. A negative porewater pressure, on the other hand, will engender an immediate expansion of the volume of voids, thus causing a decrease in the effective stresses and hence a decrease in the soil strength in the short term. With time, as the excess porewater pressure (of whatever sign) dissipates, the magnitude of the soil strength will become similar to that of an equivalent saturated soil. This type of unsaturated soil containing small gas bubbles commonly occurs just above the capillary saturation level (refer to figure 3.5).

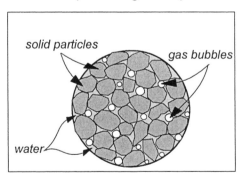

Figure 3.12: Unsaturated soil with small gas bubbles ($0.85 \leq S \leq 1$) .

If, under similar saturation conditions ($0.85 \leq S \leq 1$), the gas bubbles are larger than the void space between solid particles as shown in figure 3.13, then the soil behaviour *can no longer* be described by equation 3.18. Rather, the soil has to be modelled as a saturated soil matrix containing large gas-filled cavities.

Such modelling can be complex in nature (see for instance Toll (1990), Wheeler (1991), Sills *et al.* (1991), Thomas and He (1998)), and relies mainly on sophisticated concepts such as critical state soil mechanics, which will be presented in chapter 6.

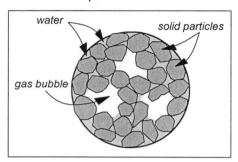

Figure 3.13: Unsaturated soil with large gas bubbles $(0.85 \leq S \leq 1)$.

It is useful to remember that this type of unsaturated soils is a common occurrence in the marine environment. Prior knowledge of their behaviour is therefore of paramount importance for foundation design of offshore structures such as oil platforms.

3.4 Stresses due to surface loading

3.4.1 Introduction

Any type of loading transmitted to a soil mass through a foundation is bound to generate a contact pressure which is three-dimensional in nature. The distribution of this pressure within the soil mass depends on the following.

  •*(a) The nature of load transmitted through the foundation*: One would expect the stresses generated by a uniform load applied at the soil surface over a relatively wide area to be different from those corresponding to a concentrated load, for instance.

  •*(b) The type of foundation transmitting the load*: The deformation of a foundation under an applied load depends on its rigidity. Thus in the case of a uniformly loaded *rigid foundation,* as depicted in figure 3.14, a uniform settlement beneath the foundation surface generates a pressure distribution whose maximum depends on the type of soil. For a clay, the maximum occurs under the foundation edges, whereas for a sand, the maximum pressure is beneath the foundation centre. In the case of a *flexible foundation*, the deformation reflecting the degree of flexibility leads to a uniform contact pressure as shown in figure 3.14. From a practical perspective, the calculation of settlements undertaken using a pressure distribution related to a flexible foundation, are corrected to take into account any foundation rigidity when applicable (refer to section 5.6.1).

• *(c) The soil type within which the contact pressure is generated:* Because of the three-dimensional nature of the pressure distribution, the soil can (justifiably) be considered as an infinite half-space compared with the foundation area, so that any stress analysis is not affected by the boundaries.

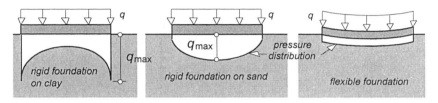

Figure 3.14: Pressure distribution within a soil mass due to a surface load.

The profiles with depth of the *vertical stress* $\Delta\sigma_z$ induced by a surface loading are of particular interest since they affect the magnitude of *settlements* as will be explained shortly in chapter 5. These profiles, which are closely related to the shape and size of the loaded area, as well as to the type of applied load, show a variable rate of *decay* of $\Delta\sigma_z$ as the depth increases, corresponding to a continuous *stress redistribution* within the soil mass. This is in sharp contrast to the *monotonous* (linear) *increase* of the vertical stress due to self weight discussed earlier. Figure 3.15 depicts a three-dimensional pear-shaped vertical stress profile under the central point of a circular loaded area of diameter *B,* transmitting a uniform pressure *q*. The profile corresponding to an (assumed) infinitely long strip of width *B,* subjected to an identical pressure *q* is no longer three- dimensional since the confinement is limited to each side of the strip; accordingly, the rate of decay of $\Delta\sigma_z$ with depth is affected by these boundary conditions.

The profile of other stress components (such as radial or shear stresses) with depth due to surface loading is equally important. For example, the design of a retaining structure requires the prior knowledge of the radial stress distribution as will be seen in chapter 11. Consequently, it is essential to develop a method by which the stress increase with depth, due to surface loading, can be calculated, if not precisely, at least with sufficient accuracy so that (with the help of a factor of safety perhaps) a safe design can be achieved.

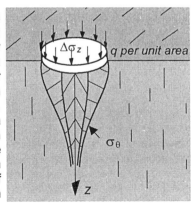

Figure 3.15: Vertical stress profile.

Natural soils, regardless of the way they were formed, are likely to be :
- *anisotropic*, in other words they have different properties in every direction of the space;
- *heterogeneous*, meaning that their stiffness varies with depth, and
- of a *restricted elastic behaviour*.

These natural conditions imply that an analytical solution to the stress distribution due to a given type of surface loading will be fraught with difficulties, the corresponding strenuous boundary conditions being very difficult to satisfy. To find a way around these difficulties (at the expense of some accuracy), the following analysis based on elastic equilibrium assumes that:
- the soil mass is a *semi-infinite* half space,
- the soil is *weightless*,
- the soil is *isotropic* and *homogeneous*, and its behaviour is *linear-elastic*,
- the load is of a *flexible* type.

Obviously, these assumptions are bound to lead to ideal stress distributions. In particular, the assumption related to elasticity is only realistic as long as the increase in stress caused by the surface load does not exceed in any significant way the yield stress as depicted in figure 3.16 in the case of a dense sand.

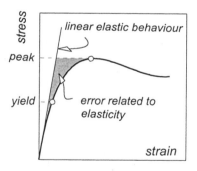

Figure 3.16: Potential errors related to the assumption of elastic soil behaviour.

Also, the assumption of a homogeneous soil can no longer apply if the soil mass is of finite thickness as in the case of a clay layer underlain by a thick layer of rock. Under such circumstances, *other* methods of analysis, mainly of a numerical type, must be applied. Despite the restrictive nature of the previous assumptions, Burland *et al.* (1977) have shown that, in many cases, the corresponding elastic solutions to the *vertical stress* distribution compare favourably with solutions obtained using more sophisticated methods of analysis. Consequently, the following analysis, which is limited mostly to vertical stresses, must be used cautiously; the radial stress distribution (when needed) can be estimated using the coefficient of earth pressure at rest of equation 3.5*b*.

3.4.2 Elastic equilibrium of a weightless soil subject to a point load: Boussinesq solution

Consider an element of a *weightless semi-infinite soil mass,* situated at a distance $R = \sqrt{r^2 + z^2}$ from a surface load P as depicted in figure 3.17. Assuming that the soil is *homogeneous* (that is identical in composition between any two chosen points), *isotropic* and *elastic* with a modulus of elasticity E and a Poisson's ratio ν, then it can be shown (see Poulos and Davis (1974)) that the differential equation of elastic equilibrium, expressed in terms of a stress function Φ in the cylindrical co-ordinates system, is as follows:

$$\nabla^4 \Phi = \nabla^2 \nabla^2 \Phi = 0 \qquad (3.16)$$

with $\quad \nabla^2 = \left(\dfrac{\partial^2}{\partial r^2} + \dfrac{1}{r}\dfrac{\partial}{\partial r} + \dfrac{\partial^2}{\partial z^2} \right)$

the stresses being related to the stress function in the following manner:

$$\sigma_r = \frac{\partial}{\partial z}\left[\nu \nabla^2 \Phi - \frac{\partial^2 \Phi}{\partial r^2} \right] \qquad (3.17a)$$

$$\sigma_\theta = \frac{\partial}{\partial z}\left[\nu \nabla^2 \Phi - \frac{1}{r}\frac{\partial \Phi}{\partial r} \right] \qquad (3.17b)$$

$$\sigma_z = \frac{\partial}{\partial z}\left[(2 - \nu)\nabla^2 \Phi - \frac{\partial^2 \Phi}{\partial z^2} \right] \qquad (3.17c)$$

$$\tau_{rz} = \frac{\partial}{\partial r}\left[(1 - \nu)\nabla^2 \Phi - \frac{\partial^2 \Phi}{\partial z^2} \right] \qquad (3.17d)$$

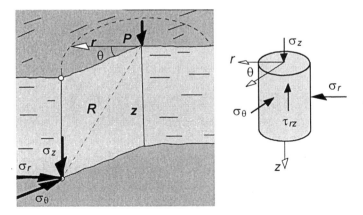

Figure 3.17: Stress field generated by a point load.

As early as 1885, Joseph Boussinesq published his *Application des potentiels à l'étude de l'équilibre et du mouvement des solides élastiques* in which he presented the solution to equation 3.16 in the case of a concentrated load *P*. The mathematical formulation of such an elegant solution, which is outside the scope of this text, can be found in Timoshenko and Goodier (1970), for instance. The solution resulted in the following *vertical and shear stresses*, respectively:

$$\Delta\sigma_z = \frac{3Pz^3}{2\pi R^5} \tag{3.18a}$$

$$\Delta\tau_{rz} = \frac{3Prz^2}{2\pi R^5} \tag{3.18b}$$

Analytical solutions to the same equation related to other types of surface loading have since been established, and in some cases, equation 3.16 has been solved numerically in the absence of closed form solutions. The stress distribution due to loads most commonly encountered in practice are presented in the following sections, and reference should be made to the comprehensive analysis of Poulos and Davis (1974).

3.4.3 Stress distribution due to a concentrated horizontal load

In this case, the vertical stress $\Delta\sigma_z$ and shear stress $\Delta\tau_{xy}$ engendered by the horizontal concentrated load depicted in figure 3.18 are:

$$\Delta\sigma_z = \frac{3Pxz^2}{2\pi R^5} \tag{3.19a}$$

$$\Delta\tau_{xy} = \frac{Py}{2\pi R^3}\left[\frac{3x^2}{R^3} + \frac{(1-2v)}{(R+z)^2}\left(R^2 - x^2 - \frac{2Rx^2}{R+z}\right)\right] \tag{3.19b}$$

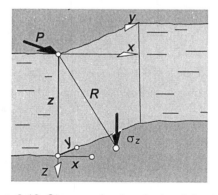

Figure 3.18: Stresses due to a horizontal point load.

3.4.4 vertical stress due to a uniformly loaded circular area

The stresses induced by this type of loading under the *centre* of the loaded area can be obtained by assuming that the vertical load applied on an elementary area such as the one depicted in figure 2.19, whose magnitude is $qr\,dr\,d\theta$, acts as a point load at the centre of the element. The stresses at any depth below the *centre* of the whole area can thence be found by integration of equations 2.19a, in which the quantity $qr\,dr\,d\theta$ is substituted for P. Knowing that:

$$R = [r^2 + z^2]^{1/2} \quad \Rightarrow \quad R^5 = z^5 \left[1 + (r/z)^2 \right]^{5/2}$$

the increase in vertical stress corresponding to figure 3.19 is then calculated as follows:

$$\Delta\sigma_z = \int_0^{2\pi} \int_0^a \frac{3q\,r\,dr\,d\theta}{2\pi z^2 \left[1 + (r/z)^2 \right]^{5/2}}$$

A straightforward integration yields :

$$\Delta\sigma_z = q \left[1 - \frac{1}{\left[1 + (a/z)^2 \right]^{3/2}} \right] \qquad\qquad (3.20)$$

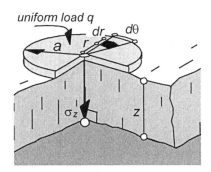

uniform load q

Figure 3.19: Stress increase due to a circular uniform load.

Equation 3.20 is *only* used in conjunction with the calculation of the vertical stress under the *centre* of the uniformly loaded circular area. For points outside the central axis, the analytical solution, though it exists (see Harr (1966), for example), is very complex in nature. However, graphical solutions to the stress distribution are available, and figure 3.20 represents the charts produced by Foster and Ahlvin (1954) for the evaluation of *vertical* stresses at any point beneath a uniformly loaded circular area. A more comprehensive graphical solution for this type of loading can be found in Poulos and Davis (1974), for instance.

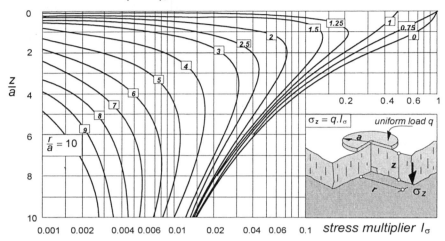

Figure 3.20: Stress multiplier for uniformly loaded circular areas due to Foster and Ahlvin (1954).

Example 3.4

A storage tank is to be built on the surface of a thick clay layer containing a pocket of softer material at a depth of 6 m below the ground as depicted in figure 3.21. When fully operational, the flexible foundation of the tank will be transmitting a uniform pressure q to the ground surface and, because of the nature of the soft material, it is required that the *increase* in vertical pressure (due to the tank) at point b (figure 3.21) should in no way exceed $\Delta\sigma_v = 60\,kN/m^2$.

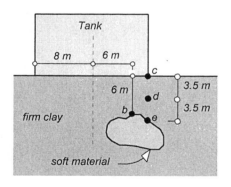

Figure 3.21: Tank dimensions.

Estimate the maximum pressure q and the corresponding increase in vertical pressure at different points indicated in the figure. First, the stress multiplier at point b is determined in the following way using the notation in figure 3.20: $r = 6\,m$, $a = 8\,m$, $z = 6\,m$, whence $r/a = z/a = 0.75$. Using the charts in figure 3.20 in conjunction with these ratios, it is seen that the stress multiplier $I_\sigma \approx 0.6$. Because of the limit imposed on the maximum vertical stress increase at b, it follows that:

$$\Delta\sigma_v = q_{max}I_\sigma = 60\,kN/m^2 \quad \Rightarrow \quad q_{max} = \frac{60}{0.6} = 100\,kN/m^2$$

Under this maximum pressure, the increase in vertical stress at points c, d, and e is (with reference to the charts in figure 3.20) such that:

- *point c:* $r/a = 1$, $z/a = 0$ $\Rightarrow$ $I_\sigma = 0.5$ $\Rightarrow$ $\Delta\sigma_v = 100 \times 0.5 = 50\,kN/m^2$,

- *point d:* $r/a = 1$, $z/a = 3.5/8 = 0.437$, $\Rightarrow$ $I_\sigma = 0.43$ $\Rightarrow$ $\Delta\sigma_v = 43\,kN/m^2$,

- *point e:* $r/a = 1$, $z/a = 7/8 = 0.875$, $\Rightarrow$ $I_\sigma \approx 0.35$ $\Rightarrow$ $\Delta\sigma_v = 35\,kN/m^2$.

3.4.5 Vertical stress due to a uniformly loaded rectangular area

The stresses due to this type of loading under a *corner* of the uniformly loaded rectangular area can be calculated by integration of Boussinesq solutions for a concentrated vertical load (equations 3.19). Referring to figure 3.22, it is seen that the load applied to the elementary area $dx\,dy$ can be assumed to act as a concentrated load of a magnitude $q\,dx\,dy$. Thus, substituting for the load P in equations 3.19 in the knowledge that $R = \sqrt{x^2 + y^2 + z^2}$, it follows that the increase in vertical stress, for instance, generated by the whole rectangular area under a corner such as the one illustrated in figure 3.22, is calculated by integration of equation 3.19a:

$$\Delta\sigma_z = \int_0^l \int_0^b \frac{3z^3 q\,dx\,dy}{2\pi(x^2 + y^2 + z^2)^{5/2}} \tag{3.21}$$

It can be shown that the calculus related to this integration (which is out of the scope of this text) yields the following solution:

$$\Delta\sigma_z = \frac{q}{4\pi}\left[\frac{2mn(m^2+n^2+2)\sqrt{m^2+n^2+1}}{(m^2+n^2+m^2n^2+1)(m^2+n^2+1)} + \tan^{-1}\left(\frac{2mn\sqrt{m^2+n^2+1}}{m^2+n^2+m^2n^2-1} \right) \right] \tag{3.22}$$

with $m = b/z$, $n = l/z$. Equation 3.22 can be rewritten as:

$$\Delta\sigma_z = qI_\sigma \tag{3.23}$$

where the stress multiplier I_σ depends on m and n, in other words on the size of the rectangle and the depth under the corner at which the stress is calculated. The corresponding graphical solution (Fadum (1948)) is reproduced in figure 3.23 in which the variables m and n are interchangeable.

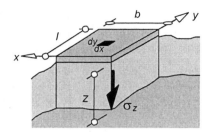

Figure 3.22: Stress due to a uniformly loaded rectangular area.

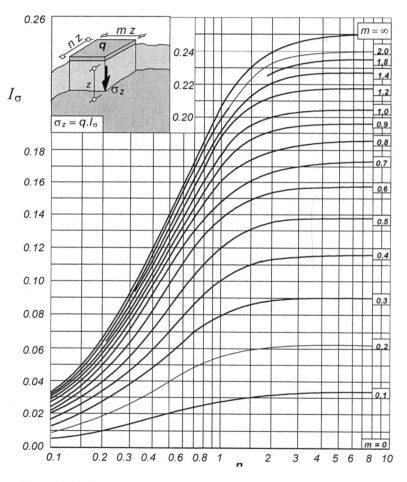

Figure 3.23: Stress multiplier for uniformly loaded rectangular areas
(Fadum, 1948).

3.4.6 Vertical stress due to any shape of a uniformly loaded area

The graphical solution devised by Newmark (1942) amounts to a brilliant idea based on rearranging the expression of the vertical stress induced by a flexible circular area subjected to uniform load q and derived previously. Using the diameter $D = 2a$, it can be seen that equation 3.20 can be rewritten as follows:

$$\frac{D}{z} = 2\left[\left(\frac{1}{1-\frac{\Delta\sigma_z}{q}}\right)^{2/3} - 1\right]^{1/2} \qquad (3.24)$$

Accordingly, the magnitude of the vertical stress increase $\Delta\sigma_z$ at a depth z, induced by a circular area of diameter D subjected to a uniform load q, depends on the ratio D/z. For instance, a stress increase $\Delta\sigma_z = 0.3q$ corresponds to a ratio $D/z = 1.036$, whence the following values:

$\Delta\sigma_z/q$	0.1	0.2	0.3	0.4	0.5	0.6	0.7	0.8	0.9	1.0
D/z	0.54	0.80	1.04	1.27	1.53	1.84	2.22	2.77	3.82	∞

Significantly, these values indicate that at a given depth z, the vertical stress generated by a flexible circular area transmitting a pressure q will have a magnitude $\Delta\sigma_z = 0.1q$ when the diameter of the loaded area is $D = 0.54z$; similarly, an increase of $\Delta\sigma_z = 0.2q$ will result from an area of diameter $D = 0.8z$, and so on. Consequently, Newmark suggested *choosing* an arbitrary scale line z for which concentric circles of diameters corresponding to the ratios in the above table are then drawn (refer to figure 3.24). The circle with the smallest diameter corresponds precisely to the flexible circular area that will engender a vertical stress increase $\Delta\sigma_z$ (at a depth z) equal to 10% of the uniform load q transmitted to the soil, so that when the area of the circle is subdivided radially into, say, 20 equal elements, the vertical stress generated at the depth z by each one of these elements is:

$$d(\Delta\sigma_z) = \Delta\sigma_z/20 = 0.1q/20 = 0.005q \qquad (3.25)$$

Referring to figure 3.24, it is seen that for a given depth z, the vertical stress induced by a uniformly loaded area of *any shape* can be estimated provided that the area in question is plotted to the scale indicated in the figure, and that the point under which the stress is calculated is placed at the centre of the circles.

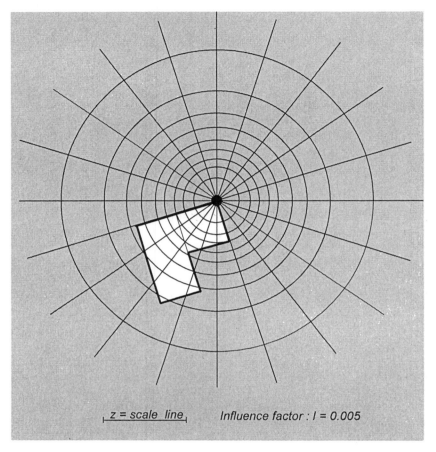

$z = scale\ line$ Influence factor : $I = 0.005$

Figure 3.24: Newmark charts for the calculation of vertical stress increases due to uniformly loaded areas of any shape.

Once the number N of elements covered by the scaled area is counted (estimating partial elements), $\Delta\sigma_z$ is then calculated as follows:

$$\Delta\sigma_z = 0.005Nq \qquad (3.26)$$

Example 3.5

Consider the flexible foundation depicted in figure 3.25 where the vertical stress, due to the uniform pressures q_1 and q_2, at point A situated at a depth $z = 6\,m$ needs to be evaluated. The scale to which the foundation is drawn in bold in figure 3.24 is such that the scale line in the figure corresponds to $z = 6\,m$ (*i.e.* the depth at which the stress needs to be estimated). Notice that the scaled foundation is drawn in a way that the point under which the stress is calculated (point A) is placed at the centre of the figure.

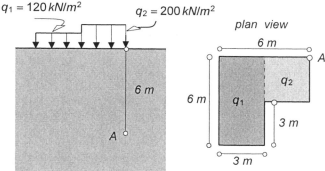

Figure 3.25: Example of a flexible, uniformly loaded foundation.

The procedure is then straightforward. It is seen that the number of elements covered by the section of foundation subjected to the uniform pressure q_1 corresponds to $N_1 \approx 10.6$, whereas the number of elements corresponding to the section subjected to q_2 is approximately $N_2 \approx 17.3$. So an increase in the (vertical) stress at point A:

$$\Delta \sigma_A = 0.005 \times (10.6 \times 120 + 17.3 \times 200) = 23.7 \, kN/m^2$$

As an alternative, Fadum's charts of figure 3.23 can be used to estimate the increase $\Delta \sigma_z$ at A. In this case, it is obvious that the method, as described earlier, needs to be adjusted, in that point A needs to be at the corner of *every* rectangle or square into which the actual foundation will be subdivided. For that to happen, some *artificial* areas are needed, so that the requirement is fulfilled; in which case care must be taken so that any stress generated by whatever *artificial* area is subtracted from the total calculated value. The procedure is best illustrated in figure 3.26, whereby the total increase in vertical stress $\Delta \sigma_{z1}$ at A is that calculated from the enlarged area ABCD subjected to q_1, from which $\Delta \sigma_{z2}$ due to the artificially added area ABEH is then subtracted, and to which $\Delta \sigma_{z3}$ due to the area AGFH subjected to q_2 is finally added. Notice that all three areas have point A at their top right-hand side corners. Accordingly, the three stress increases at a depth $z = 6 \, m$ beneath point A can now be estimated using the charts in figure 3.23 where it is seen that :

• area ABCD : $mz = nz = 6 \, m$, $z = 6 \, m$ $\Rightarrow m = n = 1 \Rightarrow I_\sigma = 0.177$,

$$\Delta \sigma_{z1} = I_\sigma q_1 = 0.177 \times 120 = 21.24 \, kN/m^2$$

- *area ABEH* : $mz = 3\,m$, $nz = 6\,m$, $z = 6\,m$ $\Rightarrow$
          $m = 0.5$, $n = 1$, $\Rightarrow$ $I_\sigma = 0.122$,

$$\Delta\sigma_{z2} = I_\sigma q_1 = 0.122 \times 120 = 14.64\,kN/m^2,$$

- *area AGFH* : $mz = nz = 3\,m$, $z = 6\,m \Rightarrow m = n = 0.5 \Rightarrow I_\sigma = 0.084$.

$$\Delta\sigma_{z3} = I_\sigma q_2 = 0.084 \times 200 = 16.8\,kN/m^2.$$

Hence the *estimated* vertical stress increase at point A:

$$\Delta\sigma_A = 21.24 - 14.64 + 16.8 = 23.4\,kN/m^2$$

A comparison with the stress increase calculated using Newmark charts shows that both methods yield remarkably similar values.

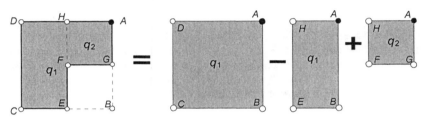

Figure 3.26: Practical aspects related to the use of Fadum charts.

3.4.7 Stresses due to a vertical line load

Under plane strain conditions (that is when a strain component in one direction of the space is very small compared with the two other components, as in the case of an embankment, for instance), the equilibrium equation 3.16 (corresponding to zero body force), expressed in terms of the stress function Φ in the Cartesian co-ordinates system, reduces to:

$$\frac{\partial^4 \Phi}{\partial x^4} + 2\frac{\partial^4 \Phi}{\partial x^2 \partial z^2} + \frac{\partial^4 \Phi}{\partial z^4} = 0 \qquad\qquad (3.27)$$

The stresses in the two dimensional stress field (see figure 3.27) are related to Φ in the following way:

$$\sigma_x = \frac{\partial^2 \Phi}{\partial z^2}, \qquad \sigma_z = \frac{\partial^2 \Phi}{\partial x^2}, \qquad \tau_{xz} = \frac{\partial^2 \Phi}{\partial x \partial z}$$

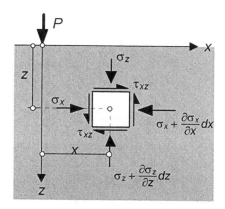

Figure 3.27: Two-dimensional stress field.

The case of a vertical line load, depicted in figure 3.28, is often referred to as the integrated Boussinesq problem, and its analytical solution can be established fairly easily by inserting the following stress function into equation 3.27:

$$\Phi = cx \tan^{-1}\left(\frac{z}{x}\right) \qquad (3.28)$$

where c is a constant. At this stage, the derivation of different stresses is easy to follow. For example, the expression of the vertical stress σ_z is:

$$\sigma_z = \frac{\partial^2 \Phi}{\partial x^2} = -\frac{2cz^3}{(x^2 + z^2)^2}$$

The constant c is evaluated from the boundary condition:

$$Q = \int_{-\infty}^{+\infty} \sigma_z \, dx = -2cz^3 \int_{-\infty}^{+\infty} \frac{1}{(x^2 + z^2)^2} \, dx$$

Q being the *load per unit length*. It can be shown that this integration yields the following c value: $c = -Q/\pi$. Whence:

$$\sigma_z = \frac{2Qz^3}{\pi (x^2 + z^2)^2} \qquad (3.29a)$$

For the shear stress increase, it is easy to establish that:

$$\tau_{xz} = \frac{2Qz^2x}{\pi (x^2 + z^2)^2} \qquad (3.29b)$$

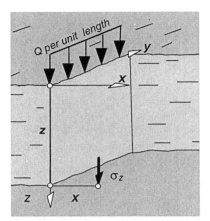

Figure 3.28: Stresses due to a vertical line load.

Example 3.6

Consider the standard gauge railway line depicted in figure 3.29, used for an 8.7 m diameter, 15 m long tunnel boring machine, with a total weight of 1750 metric tons. Since the total weight is carried by both lines, the pressure induced per linear metre is thus:

$$Q = \frac{1}{2} \times \left(\frac{1750 \times 0.981}{15} \right) = 57.22 \, kN/m$$

To evaluate the increase in both vertical and shear stresses due to Q at points A and B, equations 3.29a and b yield:

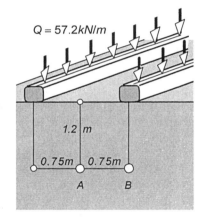

Figure 3.29: Loading conditions.

- *point A:* (remember both lines count)

$$\Delta\sigma_z = 2 \times \frac{2 \times 57.22 \times 1.2^3}{\pi(1.2^2 + 0.75^2)^2} = 31.39 \, kN/m^2$$

$\Delta\tau_{xz} = 0$ (because of symmetry)

- *point B:* applying the superposition principle, it follows that:

$$\Delta\sigma_z = \frac{2 \times 57.22 \times 1.2^3}{\pi \times 1.2^4} + \frac{2 \times 57.22 \times 1.2^3}{\pi(1.2^2 + 1.5^2)^2} = 34.98 \, kN/m^2$$

$$\Delta\tau_{xz} = \frac{2 \times 57.22 \times 1.2^2 \times 1.5}{\pi(1.2^2 + 1.5^2)^2} = 5.78 \, kN/m^2$$

3.4.8 Stresses due to a horizontal line load

In the case of a semi-infinite soil mass subject to a horizontal line load as illustrated in figure 3.30, the derivation of different stresses results in the following:

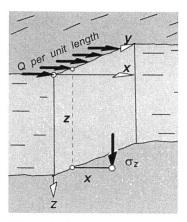

$$\Delta\sigma_z = \frac{2Qz^2x}{\pi(x^2+z^2)^2} \qquad (3.30a)$$

$$\Delta\tau_{xz} = \frac{2Qx^2z}{\pi(x^2+z^2)^2} \qquad (3.30b)$$

Figure 3.30: Stresses due to a horizontal line load.

3.4.9 Stresses due to a strip load: vertical uniform loading

If a strip, supposedly of infinite length, is transmitting a *vertical uniform load q* (*i.e.* a *load per unit area*) to the soil surface, then the stresses generated at any depth within the soil mass can be found by integration of equations 3.29, in which the load per unit area q applied through a strip of width dr as per figure 3.31 is assumed to be equivalent to the line load Q in figure 3.28. Thus, substituting $q.dr$ for Q and $(x-r)$ for x in equations 3.29, the increase in vertical and shear stresses can be found by integration between the limits $(-b, +b)$ in figure 3.31 :

$$\Delta\sigma_z = \int_{-b}^{+b} \frac{2q}{\pi}\left\{\frac{z^3}{\left[(x-r)^2+z^2\right]^2}\right\}dr \qquad (3.31a)$$

$$\Delta\tau_{xz} = \int_{-b}^{+b} \frac{2q}{\pi}\left\{\frac{z^2.(x-r)}{[(x-r^2)+z^2]^2}\right\}dr \qquad (3.31b)$$

Note that q in the above expressions represents a *load per unit area*.

On integration with reference to figure 3.31, equation 3.31a thus yields:

$$\Delta\sigma_z = \frac{q}{\pi}\left\{\tan^{-1}\left(\frac{z}{x-b}\right) - \tan^{-1}\left(\frac{z}{x+b}\right) + \frac{2bz(z^2-x^2+b^2)}{\left[(x-b)^2+z^2\right]\left[(x+b)^2+z^2\right]}\right\} \qquad (3.32)$$

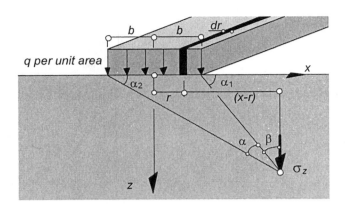

Figure 3.31: Stresses due to a vertical strip load.

Figure 3.31 shows that:

$$\alpha = \alpha_1 - \alpha_2 = \tan^{-1}\left(\frac{z}{x-b}\right) - \tan^{-1}\left(\frac{z}{x+b}\right)$$

and accordingly, equation 3.32 can be rewritten as follows:

$$\Delta\sigma_z = \frac{q}{\pi}\left\{\alpha + \frac{2bz(z^2 - x^2 + b^2)}{\left[(x-b)^2 + z^2\right]\left[(x+b)^2 + z^2\right]}\right\} \qquad 3.33$$

It can readily be shown that equation 3.33 can be equally written in terms of the angles α and β as depicted in figure 3.31, and in this respect, the reader may wish to establish that both vertical and shear stress increases at a point with co-ordinates *(x, z)*, due to a strip transmitting a vertical uniform load are as follows:

$$\Delta\sigma_z = \frac{q}{\pi}[\alpha + \sin\alpha\cos(\alpha + 2\beta)] \qquad (3.34a)$$

$$\Delta\tau_{xz} = \frac{q}{\pi}\sin\alpha\sin(\alpha + 2\beta) \qquad (3.34c)$$

α and β in both sets of equations 3.33 & 3.34 are expressed in *radians*, and q corresponds to a *load per unit area*.

Notice that, in relation to equations 3.34, whilst α represents the natural angle (i.e. always positive) subtended by the triangle at the point where the stress increase is calculated as per figure 3.31, β however is positive only when measured anti-clockwise. Readers unfamiliar with the variation of the angle β should refer to figure 3.32 for the correct sign, and are strongly advised to use equation 3.33 in conjunction with equation 3.34*a* in the first instance, if only to check the validity of their calculations.

Notice also that the quantity *b* in equation 3.33 corresponds to half the width of the uniformly loaded area.

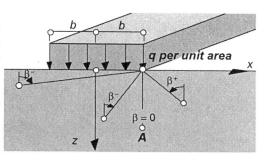

Figure 3.32: Sign convention of the angle β

3.4.10 Stresses due to a strip load: horizontal uniform loading

The stress components at a point such as the one depicted in figure 3.33 are calculated in a way similar to that used in the previous case of vertical uniform loading (β sign being as per figure 3.32):

$$\Delta\sigma_z = \frac{q}{\pi}\sin\alpha\sin(\alpha + 2\beta) \qquad\qquad (3.35a)$$

$$\Delta\tau_{xz} = \frac{q}{\pi}[\alpha - \sin\alpha\cos(\alpha + 2\beta)] \qquad\qquad (3.35b)$$

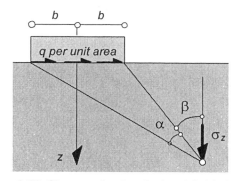

Figure 3.33: Stresses due to a horizontal strip load.

3.4.11 Stresses due to a linearly increasing vertical uniform loading

Consider the triangular area of width *B* in figure 3.34, supposedly of infinite extent, transmitting a vertical uniform load that increases linearly from zero to *q* (*load per unit area*) at the soil surface. The stresses generated at any depth within the soil mass can be found by integration of equations 3.29, in which the load per unit area q applied at a distance r from the origin through a strip of width dr as per figure 3.34 is $q.\dfrac{r}{B}.dr$.

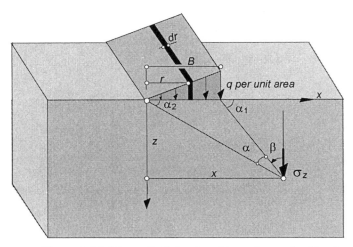

Figure 3.34: Stress field due to a triangular vertical load.

This load is then assumed to be equivalent to the line load Q in figure 3.28, and the increase in vertical and shear stresses at a point with co-ordinates (x,z) can be found by substituting $q\dfrac{r}{B}dr$ for Q and $(x-r)$ for x in equations 3.29, then integrating between the limits $(0, B)$ in figure 3.34:

$$\Delta\sigma_z = \int_0^B \frac{2q}{\pi B}\left\{\frac{z^3 r}{\left[(x-r)^2 + z^2\right]^2}\right\}dr \qquad (3.36a)$$

$$\Delta\tau_{xz} = \int_0^B \frac{2q}{\pi B}\left\{\frac{z^2 (x-r)}{\left[(x-r)^2 + z^2\right]^2}\right\}dr \qquad (3.36b)$$

On integration, equation 3.36a yields:

$$\Delta\sigma_z = \frac{q}{\pi}\left\{\frac{x}{B}\left[\tan^{-1}\left(\frac{z}{(x-B)}\right) - \tan^{-1}\left(\frac{z}{(x+B)}\right)\right] - \frac{z(x-B)}{z^2 + (x-B)^2}\right\} \qquad (3.37)$$

once more, figure 3.34 clearly indicates that:

$$\alpha = \alpha_1 - \alpha_2 = \tan^{-1}\left(\tfrac{z}{x-B}\right) - \tan^{-1}\left(\tfrac{z}{x+B}\right)$$

and on substitution into equation 3.37, it follows that:

$$\Delta\sigma_z = \frac{q}{\pi}\left\{ \frac{x}{B}\alpha - \frac{z(x-B)}{z^2 + (x-B)^2} \right\}$$ (3.38)

Equation 3.38 can relatively easily be expressed in terms of the angles α & β in figure 3.34, and it is left to the reader to show that both vertical and shear stress increases at a point with co-ordinates (x, z) within the soil mass, due to a triangular area of width B, supposedly of infinite extent transmitting a vertical uniform load that increases linearly from zero to q (*load per unit area*) are as follows:

$$\Delta\sigma_z = \frac{q}{\pi}\left[\frac{\alpha x}{B} - \frac{\sin 2\beta}{2} \right]$$ (3.39a)

$$\Delta\tau_{xz} = \frac{q}{\pi}\left[\frac{1 + \cos 2\beta}{2} - \frac{z\alpha}{B} \right]$$ (3.39b)

The angles α & β in both equations are expressed in *radians*. Furthermore, as was the case in equations 3.35, β is positive only when measured anti-clockwise. Uninitiated readers should refer to figure 3.35 for the correct sign of β, and are advised to use both equations 3.38 & 3.39a to check the validity of their calculations.

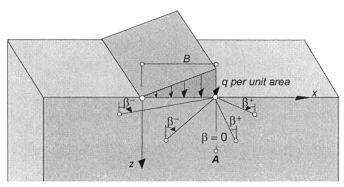

Figure 3.35: Sign convention of the angle β

Example 3.7

Consider the triangular load in figure 3.36, increasing linearly from zero at $x = 0$ to $q = 80\,kN/m^2$ at $x = B = 12\,m$. Calculate the vertical stress increase at a depth $z = 1.2\,m$ below ground at the 5 points A to E for which figures between brackets represent the ordinates in metres of each point (i.e. the distance x from the origin as per the figure).

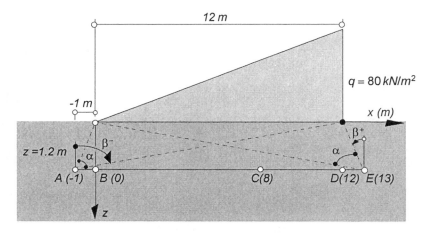

Figure 3.36: example of a triangular vertical loading

For optimum clarity of calculations, points *A* & *E* are selected for the vertical stress increase calculations using both equations 3.38 & 3.39a (which are equivalent). With the sign convention in figure 3.35 in mind, the angles α & β of both points are as follows:

- point *A*: $\beta = -\tan\left(\frac{13}{1.2}\right) = -84.7° = -1.4783\,rad$

    $\alpha = -\beta - \tan^{-1}\left(\frac{1}{1.2}\right) = 44.89° = 0.783\,rad$

- point *E*: $\beta = +\tan^{-1}\left(\frac{1}{1.2}\right) = 39.8° = 0.6946\,rad$

    $\alpha = \tan^{-1}\left(\frac{13}{1.2}\right) - \beta = 44.92° = 0.784\,rad$

Knowing that $B = 12\,m$ & $z = 1.2\,m$, equation 3.38 yields the following vertical stress increase:

$$\Delta\sigma_z^{(A)} = \frac{80}{\pi}\left(\frac{-1 \times 0.783}{12} - \frac{1.2 \times (-1 - 12)}{1.2^2 + (-1 - 12)^2}\right) = 0.67\,kN/m^2$$

$$\Delta\sigma_z^{(E)} = \frac{80}{\pi}\left(\frac{13 \times 0.784}{12} - \frac{1.2 \times (13 - 12)}{1.2^2 + (13 - 12)^2}\right) = 9.10\,kN/m^2$$

Now the stress increases at both points are calculated using equation 3.39a:

$$\Delta\sigma_z^{(A)} = \frac{80}{\pi}\left(\frac{-1 \times 0.783}{12} - \frac{\sin(2 \times -1.4783)}{2}\right) = 0.68\,kN/m^2$$

$$\Delta\sigma_z^{(E)} = \frac{80}{\pi}\left(\frac{13 \times 0.784}{12} - \frac{\sin(2 \times 0.6946)}{2}\right) = 9.10\,kN/m^2$$

Needless to say these stresses are identical, since both equations 338 & 3.39a are mathematically identical. The calculations at the remaining points can thus be undertaken in a similar way, and reference can be made to the entire variation of the vertical stress increase at a depth $z = 1.2\,m$ below ground engendered by the triangular load, and illustrated in figure 3.37

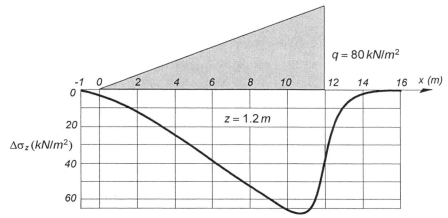

Figure 3.37: Vertical stress increase at depth $z = 1.2\,m$

The type of loading in example 3.7 is encountered during embankment construction whereby the total loaded area is formed of a strip in the middle and a triangular area, such as those illustrated in figure 3.33, on each side. The total stress increase due to an embankment can therefore be calculated at any point beneath the surface using the superposition principle: the contribution of the central strip is first calculated, and the contributions of both triangular areas are then added.

Example 3.8

Estimate the increase in the vertical stress $\Delta\sigma_z$ within the stiff clay layer at points A and B, due to the loading conditions generated by the embankment shown in figure 3.38.
Referring to figures 3.38 and 3.39, and using the notation of figure 3.33, the different quantities needed to calculate the stresses at B are such that:

$$\beta_1 = 0, \qquad \alpha_1 = \tan^{-1}\left(\tfrac{10}{2}\right) = 1.373 \; rad, \qquad \beta_2 = \alpha_1 = 1.373 \; rad,$$

$$\alpha_2 = \tan^{-1}\left(\tfrac{17}{2}\right) - \alpha_1 = 0.08 \; rad, \qquad x = 17\,m, \quad B = 7\,m$$

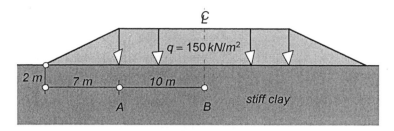

Figure 3.38: Embankment dimensions.

Because of symmetry, the increase in vertical stress at *B* can be calculated using a combination of equations 3.34*a* and 3.39*a* as follows:

$$\Delta\sigma_z = 2\left[\frac{q}{\pi}(\alpha_1 + \sin\alpha_1\cos\alpha_1) + \frac{q}{\pi}\left(\frac{\alpha_2 x}{B} - \frac{\sin 2\beta_2}{2}\right)\right]$$

$$= 2 \times \frac{150}{\pi}\left[(1.373 + \sin 1.373 \times \cos 1.373) + \left(\frac{0.08\times17}{7} - \frac{1}{2}\sin(2\times1.373)\right)\right]$$

$$= 149.7\, kN/m^2$$

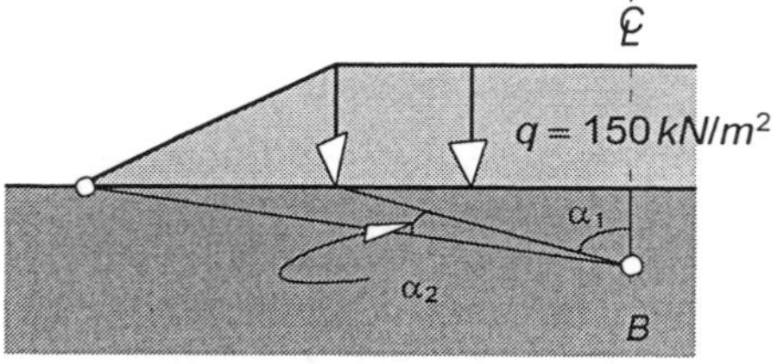

Figure 3.39: Parameters related to stress calculations at B.

It is noticeable that, because of the embankment dimensions and the central position of point *B*, the contribution of both triangular areas to the vertical stress increase is, under these circumstances, negligible. Assessing the stress increase at *A*, figure 3.40 shows clearly that the contribution of the three areas, that is the two triangles and the central rectangle, have to be evaluated separately, then added together to yield the total stress increase. Using the angles indicated in the figure, as well as the dimensions in figure 3.38, the following quantities are easily established :

- *triangle 1:* $\alpha_1 = \tan^{-1}\left(\frac{7}{2}\right) = 1.292\, rad,\quad \beta_1 = 0,\quad x_1 = 7\, m,\quad B = 7\, m.$

- *rectangle 2:* $\alpha_2 = \tan^{-1}\left(\frac{20}{2}\right) = 1.471\, rad,\quad \beta_2 = -\alpha_2 = -1.471\, rad.$

- *triangle 3:* $\alpha_3 = \tan^{-1}\left(\frac{27}{2}\right) - \alpha_2 = 0.026\,rad,\quad \beta_3 = +\alpha_2 = +1.471\,rad,$

$x_3 = +27\,m,\quad B = 7\,m$

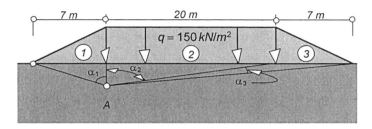

Figure 3.40: Parameters related to stress calculations at A.

Notice that the position of triangle 3 is symmetrical with respect to figure 3.36, and accordingly, not only the angle β_3 is positive, but so is the distance x_3 measured from the zero pressure point of the triangle to point A in figure 3.40.

A combination of equations 3.34a and 3.39a thus yields the following increase in vertical stress at A:

$$\Delta\sigma_z = \frac{150}{\pi}\left[\frac{1.292 \times 7}{7} - \frac{\sin(2 \times 0)}{2}\right] + \frac{150}{\pi}[1.471 + \sin 1.471 \cos(-1.471)]$$

$$+ \frac{150}{\pi}\left|\frac{0.026 \times 27}{7} - \frac{\sin(2 \times 1.471)}{2}\right|$$

$$= 61.69 + 74.97 + 0.05 = 136.7\,kN/m^2$$

Because of the position of point A, the contribution of triangle 3 (see figure 3.40) to the increase in vertical stress at A is very small indeed.

3.5 Depth of influence and stress isobars

The stress redistribution within a soil mass induced by a surface loading depends not only on the type and magnitude of the applied load, but also on the size and shape of the loaded area as shown unambiguously in figure 3.41. It is noticeable that the depth at which $\Delta\sigma_z = 0.1q$ is about $2B$ for a circular area, increasing to around $6B$ in the case of a long strip. Consequently, it can be safely assumed that any *vertical stress increase* induced by a surface loading becomes *marginal* beyond a depth of $3B$ for a circular or a rectangular foundation (*i.e.* loaded area), increasing to about $8B$ in the case of a long strip foundation; B being the diameter or width of the loaded area. These depths of influence delimit the area within which the vertical stress varies, so that a profile of stress isobars (*i.e.* the contours of equal stresses) can easily be found from the different stress expressions derived previously. It can be shown that the shapes of the stress isobars (also referred to as stress bulbs because of their shape) differ according to the foundation shape. Thus, those depicted in figure 3.42*a* correspond to a circular area, whereas the isobars of figure 3.42*b* relate to a long strip foundation. Both figures reflect the stress distribution discussed previously and, most importantly, indicate that under the same loading and soil conditions, the stressed area below a circular foundation having a diameter *B* is markedly smaller than that occurring under a strip foundation of a width *B*.

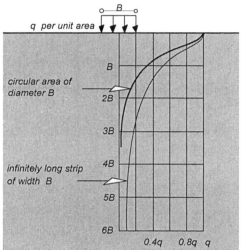

*Figure 3.41: Effect of depth on the distribution of
vertical stresses due to a uniform load.*

Moreover, ample experimental evidence shows that, in the presence of adjacent loaded areas (as in the case of foundation pads for example), the interaction between the stress bulbs results in a wider and deeper stressed area of soil as depicted in figure 3.43. If the effect of a neighbouring loaded area did not exist, then the individual stress isobars would correspond to the ones represented in broken lines in the figure. However, the interaction between adjacent areas results in the spreading of stresses within the soil mass in a way that the overall stressed area is much larger than the individual ones.

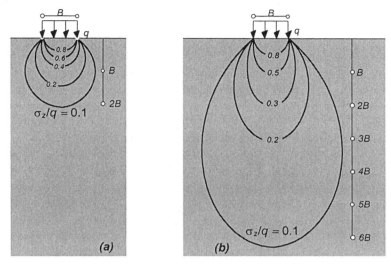

Figure 3.42: Isobars corresponding to: (a) circular area, (b) long strip.

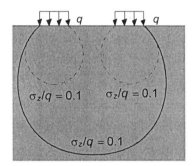

Figure 3.43: Interaction effects.

Because this stress redistribution has implications on the subsequent soil deformation (or settlement), care must be taken so as to include any interaction effect in the design. In this respect, some empirical design rules can be used cautiously. For instance, if the individual loaded areas depicted in figure 3.44 are such that:

$$\sum B \times A \geq 0.75 \times B_1 \times A_1$$

then it is advisable to consider using the area $A_1 \times B_1$ for which the stress bulb is larger than the one that takes into account the interaction effect between individual areas, leading thus to a conservative design.

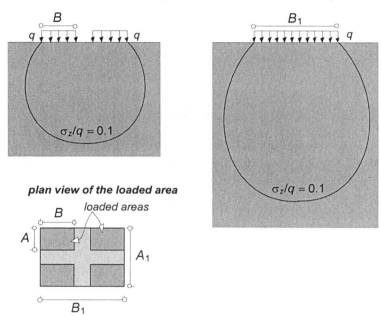

Figure 3.44: Effect of adjacent loaded areas on the stress distribution within a soil mass.

3.6 Shortcomings of elastic solutions

The solutions to the stress distribution presented earlier are based on Boussinesq analysis which *assumes* that the soil is elastic, homogeneous and isotropic. However, natural soils are usually anisotropic, heterogeneous and, most importantly, are characterised by non-linear stress–strain relationships. Experimental evidence shows that, while Boussinesq analysis can be extended to anisotropic soils, the extent of the elastic behaviour depends on the soil nature and is generally restricted to small deformations. In particular, the assumption of elastic behaviour can no longer be justified for soils such as loose sands or young normally consolidated clays; the magnitude of the corresponding yield stresses being very low as depicted in figure 3.45.

Under such circumstances, an iterative procedure is needed to evaluate the soil *stiffness* (*i.e.* the elasticity modulus) because the stress–strain relationship becomes incremental, and one solution consists of using the tangent modulus (refer to figure 3.45) defined as:

$$E = \frac{\delta \sigma'}{\delta \varepsilon} \qquad (3.40)$$

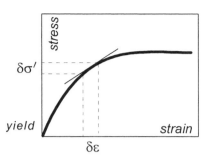

Figure 3.45: Tangent modulus for non-linear soil behaviour.

This type of analysis forms the basis of numerical techniques such as finite difference or finite element methods which are exclusively undertaken using computers. Despite their shortcomings, the solutions to the *vertical stress* distribution based on elasticity presented previously are deemed acceptable in most cases encountered in engineering practice (see Burland *et al.* (1977)). However, these solutions must be handled with great care when dealing with soils such as *loose sands* and *normally consolidated clays* (for which a comprehensive description of their behaviour is presented in section 5.1); in which case, a more sophisticated numerical modelling based on the finite elements method, for example, might be needed (see chapter 14).

Problems

2.1 A silty clay has the following characteristics:
$e = 0.94$, $C = 15\,mm^2$, $d_{10} = 1\,\mu m$, $d_{60} = 3.5\,\mu m$. Calculate the suction pressure (*i.e.* the negative porewater pressure) generated by the maximum capillary rise. Also, estimate the actual capillary saturation rise within the clay layer.

Ans: $u_c = -159.5\,kN/m^2$, $h_s = 4.56\,m$

2.2 An oil tank is built at the surface of an 8 *m* thick clay layer underlain by a sandy gravel. The groundwater level is 2 *m* below the surface and the clay has a saturated unit weight $\gamma_{sat} = 20\,kN/m^3$ and a bulk unit weight $\gamma = 18.5\,kN/m^3$.

A deep excavation needs to be undertaken near the tank and, ideally, the site engineer would like his (her) team to work under dry conditions, meaning that the water table has to be lowered.

The engineer then realised that the owners of the tank are adamant that the effective stress 5 m beneath the centre of the tank should in no way be increased by more than 20%, otherwise serious settlement problems may occur.

Estimate the depth z_w in figure p2.2 by which the water table can be lowered.

Ans: $z_w = 1.58\,m$

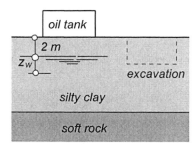

Figure p2.2

2.3   Consider the case of a 3 m deep lake above the surface of a 6 m thick layer of silty clay with a saturated unit weight $\gamma_{sat} = 20\,kN/m^3$ underlain by a stiff clay.

(a) Calculate the total, porewater and effective pressures (σ, u, and σ' respectively) at point A, 3 m below the ground surface.
(b) After an exceptionally hot summer, the lake has disappeared and the water level has receded to ground surface level. Estimate in this case the change in total, porewater and effective pressures at point A.
(c) At the peak of the dry season, the water level has further fallen to 1 m below the ground surface. Assuming a bulk unit weight $\gamma = 17\,kN/m^3$ applies above the water level, calculate the new values of σ, u and σ' at A.

(d) Plot the variation of σ, u and σ' across the silty clay layer corresponding to the three water levels.

Ans: (a) $\sigma = 90\,kN/m^2$, $u = 60\,kN/m^2$, $\sigma' = 30\,kN/m^2$,
   (b) $\sigma = 60\,kN/m^2$, $u = 30\,kN/m^2$, $\sigma' = 30\,kN/m^2$,
   (c) $\sigma = 57\,kN/m^2$, $u = 20\,kN/m^2$, $\sigma' = 37\,kN/m^2$.

2.4   Three line loads of magnitude: $Q_1 = Q_3 = 120\,kN/m$ and
$Q_2 = 200\,kN/m$ are applied on a strip (assumed to be) of infinite
length, at the surface of a very thick layer of glacial till (see figure
p2.4). Preliminary investigations showed that the water table is at a
static depth of $z_w = 5\,m$, and that, above water level, the bulk unit
weight of the soil is $\gamma = 19\,kN/m^3$, increasing to $\gamma_{sat} = 20\,kN/m^3$
below the saturation line. Given the magnitude of loading, it is
suggested that a thorough site investigation must be undertaken up
to a depth z_i at which the increase in the vertical effective stress
due to the surface loading is limited to $\Delta\sigma'_v = 0.05\sigma'_o$ beneath the
centre of the loaded surface. Knowing that σ'_o represents the
effective vertical *in situ* stress prior to the application of any
surface loading, calculate the depth z_i.

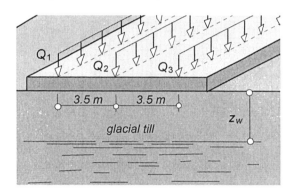

Figure p2.4

Ans: $z_i \approx 21.2\,m$

2.5   The base of a long retaining wall, assumed to be a long strip, is
transmitting a resultant load $F = 620\,kN/m$, inclined at an angle
$\beta = 12°$ to the vertical as depicted in figure *p2.5*.

(*a*) Calculate the vertical and shear stresses at point A, 1 m
beneath the centre of foundation.

(*b*) Estimate the same stresses at point B situated at the same
depth under the corner of foundation.

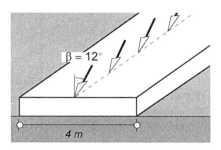

Figure p2.5

Ans: (a) $\tau_{xz} = 0$, $\sigma_z = 386.1\,kN/m^2$, (b) $\tau_{xz} = 44\,kN/m^2$, $\sigma_z = 22\,kN/m^2$.

2.6   Consider the case of the clay dam illustrated in figure p2.6, the clay having a saturated unit weight $\gamma_{sat} = 21\,kN/m^3$. Slope stability considerations require slopes of 1 to 3 and 1 to 2.5 on the upstream and downstream sides respectively.
Because of bearing capacity problems, the increase in vertical stress due to the weight of the dam at point B, 2 m deep as depicted in the figure should not exceed $150\,kN/m^2$.

Calculate under these circumstances the maximum height H of the dam.

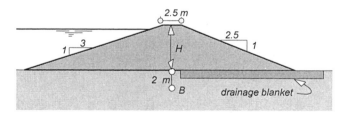

Figure p2.6

Ans: $H \approx 7.3\,m$

2.7   An oil tank with a flexible circular foundation is to be built on a layer of medium clay in the vicinity of a buried pipe as depicted in figure p2.7. When fully operational, the tank will transmit a net pressure $q = 250\,kN/m^2$ to the ground. To protect the pipe, it is suggested that any increase in effective vertical stress due to the tank loading at point A must be limited to $\Delta\sigma'_v = 5\,kN/m^2$. Calculate the distance x in figure p2.7.

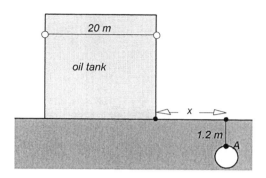

Figure p2.7

Ans: $x = 15\,m$

2.8   Consider the foundation with the shape illustrated in figure *p2.8*, transmitting a uniform pressure q to the ground.
Use Fadum's charts and estimate the ensuing increase in vertical stresses due to q at a depth $z = 1\,m$ beneath points $A, B, ..., H$.

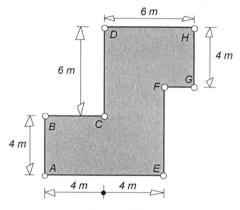

Figure p2.8

Ans: $\Delta\sigma_A \approx 0.245q$, $\Delta\sigma_B \approx 0.25q$, $\Delta\sigma_C \approx 0.724q$
$\Delta\sigma_D \approx 0.244q$, $\Delta\sigma_E \approx 0.244q$, $\Delta\sigma_F \approx 0.728q$
$\Delta\sigma_G \approx 0.247q$, $\Delta\sigma_H \approx 0.249q$.

2.9   Assume the same foundation of problem *p2.8* is now transmitting different uniform pressures q_1 and q_2 as illustrated in figure *p2.9*.

(*a*) Use the superposition principles, and estimate with the help of Fadum's charts, for instance, the increase in vertical effective stresses at a depth $z = 1\,m$ beneath points K, L and M.

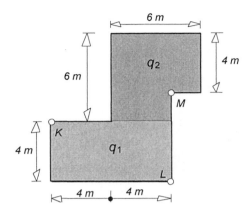

Figure p2.10

(*b*) Compare these results with those calculated in problem *p*2.8 at points *B, E* and *F*, when $q_1 = q_2$.

Ans: (*a*) $\Delta\sigma_K \approx 0.245q_1 + 0.005q_2$, $\Delta\sigma_L \approx 0.242q_1 + 0.002q_2$
          $\Delta\sigma_M \approx 0.008q_1 + 0.72q_2$.

2.10   Use Newmark charts to estimate the increase in vertical pressures at a depth $z = 10\,m$ beneath points K and M in figure *p*2.9 when $q_2 = 2q_1 = 200\,kN/m^2$.

Ans: $\sigma_K \approx 19.5\,kN/m^2$, $\sigma_M \approx 32.5\,kN/m^2$

References

Bishop, A. W. and Donald, I. B. (1961) *The experimental study of partly saturated soils in the triaxial apparatus.* Proceedings of the 5th International Conference on Soil Mechanics, Paris, 1, pp. 13–21.

Boussinesq, J. (1885) *Application des potentiels à l'étude de l'équilibre et du mouvement des solides élastiques.* Gauthier-Villars, Paris.

Burland, J. B., Broms, B. and De Mello, V. F. B. (1977) *Behaviour of foundations and structures.* State-of-the-art review. Proceedings of the 9th ICSMFE, Tokyo,Vol. 2, pp. 495–546.

Fadum, R. E. (1948) *Influence values for estimating stresses in elastic foundations.* Proceedings of the 2nd ICSMFE, Rotterdam, Vol. 3, pp. 77–84.

Foster, C. R. and Ahlvin, R. G. (1954) *Stresses and deflections induced by a uniform circular load.* Proceedings of Highway Research Board, Vol. 33, pp. 467–470.

Fredlund, D. G. (1979) *Appropriate concepts and technology for unsaturated soils.* Canadian Geotechnical Journal, 16, pp.121–139.

Harr, M. E. (1966) *Foundations of Theoretical Soil Mechanics.* McGraw-Hill, New York.

Jennings, J. E. B. and Burland, J. B. (1962) *Limitations to the use of effective stresses in partly saturated soils.* Géotechnique, 12 (2), pp. 125–144.

Mitchell, J. K. (1993) *Fundamentals of Soil Behaviour.* 2nd edn, John Wiley, New York.

Newmark, N. M. (1942) *Influence charts for computation of stresses in elastic foundations.* Engineering experiment station bulletin, No 338, University of Illinois.

Poulos, H. G. and Davis, E. H. (1974) *Elastic Solutions for Soil and Rock Mechanics.* John Wiley, New York.

Sills, G. C., Wheeler, S. J., Thomas, S. D. and Gardner, T. N. (1991) *Behaviour of off-shore soils containing gas bubbles.* Géotechnique, 41 (2), pp. 227–241.

Terzaghi, K. (1936) *The shearing resistance of saturated soils.* Proceedings of the 1st International Conference on Soil Mechanics, Harvard, pp. 54–56.

Terzaghi, K. and Peck, R. B. (1967) *Soil Mechanics in Engineering Practice.* Wiley, New York.

Thomas, H. R. and He, Y. (1998) *Modelling the behaviour of unsaturated soil using an elastoplastic constitutive model.* Géotechnique, 48 (5), pp. 589–603.

Timoshenko, S. P. and Goodier, J. N. (1970) *Theory of Elasticity.* 3rd edn, McGraw-Hill, International edition, Singapore.

Toll, D. G. (1990) *A framework for unsaturated soil behaviour.* Géotechnique, 40 (1), pp. 31–44.

Wheeler, S. J. (1991) *An alternative framework for unsaturated soil behaviour,* Géotechnique, 41 (2), pp. 257–261.

CHAPTER 4

Seepage flow

4.1 Introduction

The *flow* of water within a soil mass depends, by and large, on the soil *porosity*, in other words on the space between solid particles. A flow of water within a porous medium occurs when there is an energy imbalance, in which case, water flows from the high level energy towards the low level energy. Daniel Bernoulli established that in the case of an *incompressible* (*i.e.* constant density) *inviscid* (*i.e.* non-viscous) *fluid*, the *total energy,* often referred to as *total head* in a *steady pipe flow* remains constant regardless of the position of the point, within the flow domain, at which it is measured. Referring to figure 4.1, Bernoulli's equation is written as follows :

$$h = z + \frac{u}{\gamma_w} + \frac{v^2}{2g} = constant \qquad (4.1)$$

where z is the *elevation head* above any arbitrarily chosen datum, the quantity u/γ_w represents the *pressure head* which is in fact the height to which water would rise in a standpipe inserted into the pipe as shown in the figure, the quantity $v^2/2g$ being the *velocity head*.

N.B. A steady flow means that the velocity does not vary with time, i.e. $\partial v/\partial t = 0$

However, the nature of groundwater flow differs from that of a pipe flow in the sense that, for water to flow through a soil, it has to negotiate its way through the spaces existing between solid particles. This is bound to lead to a *loss of energy* through friction that must be accounted for in equation 4.1. Moreover, in most cases of interest in engineering practice, the flow of water in a *saturated soil* (the only type of soil under consideration) occurs at a steady state and at low velocities. Water therefore moves in layers or

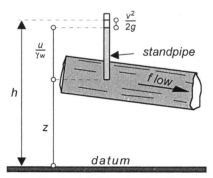

Figure 4.1: Steady pipe flow.

laminae and the corresponding flow is known as *laminar flow*. It has been established that, for a saturated soil, laminar flow conditions are maintained if Reynolds number *Re* is kept smaller than 10 (Bear (1972)), with:

$$Re = v d \, \rho / \mu \qquad (4.2)$$

where v is the discharge velocity, d is the (average) diameter of soil particles, μ is the coefficient of dynamic viscosity, and ρ is the fluid density. Under these conditions (*i.e.* soil saturation and laminar flow), an upper bound discharge velocity of 0.3 *m/s* is typical, leading to a velocity head $v^2/2g = 9 \times 10^{-2}/2 \times 9.81 = 0.0046\,m$. Considering that in all probability, the discharge velocity for most saturated sands and sandy clays will be below 0.3 *m/s*, it is clear that the velocity head can be discarded. Consequently, the total head h in equation 4.1 is no longer constant because of the loss of energy due to friction, and equation 4.1, applied to groundwater flow then becomes:

$$h = z + \frac{u}{\gamma_w} \qquad (4.3)$$

where u represents the porewater pressure and z is as per figure 4.1. The *total head loss* between any two points, due to water flow in a saturated soil is, with respect to figure 4.2:

$$\Delta h = h_1 - h_2$$

or

$$\Delta h = z_1 - z_2 + \frac{1}{\gamma_w}(u_1 - u_2) \qquad (4.4)$$

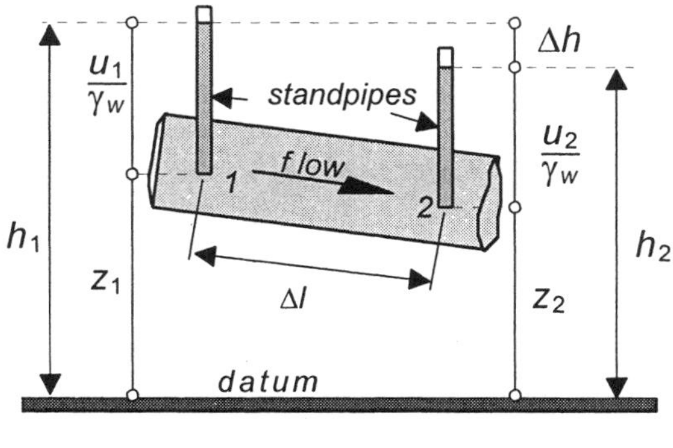

Figure 4.2: Flow in a saturated soil.

It therefore emerges that any flow rate results in a total head loss, the extent of which is related to the length of the flow path: the longer the water travels within the soil mass, the more it is subject to friction and the higher the energy loss. The opposite argument is also valid: the higher the total head loss, the longer the water has to travel within the soil mass, thus developing more friction. Whichever argument is considered, it is obvious that the flow of water within a soil mass is related to both total head loss Δh and flow path length Δl (see figure 4.2).

4.2 Darcy's law, seepage forces, critical hydraulic gradient

As early as 1856, Henri Darcy established the following simple yet powerful empirical relationship between the *rate of flow q*, the *permeability* of soil *k* and the gradient of flow *i*, better known as the *hydraulic gradient*:

$$q = Aki \qquad\qquad (4.5)$$

where *A* is the area of flow. Because the quantity *q/A* represents the flow velocity, Darcy's law is often written as:

$$v = ki \qquad\qquad (4.6)$$

with the *hydraulic gradient* defined as follows (refer to figure 4.2):

$$i = \frac{h_2 - h_1}{\Delta l} = -\frac{\Delta h}{\Delta l} \qquad\qquad (4.7)$$

so that at the limit, when $\Delta l \to 0$:

$$i = -\frac{\partial h}{\partial l} \qquad\qquad (4.8)$$

The flow velocity *v* in equation 4.6 is *assumed* to be proportional to the hydraulic gradient *i*, thus meaning that the coefficient of permeability *k* of the soil mass is constant. Accordingly, the validity of (the empirical) Darcy's law depends to a large extent on the coefficient *k* which must be carefully determined so as to be representative of the soil mass. The practical aspects related to the measurement of *k* will be thoroughly discussed shortly. However, at this stage, it is worth remembering that Darcy's law can be safely applied as long as the flow remains *laminar*. This condition is best discussed in terms of Reynolds number of equation 4.2. In fact, conclusive evidence indicates that *linear laminar* groundwater flow conditions are achieved when $1 \le Re \le 10$. Outside these boundaries *non-linear laminar* flow occurs up to $Re \approx 100$, beyond which Darcy's law is no longer valid. Consequently, equation 4.6, though still valid, is *no longer linear* at *high flow rates* through highly porous media such as fissured rocks for which $10 \le Re \le 100$; similarly, there is *non-linearity* between the *velocity* and the *hydraulic gradient* in the case of groundwater flow under *very low* hydraulic gradients corresponding to $Re < 1$.

Moreover, the velocity used in equation 4.6 is in fact an apparent (or a fictitious) one since it represents the velocity over a cross-sectional area A (refer to figure 4.3) composed of solids through which water *cannot* flow and voids *via* which water seeps. Therefore, the *actual seepage velocity v_s* is n-times the apparent velocity of equation 4.6, n being the soil's porosity, hence:

$$v_s = \frac{v}{n} = v\frac{(1 + e)}{e} \qquad (4.9)$$

Because the porosity $n < 1$, it follows that the actual seepage velocity is larger than the artificial velocity of equation 4.6.

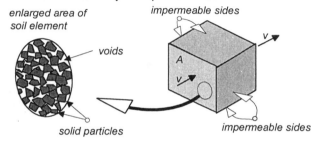

Figure 4.3: Actual seepage velocity.

The flow of water generates *seepage forces* within the soil mass, thus affecting the *effective stresses* (*i.e.* the contact pressure between solid particles). The change in effective stresses depends therefore on the orientation of these seepage forces, in other words on the direction of flow. Consider the simple flow cases represented in figure 4.4, simulating an upward and a downward water flow through a layer of an isotropic sand. In both cases, the hydraulic gradient throughout the soil is:

$$i = \frac{h}{l} \qquad (4.10)$$

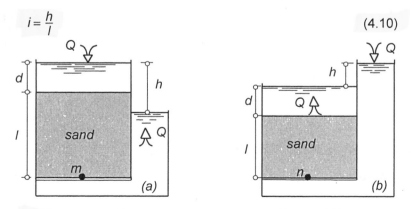

Figure 4.4: (a) Downward and (b) upward flow through an isotropic soil.

Let us now assess the stresses at the bottom of the sand layer (points m and n), starting with the downward flow (figure 4.4a). The *total stress* at m is:

$$\sigma_m = d\gamma_w + l\gamma_{sat} \qquad (4.11)$$

where γ_{sat} represents the saturated unit weight of sand and γ_w is the unit weight of water. The porewater pressure at the same point is calculated as follows:

$$u_m = (l + d - h)\gamma_w \qquad (4.12)$$

By virtue of the effective stress principle, the *effective stress* at m can now be found:

$$\sigma'_m = \sigma_m - u_m = l(\gamma_{sat} - \gamma_w) + h\gamma_w \qquad (4.13)$$

Using the effective unit weight of sand $\gamma' = (\gamma_{sat} - \gamma_w)$, and substituting for the hydraulic gradient from equation 4.10, the expression of the effective stress becomes:

$$\sigma'_m = l(\gamma' + i\gamma_w) \qquad (4.14)$$

For the upward flow case (figure 4.4b), equation 4.11 applies for the calculation of the total stress at point n. The porewater pressure however is now calculated as follows:

$$u_n = (l + d + h)\gamma_w \qquad (4.15)$$

therefore the effective stress at n is:

$$\sigma'_n = l(\gamma' - i\gamma_w) \qquad (4.16)$$

It is now becoming clear from equations 4.14 and 4.16 that the effective stresses depend on the direction of flow. This is illustrated in figure 4.5 where the *effective forces*, that is the effective stresses times the selected area of flow A, can be calculated at any depth on each side of the cut-off wall provided that the hydraulic gradient is known. Hence, on the upstream side (behind the wall):

$$A\sigma'_m = Az_m(\gamma' + i\gamma_w) \qquad (4.17)$$

and on the exit side (in front of the wall):

$$A\sigma'_n = Az_n(\gamma' - i\gamma_w) \qquad (4.18)$$

The *effective force* $A\sigma'$ exerted at any depth is therefore composed of the *effective weight of soil* $Az\gamma'$ at that depth and a *seepage force* $Azi\gamma_w$, the sign of which depends on the direction of flow as per equations 4.17 and 4.18.

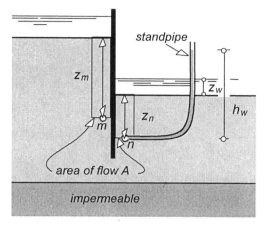

Figure 4.5: Effective stress calculations related to seepage flow.

One more important implication of the previous derivations concerns the upward flow on the downstream side of figure 3.5, represented by equation 4.18 above. This equation yields a zero effective stress when the hydraulic gradient reaches the *critical* value γ'/γ_w. Hence, using equation 2.20 established in section 2.1:

$$i_{cr} = \gamma'/\gamma_w = (G_s - 1)/(1 + e) \qquad (4.19)$$

Under such conditions, there is little or no contact between solid particles, and consequently, the sand loses its entire shear strength and behaves like a liquid. This is known as *quick conditions* which are also referred to as *piping* when they develop in a localised area. The hydraulic gradient occurring in a sand must therefore be kept smaller than the critical value at all times. The margin of safety must be such that the factor of safety against quick conditions should be at least three, ideally four or more. Notice that according to equation 4.19, $i_{cr} \approx 1$ for the vast majority of sands (loose to dense). The expression of the *critical hydraulic gradient* of equation 4.19, derived using seepage forces and effective stresses, can also be established using the following total stress analysis. Consider the soil element represented in broken lines in figure 4.5 with a depth z_n and a flow area A. A straightforward stress analysis indicates that the *total stress* applied at the bottom of the element is as follows:

$$\sigma_n = \gamma_w z_w + \gamma_{sat} z_n$$

γ_{sat} being the unit weight of saturated soil. When the element is on the verge of failure, the above total stress must balance the porewater pressure at the element base caused by the upward flow and calculated in the following manner:

$$u = h_w \gamma_w$$

Hence, equating these two quantities, then rearranging, it follows that:

$$h_w = \left(\frac{\gamma_{sat}}{\gamma_w}\right) z_n + z_w \qquad (4.20)$$

On the other hand, the hydraulic gradient calculated at the base of the element is, with reference to figure 4.5:

$$i = \frac{h_w - (z_n + z_w)}{z_n} \qquad (4.21)$$

and thus, substituting for h_w from equation 4.20 into equation 4.21 and rearranging, it is seen that:

$$i_{cr} = \left(\frac{\gamma_{sat} - \gamma_w}{\gamma_w}\right) = \frac{\gamma'}{\gamma_w} \qquad (4.22)$$

which is identical to equation 4.19 derived previously.

4.3 Permeability of soils

4.3.1 Introduction

The coefficient of permeability k of a soil is one of the key parameters on which depends the soil response to an applied loading. The rate of soil settlement, for instance, is related to the transfer from total to effective stresses. This transfer is dependent on the rate of dissipation of the excess porewater pressure induced by the loading which, in turn, depends on the ease with which water can seep through the tortuous paths connecting the voids within the soil matrix, i.e. the soil's permeability. The importance of this parameter is amplified by the difficulties associated with its measurement. This is mainly due to the fact that *permeability* is *variable* from point to point within the same soil mass because of the random arrangement of solid particles in any one direction. Moreover, k is dependent on the size of solid particles, and the *crude* empirical relationship attributed to Hazen for a variety of sands suggests that k is proportional to the square of the effective size d_{10}:

$$k \approx 10^{-2} \times d_{10}^2 \qquad (4.23)$$

where k is in m/s and d_{10} in mm. Hence there is a very wide range of *average* values of permeability associated with different types of soils as listed in the following:

gravel:	$> 10^{-2}$ m/s
sands:	$10^{-1} - 10^{-5}$ m/s
silts:	$10^{-4} - 10^{-7}$ m/s
clays:	$< 10^{-7}$ m/s

4.3.2 Laboratory measurement of the coefficient of permeability

The coefficient of permeability depends on the size of solid particles contained in a soil and on their arrangement within the soil matrix. Accordingly, it is of the utmost importance to use a *least disturbed sample* whenever the laboratory measurement of the permeability is required. Although it is accepted that some degree of disturbance is bound to occur during extraction, transportation and preparation of soil samples (especially in the case of granular soils), the operator must keep any disturbance to a minimum since a significant level of disturbance would render the measured values of permeability totally useless. Also, it can be argued that, apart from the effect of sample disturbance, the physical significance of the measured k value is largely affected by the sample size and soil structure: the smaller the sample dimensions, the less representative the permeability. Most importantly, it is well known that the vast majority of soils *in situ* are anisotropic, with a horizontal permeability far in excess of the vertical one (sometimes by three orders of magnitude). Since the flow regime applied during laboratory tests is one dimensional (*i.e.* vertical), the measured permeability is therefore expected to be well below the *actual in situ* permeability of the soil. Moreover, the permeability of a soil is affected by the viscosity of the porewater and is therefore temperature dependent (Cedergren, 1967). In this respect, the following temperature correction can be applied cautiously:

$$k_T = \frac{k_{20}}{\xi} \qquad (4.24)$$

where k_{20} represents the permeability at the standard temperature of $20°C$, k_T the permeability measured at a temperature T, and ξ is a correction factor as per figure 4.6.

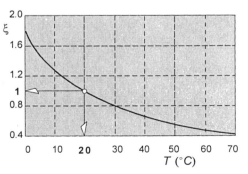

Figure 4.6: Correction related to temperature variation.

Notwithstanding these shortcomings, laboratory testing represents a useful tool that can be used to good effect to estimate the permeability of soil filters (refer to section 2.4). Two laboratory tests are widely used for permeability measurements: the falling head and the constant head tests.

•(a) Falling head test

This test is suited for relatively permeable soils (such as silts). The details of the falling head permeameter are shown in figure 4.7. According to Darcy's law, the flow rate is:

$$q = Ak\frac{h}{L} \qquad (4.25)$$

Referring to figure 3.7, it is seen that:

$$q = -a\frac{dh}{dt} \qquad (4.26a)$$

whence:
$$-a\frac{dh}{h} = \frac{Ak}{L}dt \qquad (4.26b)$$

and therefore:
$$k = \frac{La}{At} \ln \frac{h_1}{h_2} \qquad (4.27)$$

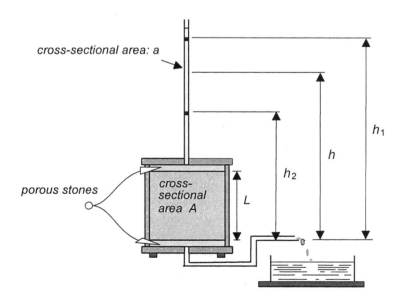

Figure 4.7: Falling head permeameter.

Example 4.1

A falling head test, undertaken on a sample of a fine silty sand 200 mm long and 100 mm in diameter, resulted in a drop of the total head $\Delta h = 400\,mm$ in a time $t = 120\,s$. Assuming the tube cross-sectional area is $a = 15\,mm^2$ and the total head $h_1 = 1200\,mm$, the permeability can then be estimated from equation 4.27:

$$k = \frac{200 \times 15}{\pi \times 50^2 \times 120} \times \ln\frac{1200}{(1200 - 400)} = 1.29 \times 10^{-3}\,mm/s$$

If the temperature in the field is only $12°C$, then the above coefficient of permeability has to be corrected according to figure 4.6 which yields a correction factor $\xi \approx 1.2$. Hence:

$$k_{12} = \frac{1.29}{1.2} \times 10^{-6} \approx 1.08 \times 10^{-6}\,m/s$$

•(b) Constant head permeameter

For more permeable soils such as sands, the constant head permeameter sketched in figure 4.8 is more suited for the measurement of permeability. According to Darcy's law, the coefficient of permeability in this case is expressed as follows:

$$k = q\frac{L}{hA} \qquad (4.28)$$

with L: length of the flow path,
h: total head loss as per figure 4.8,
A: cross-sectional area of the sample,
q: the flow rate.

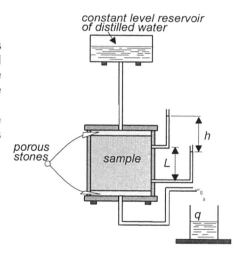

Figure 4.8: Constant head permeameter.

4.3.3 *In situ* measurement of permeability

In situ tests yield more reliable and representative values of the coefficient of permeability than laboratory tests. Not only are these tests undertaken on sites where the soil disturbance is kept to a minimum, but also they involve a larger and therefore a more representative soil volume.

The analysis of field tests is related to the type of *aquifer* (*i.e.* the permeable layer of soil) and involves *pumping* water from a well at a *steady rate* while noting the *drawdown* (or the lowering) of the *piezometric surface* (*i.e.* the surface at which the water pressure is atmospheric) at nearby observation wells.

• Pumping test: confined radial flow

In the case of a *confined aquifer*, the permeable stratum is sandwiched between two relatively impermeable soil layers as depicted in figure 4.9. Accordingly, for a well penetrating the full thickness of the aquifer, the flow is everywhere horizontal and the hydraulic gradient can be estimated as follows:

$$i = \frac{dh}{dr} \tag{4.29}$$

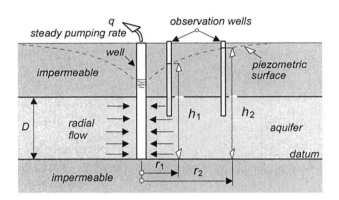

Figure 4.9: Confined radial flow.

Knowing that at a distance r from the well centre, the area through which flow occurs is $A = 2\pi r D$, and substituting for the hydraulic gradient i in Darcy's law of equation 3.5 leads to:

$$q = A k i = 2\pi k D r \frac{dh}{dr} \tag{4.30}$$

Hence:

$$q \int_{r_1}^{r_2} \frac{dr}{r} = 2\pi D k \int_{h_1}^{h_2} dh \tag{4.31}$$

and therefore:

$$k = \frac{q}{2\pi D} \frac{\ln\left(\frac{r_2}{r_1}\right)}{(h_2 - h_1)} \tag{4.32}$$

Note that when the piezometric level is above the ground surface, in other words when the water level inside a well inserted into the confined aquifer rises above the ground surface as depicted in figure 4.10, then *Artesian* conditions are said to prevail.

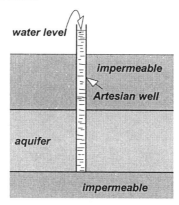

Figure 4.10: Artesian conditions.

• Pumping test: unconfined radial flow

For an *unconfined aquifer*, the permeable stratum is not overlain by an impermeable soil layer, and therefore the piezometric surface is the same as the *phreatic* surface or the *water table* as illustrated in figure 4.11. In such a case, the direction of flow towards a well inserted through the aquifer is not horizontal; however, the slope of the phreatic surface is very small according to Dupuit approximation, and therefore *the hydraulic gradient can still be calculated from equation* 4.29. The area of flow at a distance *r* from the well centre is $A = 2\pi rh$, and from Darcy's law:

$$q = A k i = 2\pi k h r \frac{dh}{dr} \tag{4.33}$$

Once integrated between the limits indicated in figure 4.11, the coefficient of permeability can then be established:

$$k = \frac{q}{\pi} \frac{\ln\left(\frac{r_2}{r_1}\right)}{\left(h_2^2 - h_1^2\right)} \tag{4.34}$$

The quantities h_1 and h_2 in equation 4.34 only represent an *approximation* of the heights to which water would rise inside the standpipes. This is due to the fact that the flow is not radial as stated earlier.

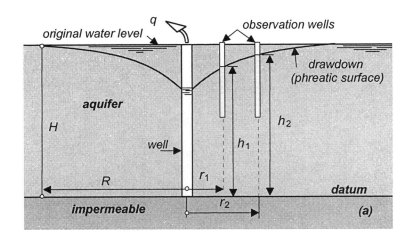

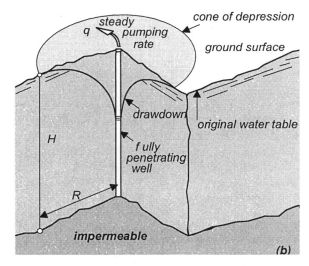

Figure 4.11: (a) Cross-sectional view of unconfined flow, (b) 3-D view.

Although the principles of flownets are yet to be detailed, figure 4.12 shows that water inside the standpipe nearest to the well rises a distance h_o corresponding to the level of the point of intersection of the equipotential line and the phreatic surface. In contrast, water is assumed to rise to the level h_1 in equation 4.34. However, it can be seen from the figure that the difference $(h_1 - h_o)$ is small and consequently, for all practical purposes, Dupuit assumption used in conjunction with equation 4.34 is in most cases appropriate.

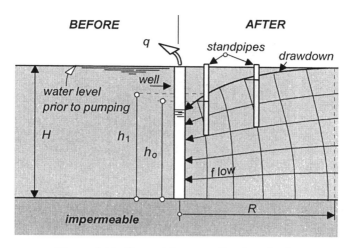

Figure 4.12: Flownet for unconfined radial flow.

• Pumping test: spherical flow

If the impermeable stratum is underlain by an aquifer of infinite thickness as illustrated in figure 4.13, a well can only partially penetrate the permeable layer. Under these circumstances, water flows radially towards the *well base* and the flow is spherical in nature. Consider the case of a well driven down to *the top* of the permeable stratum. Assuming the hydraulic gradient can still be calculated using equation 4.29, and knowing that at a distance r from the well centre, the area of the hemisphere through which flow occurs is $A = 2\pi r^2$, Darcy's law then yields:

$$q = A\,k\,i = 2\pi k r^2 \frac{dh}{dr} \qquad (4.35)$$

taking the well base as datum:

$$q \int_{r_1}^{r_2} \frac{dr}{r^2} = 2\pi k \int_{h_1}^{h_2} dh \qquad (4.36)$$

thence the expression of k:

$$k = \frac{q}{2\pi} \frac{(r_2 - r_1)}{(h_2 - h_1)\, r_2\, r_1} \qquad (4.37)$$

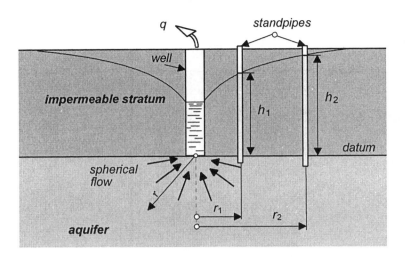

Figure 4.13: Spherical flow.

4.3.4 Design of dewatering systems

Apart from being used to yield estimates of soil permeability *in situ*, pumping wells are often used to reduce the groundwater level (in the case of unconfined flow) or the piezometric level (for confined flow) around an excavation so that work can proceed under *dry safe* conditions. An adequate reduction of the ground water or piezometric levels automatically reduces the porewater pressure applied at the bottom of excavation, thus ensuring an appropriate degree of safety against failure due to piping or to bottom heave. The design of dewatering systems depends on the type of flow (confined or unconfined) and also on the *recharge boundaries*. The following formalism applies to the case of *radial flow* (refer to figures 4.9 and 4.11). Excavations made near a river or a lake have different recharge boundaries and should be treated accordingly (see Tomlinson (1995), Somerville (1986)).

• Case of confined radial flow

Consider the case of an excavation of a size $a \times b$ to be made in a layer of relatively impermeable soil underlain by a confined aquifer of sand of a known permeability k. To ensure safety *vis à vis* bottom heave failure, relief wells (called thus because their use induces a relief in porewater pressure at the bottom of excavation) are to be installed in sufficient numbers so that the original piezometric level is reduced by a distance d_w at the centre of excavation as depicted in figure 4.14.

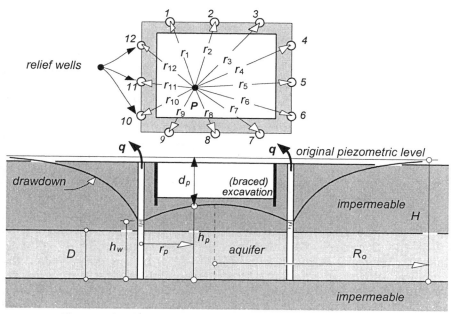

Figure 4.14: Relief wells system for confined radial flow.

In order to determine the number of wells needed to achieve a *drawdown* d_w, one has to estimate the total quantity of water to be pumped around the excavation. To do so, the entire excavation is assumed to act as an equivalent well with an average radius R_w corresponding to the area of excavation:

$$ab = \pi R_w^2 \quad \Rightarrow \quad R_w = \left(\frac{ab}{\pi}\right)^{1/2} \tag{4.38}$$

Under these circumstances, the drawdown corresponds to :

$$d_w = H - h_w$$

Equation 4.32 can thence be rearranged to calculate the total quantity of flow that needs to be pumped :

$$Q = 2\pi Dk \frac{d_w}{\ln\left(\frac{R_o}{R_w}\right)} \tag{4.39}$$

where the quantity R_o corresponds to the *radius of influence* of the equivalent well. If the soil is assumed homogeneous and isotropic, then the flow towards the well is radially symmetrical, and the drawdown d_w

decreases as the radial distance from the well centre increases. The radius of influence corresponds to the radial distance (from the well centre) beyond which the drawdown is zero (*i.e.* the radius beyond which the piezometric level remains unchanged). On the other hand, equation 4.39 indicates that the radius R_o is not constant, since an increase in the drawdown d_w or in soil permeability k results in an increase in R_o. In practice, the radius of influence is very difficult to measure accurately. However, equation 3.39 indicates that R_o occurs within a natural logarithm term and, as such, there is no need for such a quantity to be known with great accuracy. Accordingly, in the case of plane flow within an isotropic soil R_o can be estimated from Sichardt's empirical relationship (see Somerville, (1986)):

$$R_o \approx C d_w \sqrt{k}$$
(4.40)

where d_w represents the drawdown (in *metres*), k is the soil permeability (in *m/s*), and C is a constant with a value of between 1500 and 2000 (in $[s/m]^{1/2}$) for plane flow. Once the total quantity of flow is estimated, the number n of wells is then found by assuming that identical pumps yielding an identical discharge q under steady state conditions are used for each well. This assumption is realistic as long as the wells are equally spaced around the excavation. Under such conditions, the *drawdown* at *any* point such as P in figure 4.14 can be calculated using the superposition principle in conjunction with equation 4.32:

$$H - h_p = \frac{q}{2\pi D k} \sum_{j=1}^{n} \ln\left(\frac{R_o}{r_j}\right)$$
(4.41)

with : q: flow rate from each individual well,
r_j: radial distance from point P to the centre of well j
(see figure 3.14).

Example 4.2

Consider the case of a $55\,m \times 45\,m$ excavation to be made in a $20\,m$ thick layer of firm clay underlain by a $15\,m$ thick layer of sand as depicted in figure 4.14. Preliminary investigation indicated that artesian conditions prevail in that the original piezometric level was found to be $1\,m$ above the ground surface. Furthermore, carefully undertaken measurements from a pumping test carried out on a well penetrating the entire sand layer revealed that the piezometric levels at two observations wells $15\,m$ and $75\,m$ from the pumping well were reduced by $0.98\,m$ and $0.35\,m$ respectively; the corresponding steady state flow rate being $q = 7 \times 10^{-2}\,m^3/s$.

Because of the substantial depth of excavation, it is suggested that a minimum drawdown $d_w = 10.5\,m$ must be achieved at the *centre* of excavation so as to avoid any potential bottom heave. Check if this condition can be achieved using the arrangement depicted in figure 4.14, assuming the radius of influence of the entire pumped zone is $R_o = 900\,m$. First, the permeability of the aquifer must be evaluated. According to the measurements from the observation wells, and using the stated dimensions with the bottom of the sand layer as datum, it is seen that:

- *observation well 1:* $h_1 = (15 + 20 + 1) - 0.98 = 35.02\,m$, $r_1 = 15\,m$,
- *observation well 2 :* $h_2 = 36 - 0.35 = 35.65\,m$, $r_2 = 75\,m$.

Hence, from equation 4.32:

$$k = \frac{q}{2\pi D}\frac{\ln\left(\frac{r_2}{r_1}\right)}{(h_2 - h_1)} = \frac{7\times 10^{-2}}{2\times\pi\times 15}\times\frac{\ln(75/15)}{(35.65 - 35.02)} \approx 1.9\times 10^{-3}\,m/s$$

Next, the radius of the equivalent well is calculated from equation 4.38:

$$R_w = \left[\frac{50\times 45}{\pi}\right]^{1/2} = 26.76\,m$$

The total quantity of flow that needs to be pumped is then estimated from equation 4.39:

$$Q = 2\pi Dk\frac{d_w}{\ln\left(\frac{R_o}{R_w}\right)} = 2\pi\times 15\times 1.9\times 10^{-3}\times\frac{10.5}{\ln(900/26.76)} \approx 535\times 10^{-3}\,m^3/s$$

Accordingly, the capacity of each pump is such that:

$$q = Q/12 = 44.6\times 10^{-3}\,m^3/s$$

and therefore 12 pumps, each with a capacity $q = 2800\,litres/\min$ (that is $4.6\times 10^{-2}\,m^3/s$) can be selected.

Now the drawdown at the *centre* of excavation (where the total head is h_c) is checked using equation 4.41:

$$H - h_c = d_w = \frac{q}{2\pi Dk}\sum_{j=1}^{12}\ln\left(\frac{R_o}{r_j}\right)$$

Referring to figure 4.15, a straightforward calculation yields the following radii with respect to the centre of excavation:

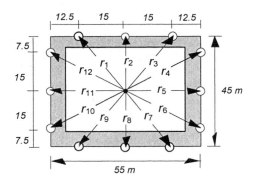

Figure 4.15: Radial distances in the case of example 3.2.

$r_1 = r_3 = r_7 = r_9 = [15^2 + 22.5^2]^{1/2} = 27.04\,m$
$r_2 = r_8 = 22.5\,m$
$r_4 = r_6 = r_{10} = r_{12} = [15^2 + 27.5^2]^{1/2} = 31.32\,m$
$r_5 = r_{11} = 27.5\,m$

Whence: $d_w = \dfrac{4.6 \times 10^{-2}}{2\pi \times 15 \times 1.9 \times 10^{-3}}[4\ln(900/27.04) + 2\ln(900/22.5)$

$+\; 4\ln(900/31.32) + 2\ln(900/27.5)] \;=\; 10.72\,m$

Note that in practice, such a drawdown depth would require the use immersed pumps.

• Case of unconfined radial flow

In this case, a similar analysis to that used for confined radial flow, this time based on equation 4.34, results in the following equation in the case of *n* wells, each yielding a flow quantity *q* as depicted in figure 4.16:

$$H^2 - h_p^2 = \frac{q}{\pi k} \sum_{j=1}^{n} \ln\left(\frac{R_o}{r_j}\right) \qquad (4.42)$$

Example 4.3

Assume the same excavation of example 4.2 is to be made in a 20 *m* thick layer of a silty sand with a permeability $k = 4 \times 10^{-4}\,m/s$, underlain by a relatively impermeable soil. . Estimate the capacity of pumps needed to achieve a minimum drawdown $d_p = 8\,m$ at point *P* with the co-ordinates $(-8\,m, -4\,m)$ with respect to the excavation centre point as depicted in figure 4.16. The original water table is at ground level, and the radius of influence of the entire pumped zone is assumed to be $R_o = 700\,m$.

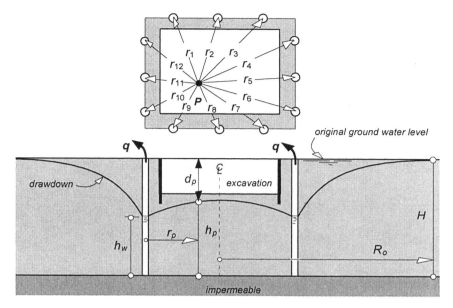

Figure 4.16: Wells system for unconfined radial flow.

The radius of the equivalent well, calculated previously is $R_w = 26.7\,m$, and therefore the total quantity of water that needs to be pumped to achieve the required drawdown $d_p = 8\,m$ at P can be estimated from equation 4.34:

$$Q = \pi k \frac{\left(H^2 - h_p^2\right)}{\ln\left(\frac{R_o}{R_w}\right)}$$

with $d_p = H - h_p \;\Rightarrow\; h_p = 20 - 8 = 12\,m$. Accordingly:

$$Q = \pi \times 4 \times 10^{-4} \times \frac{(20^2 - 12^2)}{\ln(700/26.76)} = 98.6 \times 10^{-3}\,m^3/s$$

With the 12 wells rearranged as in figure 4.16, the capacity of individual pumps is such that:

$q = Q/12 = 8.2 \times 10^{-3}\,m^3/s$

Therefore pumps with a capacity $q = 8.33 \times 10^{-3}\,m^3/s$ (that is 500 *litres/* min) can be used. Moreover, the following radii (in *m*) are calculated from the dimensions of excavation indicated in figure 4.15, in conjunction with the position of point P in figure 4.16:

r_1	r_2	r_3	r_4	r_5	r_6	r_7	r_8	r_9	r_{10}	r_{11}	r_{12}
27.4	27.7	35.1	40.3	35.7	37.2	29.5	20.1	19.8	22.4	19.9	27.2

Whence: $\qquad \sum\limits_{j=1}^{12} \ln\left(\frac{R_o}{r_j}\right) = \sum\limits_{j=1}^{12} \ln\left(\frac{700}{r_j}\right) = 38.76$

According to equation 3.34: $\qquad H^2 - h_p^2 = (q/\pi k) \sum\limits_{j=1}^{12} \ln(R_o/r_j) \qquad \Rightarrow$

$$h_p = \left[20^2 - \frac{8.33 \times 10^{-3}}{\pi \times 4 \times 10^{-4}} \times 38.76 \right]^{1/2} = 11.96 \, m$$

and the drawdown at point P:

$$d_p = H - h_p = 20 - 11.96 = 8.04 \, m$$

4.4 Seepage theory

4.4.1 Governing flow equation

For the typical soil element in figure 4.17 representing the flow of an *incompressible* fluid through a *fully saturated* soil, the condition of continuity requires that the quantity of water flowing through the entrance faces of the element *must* equal that emerging at the opposite exit faces.

Using Darcy's law in the form of equation 4.8, the hydraulic gradients at the entrance faces of the element are:

$$i_x = \partial h/\partial x \qquad\qquad (4.43a)$$
$$i_y = \partial h/\partial y \qquad\qquad (4.43b)$$
$$i_z = \partial h/\partial z \qquad\qquad (4.43c)$$

At the exit faces, the hydraulic gradients are, respectively:

$$i_x + \frac{\partial i_x}{\partial x} dx = \frac{\partial h}{\partial x} + \frac{\partial}{\partial x}\left(\frac{\partial h}{\partial x}\right) dx = \frac{\partial h}{\partial x} + \frac{\partial^2 h}{\partial x^2} dx \qquad\qquad (4.44a)$$

$$i_y + \frac{\partial i_y}{\partial y} dy = \frac{\partial h}{\partial y} + \frac{\partial^2 h}{\partial y^2} dy \qquad\qquad (4.44b)$$

$$i_z + \frac{\partial i_z}{\partial z} dz = \frac{\partial h}{\partial z} + \frac{\partial^2 h}{\partial z^2} dz \qquad\qquad (4.44c)$$

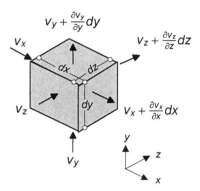

Figure 4.17: Flow through a typical soil element.

the quantity h in both sets of equations being the total head. Equating the flow quantities at the entrance to those at the exit faces leads to the *continuity equation*:

$$\frac{\partial v_x}{\partial x} + \frac{\partial v_y}{\partial y} + \frac{\partial v_z}{\partial z} = 0 \qquad (4.45)$$

Introducing Darcy's law in the form of equation 4.6 in the above expression, the general governing equation of flow can be established :

$$k_x \frac{\partial^2 h}{\partial x^2} + k_y \frac{\partial^2 h}{\partial y^2} + k_z \frac{\partial^2 h}{\partial z^2} = 0 \qquad (4.46)$$

This equation, represents the general expression of flow in the space (x, y, z), and indicates that the flow depends on the three components of permeability k_x, k_y, k_z. Assuming that the flow in figure 4.17 is mainly planar, and neglecting accordingly the flow component in the z-direction, equation 4.46 can then be reduced to the following:

$$k_x \frac{\partial^2 h}{\partial x^2} + k_y \frac{\partial^2 h}{\partial y^2} = 0 \qquad (4.47)$$

In practice, only few boundary value problems represented by the simple Laplacian associated with equation 4.47 have been solved analytically, principally because the boundary conditions related to the closed form solution of this equation are often difficult to satisfy. Fortunately, an approximate method of solution is at hand in that a graphical flownet, when drawn skilfully, can lead to accurate estimates of different parameters such as seepage quantities and porewater pressures. A brief description of the essential mathematical features of this technique follows.

4.4.2 Confined flow

When all boundaries of the flow domain are known *ab initio*, the flow is referred to as *confined flow*. From a mathematical view point, equation 4.47 produces families of curves, four of which are plotted in figure 4.18. The curves referred to as *flow lines* represent the flow paths of trickles of water, whereas an *equipotential line* corresponds to a line through which the *total head* remains constant, so that if two standpipes were inserted at different locations in a way that their bases are on the same equipotential line, the water in both standpipes will rise to the same level as depicted in the figure. As one moves to the next equipotential line in the direction of flow, the total head drops by an amount Δh.

Let us examine the conditions that one *must* satisfy to obtain an acceptable flownet. With reference to figure 4.18, the slope of the flow line at the point *I* (where it crosses an equipotential line) is:

$$\tan \alpha = -\frac{v_y}{v_x} \tag{4.48}$$

N.B. The vectors v_x and dx are not represented in figure 4.18 for the sake of clarity.

Substituting for the velocity from equation 4.19:

$$\tan \alpha = -\frac{k_y}{k_x}\frac{\partial h/\partial y}{\partial h/\partial x} \tag{4.49}$$

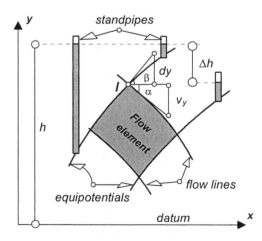

Figure 4.18: Flow and equipotential lines.

Moreover, the total head h has a constant value, with respect to any chosen datum, along any equipotential line, and in particular along the one passing through the point l. Under these circumstances, the total differential dh is zero, hence:

$$dh = \frac{\partial h}{\partial x}dx + \frac{\partial h}{\partial y}dy = 0 \qquad (4.50a)$$

alternatively :

$$\frac{dy}{dx} = -\frac{\partial h/\partial x}{\partial h/\partial y} \qquad (4.50b)$$

Furthermore, figure 4.18 shows that:

$$\frac{dy}{dx} = \tan\beta \qquad (4.51)$$

where b represents the slope of the equipotential line at l. We now, therefore, have a relationship between a and b such that:

$$\tan\beta = \frac{k_y}{k_x}\frac{1}{\tan\alpha} \qquad (4.52)$$

Three cases arise from the above equation as follows.

• (a) Case of isotropic homogeneous soils

In this case, by virtue of isotropy, $k_x = k_y$ and, accordingly, equation 4.47 becomes a *Laplace* equation:

$$\frac{\partial^2 h}{\partial x^2} + \frac{\partial^2 h}{\partial y^2} = 0 \qquad (4.53)$$

equation 4.52 is thence reduced to:

$$\tan\beta - \frac{1}{\tan\alpha} = 0$$

which has a solution : $\alpha + \beta = \frac{\pi}{2}$.

This solution implies that for *isotropic homogeneous soils*:

- the flow is *independent* of the *permeability*, and
- flow lines and equipotential lines always cross at *right angles*.

Also, figure 4.19 shows the total head h decreasing continuously in the direction of the flow, indicating that *adjacent equipotential lines must never cross*. It is also clear, from the same figure, that the quantity of water per unit length, flowing within any *flow channel* (*i.e.* the space between adjacent flowlines) is constant.

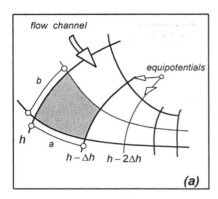
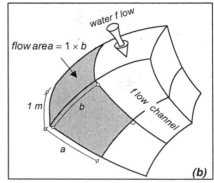

Figure 4.19 : (a) Flow and equipotential lines and (b) 3-D flow element.

Applying Dracy's law to the shaded element:

$$q = (1 \times b)\, k \frac{\Delta h}{a} \text{ per flow channel per unit length} \qquad (4.54)$$

If the flownet is drawn such that the elements of flow are *curvilinear squares*, then $b \approx a$ and:

$$q = k\Delta h \text{ per flow channel per unit length} \qquad (4.55)$$

Referring to the number of intervals between equipotential lines as N_d, the quantity Δh is then related to the total head h through the relationship :

$$\Delta h = \frac{h}{N_d} \qquad (4.56)$$

Accordingly, for a flownet having N_f flow channels, the total flow quantity per unit length is therefore:

$$Q = qN_f = kh\frac{N_f}{N_d} \text{ per unit length} \qquad (4.57)$$

Example 4.4

Figure 4.20 depicts an example of a confined flow represented by a sheet-pile cut-off wall driven in an isotropic homogeneous sand characterised by a permeability $k = 2 \times 10^{-5}\, m/s$, underlain by an impervious material. Let us estimate the quantity of flow per unit width of the wall, then calculate the distribution of the porewater pressure along the sheet-pile, as well as the exit hydraulic gradient and the factors of safety against piping and against bottom heave.

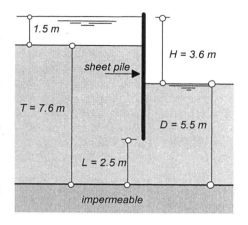

Figure 4.20: Sheet pile cut-off wall.

The corresponding flownet is depicted in figure 4.21. Notice that, in this case, the flownet has four flow channels and eleven equipotential lines labelled with their respective total heads in the figure (N_d being the number of intervals between adjacent equipotential lines); whence: $N_f = 4$, $N_d = 10$.

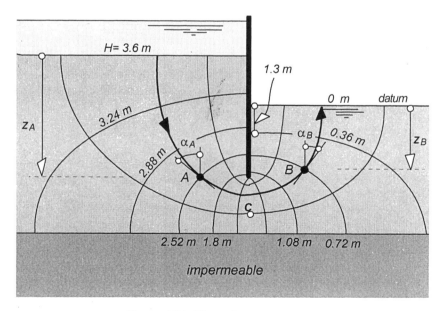

Figure 4.21: Flownet.

The flow quantity per unit width is therefore:

$$Q = kH\frac{N_f}{N_d} = \frac{2 \times 3.6 \times 4}{10} \times 10^{-5} = 2.88 \times 10^{-5}\ m^3/s\ per\ metre\ run$$

As for the porewater pressure, it can be estimated at any point from the flownet, since at any location, the total head as well as the elevation head (with respect to the chosen datum) can be measured. For example at point A, the total head is: $h_A = 2.52\ m$; the elevation head (scaled from the figure) being $y_A = -3.2\ m$. Similarly at B: $h_B = 0.72\ m$ and $y_B = -2.6\ m$. The porewater pressures at A and B are therefore (note the negative sign assigned to y_A & y_B due to the fact that both points A & B are situated below the datum line):

- $u_A = \gamma_w(h_A - y_A) \approx 10 \times (2.52 + 3.2) = 57.2\ kN/m^2$

- $u_B = \gamma_w(h_B - y_B) \approx 10 \times (0.72 + 2.6) = 33.2\ kN/m^2$

At the exit, the hydraulic gradient is measured from the square nearest to the pile at the top of the discharge area. From figure 4.21, the corresponding total head loss across the element is 0.36 *m,* and the flow path is 1.3 *m* long, thence:

$$i_e = \frac{0.36}{1.3} = 0.28$$

Using the critical hydraulic gradient defined earlier through equation 4.19, the factor of safety against piping (*i.e.* localised quick conditions) is:

$$F = \frac{i_{cr}}{i_e} \approx \frac{1}{0.28} = 3.6$$

Figure 4.22 illustrates the possibility of the soil mass, represented by the white element in front of the pile, failing by being carried upward by seepage forces. This may occur were the seepage forces at the element base to be larger than the submerged weight of the soil contained within the element. An adequate factor of safety is therefore essential in order to prevent this possibility from occurring. In this respect, the empirical Terzaghi procedure which consists of selecting an element with a volume $1 \times D \times D/2$, where D represents the depth of embedment as per figure 4.22, can be adopted. The factor of safety against bottom heave is therefore defined as the ratio of the submerged weight of the element to the upward seepage force exerted on its base:

$$F = \frac{\gamma_{sat}\frac{D^2}{2}}{u\frac{D}{2}} = \frac{\gamma_{sat}}{u}D \qquad (4.58)$$

where u represents the *average* porewater pressure exerted at the element base. Thus, referring to figure 4.22, it can be seen that both the total head and elevation head at the middle of the element base are: $h = 1.08\,m$, $h_e = -3\,m$. Hence a pressure head: $h_p = h - h_e = 4.08\,m$.

Assuming that the saturated unit weight of sand is $\gamma_{sat} = 21\,kN/m^3$, and knowing that $D = 3\,m$, equation 3.58 then yields the following factor of safety:

$$F = \frac{21}{4.08 \times 10} \times 3 = 1.54$$

Obviously this value is linked to that of the factor of safety against piping, whose value must be ideally 4 or more as suggested earlier.

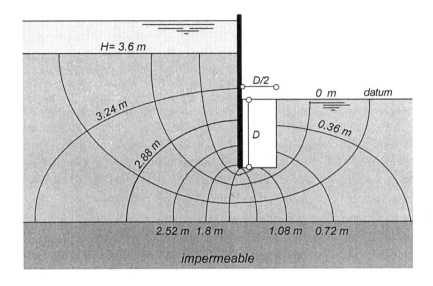

Figure 4.22: Bottom heave of an excavation.

• General case of effective stress calculations

Interestingly, the effective stresses can be calculated anywhere within the flow domain using a similar analysis to that developed earlier in section 4.2 in the case of vertical flow. However in this instance, the flow patterns represented by the flow lines in figure 4.21 are all curved, except from the two vertical flow lines corresponding to either side of the sheet pile, and the horizontal flow line representing the top of the impermeable stratum.

Consider the flow line in figure 4.21 containing points A, B, and C, for which the direction of flow is indicated by the black arrows. Both equations 4.14 & 4.16 developed in the case of vertical downward and upward flow can easily be extended to include any direction of flow.
- on the upstream side (such as point A in figure 4.21), the effective stress can be calculated as follows:

$$\sigma_A' = z_A(\gamma' + i_A.\gamma_w.\cos\alpha_A) \qquad (4.59a)$$

- on the downstream side (such as point B in figure 4.21):

$$\sigma' = z_B(\gamma' - i_B.\gamma_w.\cos\alpha_B) \qquad (4.59b)$$

In both equations, $\gamma' = (\gamma_{sat} - \gamma_w)$ is the effective unit weight of soil, i is the hydraulic gradient, α is the angle the tangent to the flow line at the point in question makes with respect to the vertical, and z is the depth from the saturated ground level to the point at which the effective stress is sought. Referring to figure 4.21, it is seen that at point C, the flow is horizontal, and therefore $\alpha_C = 90°$. Accordingly, the contribution to the effective stress due to the hydraulic gradient as per equations 4.59 reduces to zero, indicating that effective stresses are not affected by horizontal flow. As far as the effective stresses at points A and B in figure 4.21, the reader may wish to use the flownet solution to check the following quantities: $z_A = 5.3\,m$, $z_B = 2.6\,m$, $\alpha_A \approx 49°$, $\alpha_B \approx 32°$ Also, the hydraulic gradients (averaged from the 4 elements attached to each point) at both A & B are:

$$i_A \approx 0.29 \qquad\qquad i_B \approx 0.28$$

Thus, assuming the soil saturated unit weight is $\gamma_{sat} = 21\,kN/m^3$, and applying equations 4.59, it follows that:

$$\sigma_A' = 5.3 \times (11 + 0.29 \times 10 \times \cos 49) = 68.4\,kN/m^2$$

$$\sigma_B' = 2.6 \times (11 - 0.28 \times 10 \times \cos 32) = 22.4\,kN/m^2$$

The validity of these calculations can easily be checked using the effective stress principle equation 3.7 (see section 3.1), given that the porewater pressure at both points A and B were calculated earlier from the flownet of figure 4.21, and thus:

$$\sigma_A' = \sigma_A - u_A = 15 + 5.3 \times 21 - 57.2 = 69.1\,kN/m^2$$

$$\sigma_B' = \sigma_B - u_B = 2.6 \times 21 - 33.2 = 21.4\,kN/m^2$$

These results are similar to those calculated above using equations 4.59.

• (b) case of anisotropic homogeneous soils

Natural soils usually exhibit *anisotropic properties* since they have been, originally, laid down in layers. The values of horizontal and vertical permeabilities are, therefore, considerably *different*, and due to the formation process, the coefficient of permeability in the horizontal direction is usually higher (by as much as three orders of magnitude in some cases) than the one in the vertical direction. Consequently, the permeability of a homogeneous soil depends on the *direction of the flow*. Let us examine the three distinctive possibilities.

• (b.1) The water flow is parallel to the bedding

When dealing with anisotropic homogeneous soils, if the water flows parallel to the bedding (assumed to be horizontal), the entire soil mass can be considered to be isotropic if an *equivalent horizontal permeability* is used. Consider the case of horizontal flow represented in figure 4.23a where water seeps through n layers of soil, each of which having a thickness t and a permeability k. The total head loss is H, and the length of flow path is L. The figure indicates that the total flow quantity per metre width seeping through the soil is the sum of the flow passing *via* each layer:

$$Q = q_1 + q_2 + \ldots + q_n = \sum_{p=1}^{n} q_p$$

Moreover, the figure shows that all layers have the same hydraulic gradient: $i = H/L$.

Thus, in accordance with Darcy's law, the total flow quantity per unit width is:

$$Q = \frac{H}{L} \sum_{p=1}^{n} t_p k_p \qquad (4.60)$$

On the other hand, if, all other things being equal, the n layers of soil are replaced by a unique homogeneous layer of permeability k'_h as per figure 4.23b, with a thickness T (equal to the sum of individual thicknesses in figure 4.23a), then the total flow quantity seeping through the new layer becomes:

$$Q = T \frac{H}{L} k'_h \qquad (4.61)$$

Manifestly, the flow quantities given by equations 4.60 and 4.61 are identical, hence the *equivalent horizontal permeability*:

$$k'_h = \frac{\sum\limits_{p=1}^{n} t_p k_p}{\sum\limits_{p=1}^{n} t_p} \qquad (4.62)$$

where n is the number of layers and t and k are, respectively, the thickness and permeability of each individual layer.

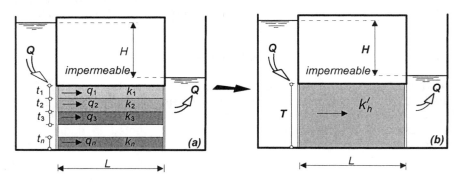

Figure 4.23: (a) Layered soil, (b) equivalent isotropic soil.

• (b.2) The water flow is perpendicular to the bedding

This time, the same total flow quantity per unit width seeps through each of the n soil layers represented in figure 4.24a in which the bottom layer is assumed to be infinitely permeable. Thence, for the pth layer, having a thickness l_p and a permeability k_p, Darcy's law states that::

$$Q = A k_p i_p \qquad (4.63)$$

where A represents the flow area which is identical to all layers. Furthermore, the thickness l_p is also the length of the flow path through the pth layer. Therefore, the corresponding hydraulic gradient is:

$$i_p = \frac{h_p}{l_p}$$

Inserting this quantity into equation 4.62 leads to the head loss occurring across the pth layer: $h_p = Q l_p / A k_p$. The total head loss can now be written as the sum of individual head losses:

$$H = \sum_{p=1}^{n} h_p = \frac{Q}{A} \sum_{p=1}^{n} \frac{l_p}{k_p} \qquad (4.64)$$

Consider what happens if the n layers were replaced by a single homogeneous layer, as in figure 4.24b, with a total thickness L equal to the sum of individual thicknesses, and a unique permeability k_v'. All other things being equal, the same quantity of flow Q seeps through the same area A and an identical total head loss H occurs across the flow path L. Making use of Darcy's law:

$$Q = A k_v' \frac{H}{L}$$

The quantity H in equation 4.64 can now be inserted into the above expression which, once rearranged yields the *equivalent vertical permeability* k_v':

$$k_v' = \frac{\displaystyle\sum_{p=1}^{n} l_p}{\displaystyle\sum_{p=1}^{n} l_p/k_p} \qquad (4.65)$$

The latter equation represents the equivalent vertical permeability in the case of a normal flow through a soil containing n layers, each of which has a thickness l and a coefficient of permeability k. It is clear from both equations 4.62 and 4.65 that the equivalent horizontal permeability is *larger* than the vertical one.

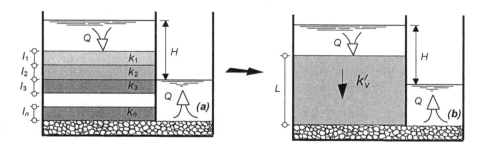

Figure 4.24: (a) Layered soil, (b) equivalent isotropic layer.

- **(b.3) The water flow is two-dimensional**

In this case, the flow is governed by equation 4.47 which can be rewritten as:

$$\frac{k_x}{k_y}\frac{\partial^2 h}{\partial x^2} + \frac{\partial^2 h}{\partial y^2} = 0 \qquad\qquad (4.66)$$

A closer analysis of the above equation indicates that a simple Laplacian may be engendered if an adequate change of variable is used. Let us rewrite the same equation using $X = cx$ (where c is a constant):

$$\frac{\partial^2 h}{\partial X^2} + \frac{\partial^2 h}{\partial y^2} = \frac{\partial^2 h}{\partial (cx)^2} + \frac{\partial^2 h}{\partial y^2} = 0 \qquad\qquad (4.67a)$$

or

$$\frac{\partial^2 h}{\partial X^2} + \frac{\partial^2 h}{\partial y^2} = \frac{1}{c^2}\frac{\partial^2 h}{\partial x^2} + \frac{\partial^2 h}{\partial y^2} = 0 \qquad\qquad (4.67b)$$

The constant c is then identified by comparing equations 4.66 and 4.67b:

$$c = \sqrt{k_y/k_x} \qquad\qquad (4.68)$$

The flow is therefore dependent on the ratio of horizontal to vertical permeabilities, and the flownet associated to equation 4.66 is characterised by curvilinear rectangles of a sides ratio $\sqrt{k_x/k_y}$. Furthermore, equation 4.52 indicates that, for $k_x \neq k_y$, equipotential and flow lines do *not* cross at right angles since, at any crossing point, the tangent to the flow line does not correspond to the normal to the equipotential line as was the case for isotropic soils. As a result, the flow net is this time harder to sketch because the sides of *every* quadrangle in the net must have a ratio $\sqrt{k_x/k_y}$.

However, by choosing a co-ordinate system whereby $X = x\sqrt{k_y/k_x}$, it is possible to create an artificial domain known as *the transformed section*, where the flow is represented by a Laplacian, and where the soil can be considered isotropic. The implications are that the corresponding flownet must satisfy the less stringent conditions of an isotropic soil, *i.e.* the elements of the mesh are curvilinear squares. Also, because the soil is isotropic in the transformed section, its coefficient of permeability has a unique value k_t known as the *transformed permeability*, and the flow is, hence, independent of the permeability, the result of which are right-angled crossings between flow and equipotential lines. The task of finding the expression of the transformed permeability k_t is greatly simplified by considering the vertical flow corresponding to figure 4.25.

Starting with the natural section, the flow quantity per unit length is :

$$Q = (L \times 1)\, k_y i$$

Within the transformed section, the same quantity of flow is calculated as follows:

$$Q = \left\lfloor 1 \times L\sqrt{k_y/k_x} \right\rfloor k_t i$$

Comparing the two expressions, the transformed permeability is then established:

$$k_t = \sqrt{k_x k_y} \tag{4.69}$$

The same expression could have been found using the flow in the *horizontal* direction. Remember, then, the hydraulic gradient changes from $i = H/L$ in the natural section to $i = H/L\sqrt{k_y/k_x}$ in the transformed section.

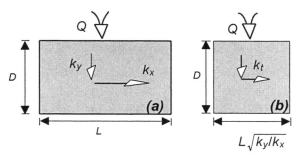

Figure 4.25: (a) *Flow through natural anisotropic section,* (b) *flow through transformed (isotropic) section.*

Example 4.5

Figure 4.26 depicts a concrete dam which is built on a layer of a homogeneous anisotropic clay having permeabilities $k_x = 16 \times 10^{-8}\,m/s$ and $k_y = 10^{-8}\,m/s$. To control seepage pressures, a cut-off sheet pile is driven on the upstream side of the dam to a depth of 4.6 m. Required are: the flow quantity seeping on the downstream side of the dam, the uplift force at the base of dam, the factor of safety against piping as well as the factor of safety against heave at the toe of the dam. Because of anisotropy, a flownet needs to be sketched on a transformed section. The dimensions represented in figure 3.26 need only be reduced in the horizontal direction by a factor:

$$c = \sqrt{k_y/k_x} = \frac{1}{4}$$

Within the transformed section, the soil is considered *isotropic* with a *transformed permeability*:

$$k_t = \sqrt{k_x k_y} = 4 \times 10^{-8}\,m/s$$

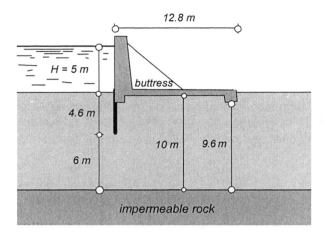

Figure 4.26: Flow through anisotropic soil.

The corresponding flownet, drawn in figure 4.27, has five flow channels ($N_f = 5$) and ten equipotential drops ($N_d = 10$). The flow quantity per unit length is therefore:

$$Q = k_t H \frac{N_F}{N_d} = 4 \times 5 \times \frac{5}{10} \times 10^{-8} \, m^3/s/m = 10^{-7} \, m^3/s/m$$

In order to calculate the uplift force applied to the base of the dam, one needs, first, to estimate the porewater pressure at the five selected points at the base of the dam represented by open circles in figure 4.27. The porewater pressure is calculated as follows:

$$u = \gamma_w(h - y)$$

where γ_w is the unit weight of water ($\approx 10 \, kN/m^3$), h is the total head (estimated from the flownet) and y is the elevation head (scaled from the flownet) with respect to the indicated datum. The following results correspond to the five points depicted in the figure, starting from the upstream side.

point	h (m)	y (m)	u (kN/m²)
1	1.20	−1.0	22.0
2	1.12	−0.6	17.2
3	1.04	−0.6	16.4
4	0.9	−0.6	15.0
5	0.6	−1.0	16.0

It is clear that the porewater pressure does not vary considerably at base level (bearing in mind that a transformed section is used and that the *actual* width of the base is 12.8 *m*). A value $u \approx 17\,kN/m^2$ represents a fair average of the porewater pressure at that level and, consequently, the uplift force per unit length beneath the dam is:

$$F_{up} = u \times area = 17 \times 12.8 \times 1 = 217.6\ kN/m$$

Now that the uplift force is known, the cross-sectional area of the dam in figure 4.27 can be chosen so that the total weight W per metre run of the dam can be calculated, securing in the process a factor of safety against uplift:

$$F = W/F_{up}$$

typically in the range 1.2 to 1.5. The exit hydraulic gradient i_e is estimated from the upper flow square nearest to the toe of the dam. This square is roughly 1.1 *m* long, and through it, the head drops by 0.5 *m*. Thus:

$$i_e = 0.5/1.1 = 0.45$$

Piping, which occurs at the toe of the dam, as illustrated in figure 4.28, can cause considerable damage and, therefore, there is a need for a good factor of safety to prevent piping from occurring. The factor of safety against piping is calculated according to the following:

$$F = i_{cr}/i_e \approx 1/0.45 = 2.22$$

i_{cr} being the critical hydraulic gradient.

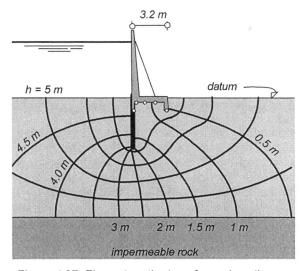

Figure 4.27: Flownet on the transformed section.

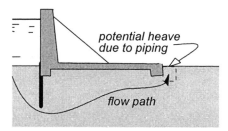

potential heave
due to piping

flow path

Figure 4.28: Piping related problems.

In practice, factors of safety against piping should have ideally a minimum value of 4, although some engineers would settle for smaller values. In this particular example, a larger factor of safety is needed, and this can be achieved by reducing the exit hydraulic gradient. For that to happen, the flow path must be increased so that the total head within the element of soil shown in broken lines (at the toe of the dam in figure 4.28) is substantially reduced. One solution consists of driving a sheet pile at the toe of the dam, or increasing the length of the pile used on the upstream side.   For the factor of safety against heave due to piping, equation 4.58 is applied. Considering therefore the prism shown in broken lines at the toe of the dam (figure 4.28) with dimensions of 1 *m* depth, 0.5 *m* width and 1 *m* length. The factor of safety against heave corresponds to the ratio of the *submerged weight* of the prism to the *uplift force* due to the porewater pressure at the base of the prism, that is:

$$F = \frac{(\gamma_{sat} - \gamma_w) \times 0.5 \times 1 \times 1}{u \times 0.5 \times 1}$$

Assuming that the soil has a saturated unit weight $\gamma_{sat} = 20\,kN/m^3$, and considering an average porewater pressure at the base of the prism of $13\,kN/m^2$, the ratio is therefore:

$$F = 10 \times 0.5/13 \times 0.5 = 0.77$$

This value is obviously unacceptable because it indicates that the soil at the toe of the dam will heave. To prevent this from occurring, a coarse filter can be applied in front of the dam so as to increase the effective weight of the soil mass in question. Notice that an increase in the factor of safety against piping would mean a decrease in the porewater pressure at the base of the soil element shown in figure 4.28, therefore causing an improvement in the factor of safety against heave due to piping. Once all calculations are undertaken, the flownet is scaled back to the natural section by multiplying all dimensions in the x-direction by a coefficient $1/c = 4$. The resulting effect is shown in figure 4.29 which represents the *actual* flownet and, most importantly, indicates how difficult it would have been to obtain such a net had a transformed section not been used in the first instance. The difficulties being twofold in that the flow elements are *not* squares and the crossings between flow and equipotential lines are *not* right angles. The scaling back operation is performed using the flownet of the transformed section in figure 4.27. This tedious operation consists, for every crossing point between flow and equipotential lines of:

- measuring, on the transformed section of figure 4.27 the co-ordinates (X,y);
- calculating the natural co-ordinates (x,y) by multiplying X by a factor of 4 (y is not affected) and
- plotting the point (x,y) on the natural section in figure 4.26.

A flownet is then sketched on the natural section by joining smoothly all the points.

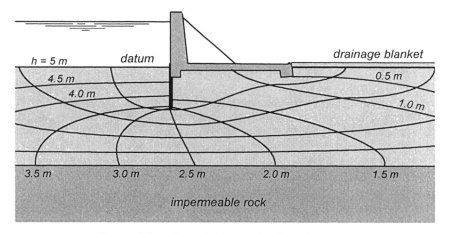

Figure 4.29: Flownet in the natural section.

• (c) Case of multi-layered soils

When dealing with non homogeneous soils (*i.e.* soils comprising layers with inherently different permeabilities), the flow patterns change according to the relative permeabilities of adjacent soil layers. If, for instance, water flows from a high permeability layer to a lower permeability one, the energy dissipated through friction increases as a result of a steeper hydraulic gradient. At the boundary between adjacent layers, flow lines bend according to the incidence law in optics. The flownet must therefore reflect the change in permeability. As shown in figure 4.30, when water flows from one layer having a permeability k_1, to the next characterised by a permeability k_2, the shape of the flow elements changes to account for the change in permeability in such a way that the ratio between the sides of each element in the bottom layer is related to the ratio of permeabilities as follows:

$$\frac{c}{d} = \frac{k_2}{k_1}$$

(4.70)

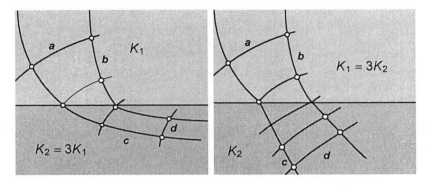

Figure 4.30: Flow through multilayered soils.

Example 4.6

Consider the dam represented in figure 4.31, built at a site characterised by two layers of isotropic clay underlain by impervious rock. The top clay layer is 2 m thick and has a permeability k_1. The bottom layer is 2.7 m thick and is three times more permeable than the overlaying soil ($k_2 = 3k_1$).

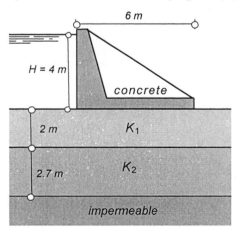

Figure 4.31: Flow through a multi-layered soil.

The corresponding flownet, sketched in figure 4.32, shows how the flow elements change from being curvilinear squares in the top layer to curvilinear rectangles in the underlying layer. In fact, the flow elements in the bottom layer have been elongated in such a way that the ratio of the sides of each rectangle is equal to $k_2/k_1 = 3$.

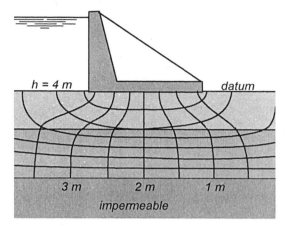

Figure 4.32: Flownet for the multi-layered soil corresponding to figure 4.31.

4.4.3 Unconfined flow

When the boundaries of flow are in part not known *a priori*, the flow is referred to as *unconfined* since it contains a *free surface* at which the pressure is atmospheric. Consider, for example, the case of seepage across an earth dam where the position of the flow patterns are, *prima facie*, hard to predict. Yet, the position of the top flowline, also known as the *phreatic surface*, is entirely defined by the fact that it represents a flowline on which the total head varies linearly with the elevation above any chosen datum. Referring to figure 4.33, the pressure head h_p (read the water pressure) at the points *A, B, C* and *D* is zero since these points are on the phreatic surface where the pressure is atmospheric. Consequently, if the equipotential line going through *A* corresponds to a total head h_A, then one can write: $h_p = h_A - y_A = 0$

which shows that at *A*, the total head is equal to the elevation head y_A measured with respect to any chosen datum. For the equipotential lines going through *B* , *C* and *D*, corresponding respectively to a total head $h_A - \Delta h$, $h_A - 2\Delta h$ and $h_A - 3\Delta h$, it follows that:

$$h_A - \Delta h - y_B = 0 \qquad (4.71a)$$
$$h_A - 2\Delta h - y_C = 0 \qquad (4.71b)$$
$$h_A - 3\Delta h - y_D = 0 \qquad (4.71c)$$

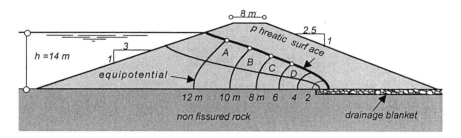

Figure 4.33: Phreatic surface for unconfined flow.

A straightforward manipulation of equations 4.71 leads to:

$$y_C - y_D = y_B - y_C = y_A - y_B = \Delta h$$

indicating that equipotential lines drawn at *equal* intervals of total head Δh intersect the free surface at the *same* Δh in the vertical direction as shown in figures 4.34a and 4.34b where the shape of both flownets, corresponding to the same seepage problem through the same soil, is affected by the extent of the drainage blanket (*i.e.* a highly permeable drainage layer). Having this condition in mind, the problem of sketching a correct flownet then becomes a matter of practice.

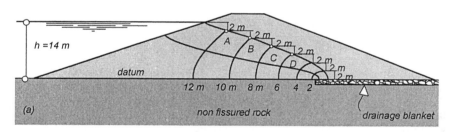

Figure 4.34: (a) Flownet construction for unconfined flow,

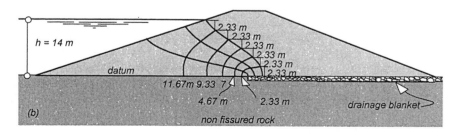

Figure 4.34: (b) effect of the use of a wider drainage blanket.

Once an acceptable flownet is obtained, it can be used to estimate different quantities such as the porewater pressure at any location, the hydraulic gradient or the total flow quantity. Note that aspects related to safety calculations of this type of construction, especially that concerned with the *rapid draw down conditions*, simulating a sudden decrease in the level of retained water, are presented in detail in Azizi (2007).

4.5 Conformal mapping

4.5.1 Velocity potential – stream function

As mentioned earlier, only a handful of seepage problems have been solved analytically, mainly because of the difficulties arising from the boundary conditions of the flow equation which cannot always be satisfied. However, a theoretical approach to the analysis of some seepage problems has been developed and, notwithstanding its reliance on advanced mathematical concepts such as elliptic functions and conformal mapping, the solutions obtained are none the less very elegant. The aim of this section is to use a special conformal mapping technique developed by Mandel (1951) to solve analytically seepage problems of *steady state confined flow* in *isotropic soils*, related to excavations, trenches and cofferdams. For more thorough analysis, the reader is referred to the excellent work of Pavlovsky (widely reported by Harr (1962)), Halek and Svec (1979) and Polubarinova-Kochina (1962).

Consider the two-dimensional form of the continuity equation established earlier *via* equation 3.45:

$$\frac{\partial v_x}{\partial x} + \frac{\partial v_y}{\partial y} = 0 \tag{4.72}$$

If the *velocity potential* is defined as $\Phi(x, y) = -kh$, then, according to Darcy's law:

$$v_x = \frac{\partial \Phi}{\partial x} \qquad \text{and} \qquad v_y = \frac{\partial \Phi}{\partial y}$$

Substituting for v_x and v_y into equation 4.72 leads to the following *Laplace* equation:

$$\nabla^2 \Phi = \frac{\partial^2 \Phi}{\partial x^2} + \frac{\partial^2 \Phi}{\partial y^2} = 0 \tag{4.73}$$

The *stream function* is defined as $\Psi(x, y)$, such that:

$$v_x = \frac{\partial \Psi}{\partial y} \qquad \text{and} \qquad v_y = -\frac{\partial \Psi}{\partial x}$$

Substituting for v_x and v_y from the above expressions yields the *Cauchy–Reimann* equations:

$$\frac{\partial \Phi}{\partial x} = \frac{\partial \Psi}{\partial y} \quad \text{and} \quad \frac{\partial \Phi}{\partial y} = -\frac{\partial \Psi}{\partial x}$$

Moreover, using the velocity potential, it is seen that:

$$\frac{\partial v_x}{\partial y} = \frac{\partial v_y}{\partial x} = \frac{\partial^2 \Phi}{\partial x \, \partial y}$$

so that when the stream function is substituted for the velocity potential in the last equation, the following Laplacian is established in a straightforward way :

$$\nabla^2 \Psi = \frac{\partial^2 \Psi}{\partial x^2} + \frac{\partial^2 \Psi}{\partial y^2} = 0 \tag{4.74}$$

Both equations 4.73 and 4.74 indicate that the potential and stream functions are *harmonic functions*. More importantly, it can be shown that if the *complex potential* $\omega = \Phi + i\Psi$ is an *analytic function* of the complex variable $z = x + iy$, then Φ and Ψ are *conjugate harmonic functions,* meaning that curves representing constant potentials and constant stream lines intersect at right angles. Accordingly, an analytical solution to a seepage problem can be developed *if* an appropriate complex potential can be found for which both stream and potential functions are conjugate harmonic functions. In what follows, the mathematical details of the analytical solutions developed by Mandel, relating to steady state confined seepage flow through isotropic soils, are presented.

4.5.2 Seepage along a sheet pile cut-off wall driven in a homogeneous soil layer of infinite thickness: exact solution

Consider the case of a sheet pile wall embedded in a *homogeneous* layer of soil, assumed to be of infinite thickness as depicted in figure 4.35. It is important to bear in mind that the following analysis applies equally to an *excavation* (where the water level behind the pile is below the ground) and a *cofferdam* (for which water behind the pile is above the ground surface). In order to study the nature of seepage around the pile, Mandel considered the following mapping function:

$$z = \alpha \sinh\left(-\frac{i\omega}{\lambda}\right) + \frac{i\omega}{\lambda}\beta$$

which can be rewritten as:

$$x + iy = \alpha \sinh\left(\frac{\psi - i\Phi}{\lambda}\right) - \beta\frac{\psi - i\Phi}{\lambda} \tag{4.75}$$

where α, β and λ are positive real numbers ($\alpha > \beta$).

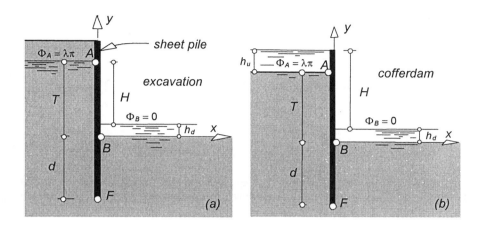

*Figure 4.35: Seepage around a sheet pile cut-off wall in the case of
(a) an excavation, and (b) a cofferdam.*

Knowing that:

$$\sinh z = \sinh x \cos y + i \cosh x \sin y$$

equation 3.74 then yields the quantities x and y:

$$x = \alpha \sinh \frac{\Psi}{\lambda} \cos\left(\frac{\Phi}{\lambda}\right) - \beta \frac{\Psi}{\lambda} \qquad (4.76a)$$

$$y = -\alpha \cosh \frac{\Psi}{\lambda} \sin\left(\frac{\Phi}{\lambda}\right) + \beta \frac{\Phi}{\lambda} \qquad (4.76b)$$

Referring to figure 4.35, it is seen that the associated boundary conditions are:

$$\Phi = 0, \qquad y = 0 \quad \text{and} \quad x \geq 0$$
$$\Phi = \lambda\pi, \quad y = \beta\pi \quad \text{and} \quad x \leq 0$$

Because both sides of the pile represent a flow line, the stream function along these frontiers (*AF* on the upstream side and *FB* on the downstream face) is therefore $\Psi = 0$. Consequently, along the pile, equations 4.76 are reduced to:

$$x = 0 \qquad (4.77a)$$

$$y = \beta \frac{\Phi}{\lambda} - \alpha \sin \frac{\Phi}{\lambda} \qquad (4.77b)$$

At the foot of the pile (*i.e.* point F in figure 4.35), the co-ordinate y is at its minimum and hence $\partial y / \Phi = 0$. Accordingly, if the velocity potential at F is

Φ_F, then the first derivative of equation 4.77b with respect to F at the foot of the pile yields:

$$\beta = \alpha \cos \frac{\Phi_F}{\lambda} \tag{4.78}$$

Moreover, with reference to figure 4.35, it can be seen that the quantities λ and β are such that:

$$\Phi_A - \Phi_B = H = \lambda\pi \tag{4.79a}$$

$$T = \beta\pi \tag{4.79b}$$

Hence, the quantity y_F at F:

$$y_F = d = \alpha \sin\left(\frac{\Phi_F}{\lambda}\right) - \beta\frac{\Phi_F}{\lambda} \tag{4.80}$$

T is the depth of water behind the wall. When the water level is at or above ground level, T is taken as the height of the ground behind the wall, d being the depth of embedment. *Notice that at F, the quantity y_F is negative, hence the change of sign in equation 4.80 compared with equation 4.77b.* Eliminating α between equations 4.78 and 4.80, and introducing the quantity $\beta = T/\pi$, it follows that:

$$\tan\left(\frac{\Phi_F}{\lambda}\right) - \frac{\Phi_F}{\lambda} = \pi\frac{d}{T} \tag{4.81}$$

If the ratio of the head loss occurring in the downstream side (between B and F) to the total head loss between A and B is:

$$\eta = \frac{\Phi_F - \Phi_B}{\Phi_A - \Phi_B} = \frac{\Phi_F}{\lambda\pi}$$

(since, from the boundary conditions, $\Phi_B = 0$ at $y = 0$), then equation 4.81 can be rewritten as follows:

$$\tan(\pi\eta) - \pi\eta = \pi d/T \tag{4.82}$$

Equation 4.82 is a *transcendental equation* that depends on the ratio T/d and which can be solved using, for instance, the chart represented in figure 4.36. *Notice that the chart is plotted in terms of the quantity T/d as opposed to d/T used in the equation.* The velocity potential at the foot of the pile (point F) is then:

$$\Phi_F = \eta H \tag{4.83}$$

and the expressions for the three constants can therefore be established:

$$\lambda = \frac{\Phi_A - \Phi_B}{\pi} = \frac{H}{\pi} \qquad (4.84a)$$

$$\beta = \frac{T}{\pi} \qquad (4.84b)$$

$$\alpha = \frac{\beta}{\cos\left(\frac{\Phi_F}{\lambda}\right)} = \frac{T}{\pi \cos(\eta\pi)} \qquad (4.84c)$$

so that at any depth y along *both sides* of the sheet pile, the velocity potential can be calculated using equation 4.77b, that is:

$$y = \frac{\Phi_y}{\lambda} - \alpha \sin \frac{\Phi_y}{\lambda} \qquad (4.85)$$

Notice that according to figure 4.35, y is negative between B and F on both sides of the pile. Also, the quantities Φ_F/λ and Φ_y/λ in equations 4.84c and 4.85 are expressed in *radians*.

Figure 4.36: Graphical solution to equation 4.82.

The hydraulic gradient is thereafter determined according to the following expressions:
• on the upstream side (from A to F in figure 4.35):

$$i_u = \frac{\Phi_A - \Phi_y}{T - y} = \frac{H - \Phi_y}{T - y} \qquad (4.86a)$$

- on the downstream side (from B to F):

$$i_d = -\frac{\Phi_y - \Phi_B}{y} = -\frac{\Phi_y}{y} \qquad (4.86b)$$

The porewater pressure at any depth y on either side of the pile is calculated from the general expression:

$$u = \gamma_w(h - y)$$
$$= \gamma_w[(\Phi_y + h_d) - y] \qquad (4.87)$$

where γ_w is the unit weight of water and $(\Phi_y + h_d)$ represents the excess head at the depth y. The quantity Φ_y is calculated from equation 4.85 and h_d corresponds to the height of the tailwater in front of the wall as shown in figure 4.35.

Example 4.7

Examine the distribution of porewater pressure along the sheet pile cut-off wall depicted in figure 4.37, and driven in a layer of isotropic sand (assumed to be infinitely thick) having a permeability k. From the figure, it is seen that:

$$h_u = 1.5\,m, \quad h_d = 0.5\,m, \quad H = 4\,m, \quad T = 3\,m, \quad d = 4\,m$$

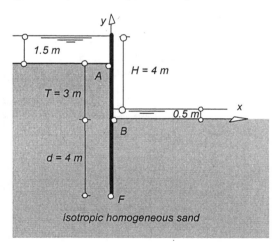

Figure 4.37: Seepage flow along a cut-off wall embedded in an isotropic homogeneous sand.

First, solve for η using equation 4.82 and figure 4.36 *(Note: figure 4.36 is used in conjunction with the quantity T/d)*:

$$\tan(\pi\eta) - \pi\eta = \pi d/T = 4.189 \quad \Rightarrow \quad \eta \approx 0.443$$

The velocity potential at the foot of the pile *(point F)* is thereafter calculated from equation 4.83:

$$\Phi_F = \eta H = 1.774\,m$$

Now that the values of the velocity potential at A, F and B are known, *i.e.*:

$$\Phi_A = H = 4\,m, \quad \Phi_F = 1.774\,m \quad \text{and} \quad \Phi_B = 0$$

the coefficients λ, β and α are then determined from equations 4.84:

$$\lambda = \frac{\Phi_A - \Phi_B}{\pi} = 1.273\,m, \quad \beta = \frac{T}{\pi} = 0.955\,m, \quad \alpha = \frac{\beta}{\cos\frac{\Phi_F}{\lambda}} = 5.416\,m$$

(Φ_F/λ in radians).

Equation 4.85 can now be readily established:

$$y = 0.785\Phi_y - 5.416 \sin\left(\frac{\Phi_y}{1.273}\right)$$

(the quantity $\Phi_y/1.273$ is expressed in radians).
For the sake of clarity, the above equation is first solved for the upstream side of the pile (where y varies from $+3\,m$ at A to $-4\,m$ at F, and the potential changes from $\Phi_A = 4\,m$ to $\Phi_F = 1.77\,m$), then for the downstream side for which y ranges from 0 at B to $-4\,m$ at F (with $\Phi_B = 0$). The results, presented in tabular form, include the values of:
- the hydraulic gradient computed using equations 4.86,
- the porewater pressure according to equation 4.87.

• *Upstream side of the pile*:

$\Phi_y(m)$	$y(m)$	i_u	$h(m)$	$u(kN/m^2)$
4.00	3.00	–	4.50	15
3.75	1.76	0.20	4.25	25
3.50	0.55	0.20	4.00	34
3.25	−0.57	0.21	3.75	43
3.00	−1.58	0.22	3.50	51
2.75	−2.44	0.23	3.25	57
2.50	−3.13	0.24	3.00	61
2.25	−3.62	0.26	2.75	64
2.00	−3.92	0.29	2.50	64
1.78	−4.00	0.32	2.28	63

● *Downstream face of the pile*:

$\Phi_y(m)$	$y(m)$	i_d	$h(m)$	$u(kN/m^2)$
0.00	0.00	–	0.50	5
0.25	–0.87	0.29	0.75	16
0.50	–1.70	0.29	1.00	27
0.75	–2.44	0.31	1.25	37
1.00	–3.08	0.32	1.50	46
1.25	–3.57	0.35	1.75	53
1.50	–3.88	0.39	2.00	59
1.78	–4.00	0.44	2.28	63

It is worth mentioning that in these tabulated values, the hydraulic gradient on each side of the pile increases with depth and reaches its maximum value at the foot of the pile. The results are plotted in figure 4.39 where the hydrostatic pressure $(u = \gamma_w h_w)$, as well as the porewater pressure estimated from the flownet of figure 4.38, are included. The hydrostatic pressure is plotted purely for comparison purposes. Also, notice how well the results measured from the flownet compare to the analytical solution.

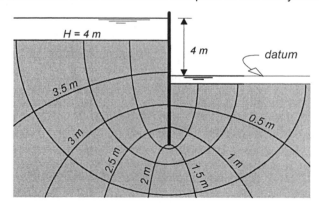

Figure 4.38: Flownet solution to example 4.7.

The discharge area in the downstream side is of particular interest to the designer in that the hydraulic gradient should always be kept smaller than the critical hydraulic gradient i_c by an adequate factor of safety. From the downstream values tabulated earlier, the hydraulic gradient varies between $i \approx 0.29$ at the top of the discharge area and $i = 0.44$ at the foot of the pile. On the other hand, the flownet of figure 4.38 yielded a hydraulic gradient of 0.33 at the top and 0.41 around the foot of the pile (on the downstream side); values that compare favourably with those calculated analytically.

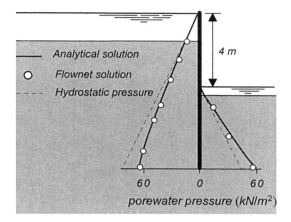

*Figure 4.39: Analytical solution of the porewater
pressure distribution along the pile.*

4.5.3 Seepage along a sheet pile cut-off wall driven in a homogeneous soil layer of finite thickness

Consider the sheet pile driven in a soil having a permeable layer of thickness T, underlain by an impervious material as depicted in figure 4.40.

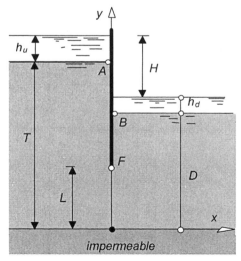

*Figure 4.40: Seepage around a pile embedded in
a permeable soil layer of finite thickness.*

This time, Mandel chose the following mapping function:

$$z = iL \cosh \frac{\omega}{\xi}$$

which can be equally expressed in the following way:

$$x + iy = iL \cosh \frac{\Phi + i\psi}{\xi}$$

where L is the depth of the impervious layer measured from the foot of the pile and ξ is a positive real number. It is straightforward to show that:

$$x = -L \sinh \frac{\Phi}{\xi} \sin \frac{\psi}{\xi} \qquad (4.88a)$$

$$y = L \cosh \frac{\Phi}{\xi} \cos \frac{\psi}{\xi} \qquad (4.88b)$$

The boundary conditions are as follows:

$$y = 0, \quad x = 0, \quad y \geq L,$$
$$\psi = \frac{\pi}{2}\xi, \quad y = 0, \quad \text{and} \quad -\infty < x < +\infty.$$

So that in the vicinity of the pile, these conditions are virtually satisfied and amount to the following:

$$x = 0, \quad \psi = 0$$
$$y = L \cosh \frac{\Phi}{\xi} \qquad (4.89)$$

Making a change of variables so that $y/L = x$ and $\Phi/\xi = \sigma$, equation 4.89 can then be rewritten as follows: $x = \cosh \sigma$

or, alternatively : $\quad (e^{\sigma} - x)^2 - (x^2 - 1) = 0$

which has a straightforward solution:

$$e^{\sigma} = x \pm \sqrt{x^2 - 1} \qquad (4.90)$$

Taking into account the change of variables made earlier, the expression of the potential along the sheet pile is obtained by rearranging equation 4.90, so that the velocity potential at a depth y along the upstream side of the pile *(AF in figure 4.40)* is:

$$\Phi_y = \xi \ln \left(\frac{y}{L} + \sqrt{\frac{y^2}{L^2} - 1} \right) \qquad (4.91a)$$

and along the downstream face *(FB)*:

$$\Phi_y = -\xi \ln \left(\frac{y}{L} + \sqrt{\frac{y^2}{L^2} - 1} \right) \qquad (4.91b)$$

Whence the velocity potentials at A (where $y = T$), F (where $y = L$) and B (where $y = D$) are:

$$\Phi_A = \xi \ln\left(\frac{T}{L} + \sqrt{\frac{T^2}{L^2} - 1}\right) \qquad (4.92a)$$

$$\Phi_F = 0 \qquad (4.92b)$$

$$\Phi_B = -\xi \ln\left(\frac{D}{L} + \sqrt{\frac{D^2}{L^2} - 1}\right) \qquad (4.92c)$$

On the other hand, figure 4.40 indicates that:: $\Phi_A - \Phi_B = H$. Making use of equations 4.92, the value of the quantity x can then be established:

$$\xi = \frac{H}{\ln\left(\frac{T}{L} + \sqrt{\frac{T^2}{L^2} - 1}\right) + \ln\left(\frac{D}{L} + \sqrt{\frac{D^2}{L^2} - 1}\right)} \qquad (4.93)$$

Having set the relationships leading to the velocity potential at any depth along each side of the pile through equations 4.91, and having also determined its precise nature at the upstream ground level *(point A)*, at the foot of the pile *(point F)* and at the downstream ground level *(point B) via* equations 4.92, the hydraulic gradient at any level is then calculated as follows:
- on the upstream side (between A and F in figure 4.40):

$$i_u = \frac{\Phi_A - \Phi_y}{T - y} \qquad (4.94a)$$

- on the downstream side (from F to B):

$$i_d = \frac{\Phi_y - \Phi_B}{D - y} \qquad (4.94b)$$

The porewater pressure is subsequently calculated in the usual way, that is:

$$u = \gamma_w(h - y) \qquad (4.95)$$

with h representing the total head, at the depth y, calculated as follows:
- behind the wall (upstream side):

$$h = (h_u + T) - i_u(T - y)$$
$$= \Phi_y - \Phi_A + (h_u + T)$$

- in front of the wall (downstream face) :

$$h = (h_d + D) + i_d(D - y)$$
$$= \Phi_y - \Phi_B + (h_d + D)$$

where D is the depth of the impervious layer measured from the bottom of the excavation in front of the wall and T is the thickness of the same impervious layer behind the wall; h_u and h_d being as indicated in figure 4.40.

Example 4.8

Let us re-examine the sheet pile studied previously with the help of a flownet in section 4.4.2 (example 4.4, figure 4.20). The dimensions as well as the co-ordinate systems are replotted in figure 4.41. Required : use the theoretical analysis to study the porewater pressure distribution along the pile. Known are:

$$h_u = 1.5\,m, \quad h_d = 0, \quad T = 7.6\,m, \quad L = 2.5\,m, \quad D = 5.5\,m, \quad H = 3.6\,m$$

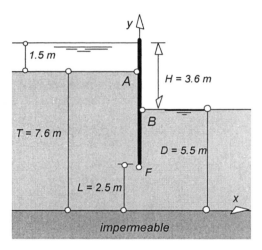

Figure 4.41: Seepage along a sheet pile embedded in a permeable soil of finite thickness.

First, use equation 4.93 to calculate the quantity ξ:

$$\xi = \frac{3.6}{\ln\left[\frac{7.6}{2.5} + \sqrt{\left(\frac{7.6}{2.5}\right)^2 - 1}\right] + \ln\left[\frac{5.5}{2.5} + \sqrt{\left(\frac{5.5}{2.5}\right)^2 - 1}\right]} = 1.124\,m$$

The velocity potentials Φ_A at ground level behind the wall, Φ_F at the foot of the pile and Φ_B at ground level in front of the wall, are thereafter computed from equations 4.92, leading to:

$$\Phi_A \approx 2\,m, \quad \Phi_F = 0, \quad \text{and} \quad \Phi_B = -1.60\,m$$

The sequence of subsequent calculations is then as follows:

- evaluate the velocity potential along the pile using equations 4.91,
- calculate the hydraulic gradient according to equations 4.94,
- estimate the porewater pressure with the help of equation 4.95.

The results, tabulated below are plotted in figure 4.42. Once more, the precise nature of the results calculated from the flownet in figure 4.21 is noticeable.

• *Behind the wall (upstream side)*:

$y(m)$	$\Phi_y (m)$	i_u	$h(m)$	$u(kN/m^2)$
7.6	2.00	–	9.10	15
6.5	1.81	0.17	8.91	24
5.5	1.60	0.19	8.70	32
4.5	1.34	0.21	8.44	39
3.5	0.97	0.25	8.07	46
3.0	0.70	0.28	7.80	48
2.5	0.00	0.39	7.10	46

• *In front of the wall (downstream face)*:

$y(m)$	$\Phi_y (m)$	i_d	$h(m)$	$u(kN/m^2)$
5.5	−1.60	–	5.50	0
5.0	−1.48	0.24	5.62	6
4.5	−1.34	0.26	5.76	13
3.5	−0.97	0.32	6.13	26
3.0	−0.70	0.36	6.40	34
2.5	0	0.53	7.10	46

At the discharge area, the emphasis would be on the exit gradient whose value is of paramount importance to the stability of the wall. From the above tables, the exit gradient has a value $i_e = 0.24$. The flownet of figure 4.21 yielded an exit gradient of 0.28.

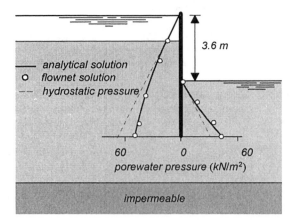

Figure 4.42: Analytical solution to the distribution of porewater pressure along the pile.

4.6 The method of fragments

Thus far, different types of two dimensional seepage problems for which the flow occurs mainly in the (x, y) plane have been considered. The method of fragments, first developed by Pavlovsky (1933), is an approximate theoretical method of solution that can be applied to any type of *confined flow* occurring within a *finite depth*. In this method, the flow region is subdivided into sections or *fragments*, each of which is assumed to have a *straight vertical equipotential line* at its various parts. For example, in the case of the seepage problem corresponding to the cofferdam in figure 3.43, the flow region is subdivided into two fragments, and the equipotential line at the foot of the pile is assumed to be vertical. If a standpipe was inserted at each side of the pile in a way that their bases are on the same equipotential line, then water will rise to the same level inside both tubes. Manifestly, the loss of total head in fragment *I* [h_1] is different from the one occurring through fragment *II* [h_2] since the length of flow path and the nature of flow are different on both sides of the pile.

The total head loss is such that : $H = h_1 + h_2$. Furthermore, equation 4.57 giving the flow quantity per unit width, can be rearranged as follows:

$$Q = k\frac{H}{\phi} \tag{4.96}$$

where ϕ represents a (dimensionless) *form factor*. Since the same flow quantity per unit width seeps through the entire region, equation 4.96 can therefore be used *ad lib* in conjunction with h_1 and h_2, so:

$$k.\frac{H}{\phi} = k.\frac{h_1}{\phi_1} = k.\frac{h_2}{\phi_2} \qquad (4.97)$$

ϕ_1 and ϕ_2 are the form factors associated, respectively, with fragments *I* and *II*:

$$\phi_1 = h_1\phi/H \qquad \text{and} \qquad \phi_2 = h_2\phi/H.$$

Whence: $\phi = \phi_1 + \phi_2$ $\qquad\qquad (4.98)$

Substituting for ϕ into equation 4.96 yields the relationship between the quantity of flow Q and the form factors ϕ_1 and ϕ_2:

$$Q = kH\frac{1}{\phi_1 + \phi_2} \qquad (4.99)$$

As for the *average* hydraulic gradient in the discharge area, it can be estimated from the ratio of total head loss h_2 in the discharge area (*i.e.* the total head at the foot of the pile) to the length of the flow path *I* indicated in figure 4.43:

$$i_{av} \approx \frac{h_2}{I} \qquad (4.100)$$

with:

$$h_2 = H\frac{\phi_2}{\phi_1 + \phi_2} \qquad (4.101)$$

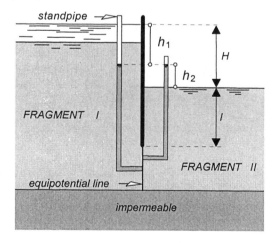

*Figure 4.43: Fragments corresponding
to seepage around a sheet pile.*

Pavlovsky based his theoretical method on elliptic functions to establish a series of typical form factors and the mathematical details can be found in Harr (1962), for instance. To make the method more appealing to practising engineers, Davidenkoff and Franke (1965, 1966) have used the electrical analogue method to study the problem of seepage through trenches and cofferdams (problems characterised by two fragments), and have established charts from which the form factors ϕ_1 and ϕ_2 are obtained. The *modus operandi* of these charts, reproduced in figure 4.45, consists of:

1- calculating, from the geometry of the problem, the dimensionless quantities d_1/T_1, d_2/T_2 and T_2/b (d_1, d_2, T_1, T_2 and b are as indicated in figure 3.44),

2- reading the form factor $\phi_1 = F(d_1/T_1, T_2/b = 0)$ on the curve $T_2/b = 0$ in conjunction with the ratio d_1/T_1, and finally

3- reading the form factor $\phi_2 = F(d_2/T_2, T_2/b)$ on the curve corresponding to the ratio T_2/b, in association with the quantity d_2/T_2 (use your judgement if an extrapolation is needed).

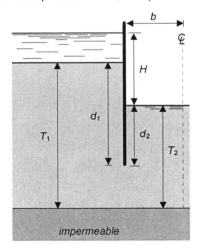

Figure 4.44: Dimensions used in conjunction with the charts in figure 4.45.

The charts can be used to estimate the total head loss in the discharge area as well as the flow quantity *per unit length of perimeter* in the three following cases:

1- *Trench having a width 2b and an infinite length*:

$$h_2 = H\frac{\phi_2}{\phi_1 + \phi_2} \tag{4.102}$$

$$q = kH\frac{1}{\phi_1 + \phi_2} \tag{4.103}$$

2- *Circular cofferdam of a diameter 2b*:

$$h_2 = 1.3H\frac{\phi_2}{\phi_1 + \phi_2}$$ (4.104)

$$q = 0.8kH\frac{1}{\phi_1 + \phi_2}$$ (4.105)

3- *Square cofferdam of a side 2b:*

$$h_2 = 1.3H\frac{\phi_2}{\phi_1 + \phi_2}$$ *(in the middle of the sides)* (4.106)

$$h_2 = 1.7H\frac{\phi_2}{\phi_1 + \phi_2}$$ *(in the corners)* (4.107)

$$q = 0.75kH\frac{1}{\phi_1 + \phi_2}$$ (4.108)

In all cases, the *average* hydraulic gradient on the downstream side is calculated from equation 3.99.

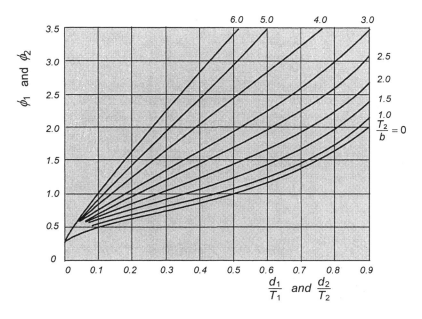

Figure 4.45: Davidenkoff and Franke form factors charts (reproduced by permission of Ernst & Sohn).

Example 4.9

Examine the flow problem for which the planar dimensions are as represented in figure 4.46. The permeable soil layer consists of an isotropic sandy clay with a permeability $k = 10^{-6}\,m/s$.

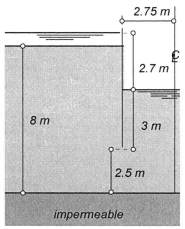

The corresponding two-dimensional flownet is sketched in figure 4.47, where it can be assumed that the equipotential line at the foot of the pile is vertical. The flownet has six flow channels (only one half on the flownet is produced in figure 4.47 because of symmetry) and nine equipotential drops, thence:

$$Q = 2.7 \times \tfrac{6}{9} \times 10^{-6} = 1.8 \times 10^{-6}\,m^3/s/m.$$

Figure 4.46: Seepage problem.

The exit gradient is estimated from element a in figure 4.47:

$$i_e \approx \tfrac{0.3}{0.72} = 0.41$$

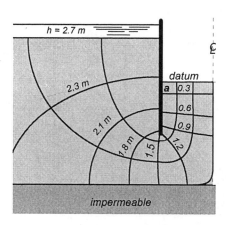

Figure 4.47: Flownet solution.

Let us now apply the Davidenkoff and Franke method. The following quantities can be calculated from figure 3.46, using the notation of figure 4.44:

$$\frac{d_1}{T_1} = \frac{5.5}{8} = 0.69, \quad \frac{d_2}{T_2} = \frac{3}{5.5} = 0.545, \quad \frac{T_2}{b} = \frac{5.5}{2.75} = 2$$

The form factors are read from the charts in figure 4.45 (note that ϕ_1 is read on the curve corresponding to $T_2/b = 0$):

$$\phi_1 = 1.35, \quad \phi_2 = 1.6$$

As drawn in the plane, figure 4.47 can be projected in the third dimension to form one of three cases which are of particular interest.

- **Case 1: Trench of infinite length, having a width 2b = 5.5 m**

The three-dimensional flownet sketched in figure 4.48, gives a clear indication as regards the flow patterns. The quantities h_2 and q are calculated from equations 4.102 and 4.103:

$$h_2 = 2.7 \times \frac{1.6}{1.35+1.6} = 1.462\,m$$

$$q = \frac{2.7}{1.35+1.6} \times 10^{-6} = 9.1 \times 10^{-7}\,m^3/s \text{ per metre of perimeter}$$

hence the total flow quantity on both sides of the trench:

$$Q = 2q \quad = 1.82 \times 10^{-6}\,m^3/s \text{ per metre run}$$

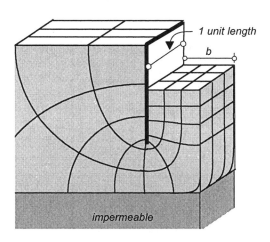

Figure 4.48: 3-D flownet in the case of a trench of infinite length.

The average gradient is estimated from equation 4.100:

$$i_{av} = \frac{h_2}{l} = \frac{1.46}{3} = 0.49$$

These results are in close agreement with those calculated from the flownet of figure 4.44:

	flownet solution	Davidenkoff and Franke method
$Q\,(m^3/s/m)$	1.8×10^{-6}	1.82×10^{-6}
i_e	0.41	$i_{av} = 0.49$

- **Case 2: Circular cofferdam of diameter 2b = 5.5 m (perimeter 2πb)**

A cross-section of the corresponding three-dimensional flownet is shown in figure 4.49. In this case, equations 4.104 and 4.105 are used to calculate h_2 and q:

$$h_2 = 1.3 \times 2.7 \times \frac{1.6}{1.35+1.6} = 1.90\,m$$

$$q = \frac{0.8 \times 2.7}{1.35+1.6} \times 10^{-6} = 7.3 \times 10^{-7}\,m^3/s \text{ per metre of perimeter}$$

hence the total flow quantity:

$$Q = 2\pi b q = 1.26 \times 10^{-5}\,m^3/s$$

The average gradient is in this case: $i_{av} = \frac{1.90}{3} = 0.63$

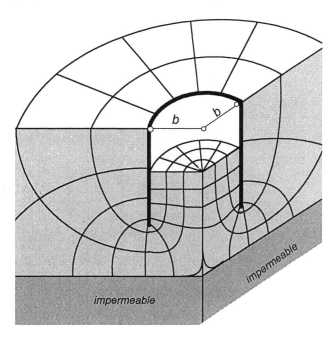

Figure 4.49: Cross-section of the 3-D flownet for a circular cofferdam.

• *Case 3: Square cofferdam of side 2b = 5.5 m (perimeter 8b)*

Figure 4.50 depicts a cross-section of the three-dimensional flownet associated with this case. The quantities h_2 and q are computed according to equations 4.106 to 4.108:

$$h_2 = 1.3 \times 2.7 \times \frac{1.6}{1.35+1.6} = 1.90\,m \text{ (in the middle of each side)}$$

$$h_2 = 1.7 \times 2.7 \times \frac{1.6}{1.35+1.6} = 2.49\,m \text{ (in the corners)}$$

$$q = \frac{0.75 \times 2.7}{1.35+1.6} \times 10^{-6} = 6.9 \times 10^{-7}\,m^3/s \text{ per metre of perimeter}$$

so that the total flow rate is:

$$Q = 8bq = 1.52 \times 10^{-5}\,m^3/s$$

Finally the average hydraulic gradient is:

$$i_{av} = \frac{1.90}{3} = 0.63 \text{ (in the middle of each side)}$$

$$i_{av} = \frac{2.49}{3} = 0.83 \text{ (in the four corners)}$$

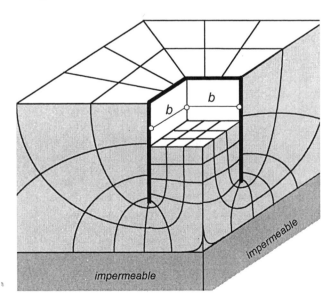

Figure 4.50: Cross-section of the 3-D flownet in the case of a square cofferdam.

Example 4.10: Asymmetric trench

Consider the problem of seepage flow beneath an asymmetric trench assumed to be of infinite length, whose dimensions are as indicated in figure 4.51. The pervious soil is an isotropic homogeneous sand of permeability k (m/s).

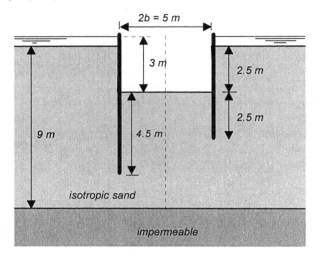

Figure 4.51: Asymmetric seepage flow.

The corresponding flownet solution, sketched in figure 4.52, reflects the asymmetrical nature of flow (five flow channels on the right-hand side and only three on the left-hand side). Based on the flownet, the flow rate can be estimated using equation 4.57:

$$Q = kH\frac{N_f}{N_d} = 3k\frac{(5+3)}{13} \approx 1.85k \; (m^3/s/m)$$

With reference to figure 4.52, it is seen that the exit hydraulic gradient has different values on either side of the trench. On the left-hand side, the exit gradient calculated from element a in the flownet is:

$$i_e \approx \frac{0.23}{0.66} = 0.35$$

On the right-hand side, however, the exit gradient is calculated from element b in the flownet:

$$i_e \approx \frac{0.23}{0.46} = 0.50$$

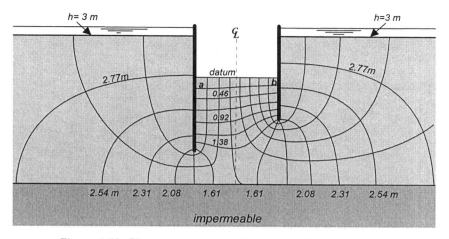

Figure 4.52: Flownet associated with asymmetric flow.

An alternative way of solving this flow problem would be to use the charts of figure 4.45. The flownet of figure 4.52 shows that both equipotential lines at the foot of the piles can be assumed to be vertical. The asymmetry dictates that the superposition of figure 4.53 is used.

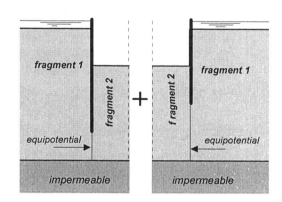

Figure 4.53: Superposition of fragments in the case of asymmetric flow problem.

The different parameters used in conjunction with the charts (refer to figures 4.44 and 4.51), as well as the ensuing results are:

• *on the left-hand side of the trench:*

$$b = 2.5\,m, \quad d_1/T_1 = 0.78, \quad d_2/T_2 = 0.69, \quad T_2/b = 2.6$$

Hence the form factors : $\phi_1 = 1.58$, $\phi_2 = 2.3$.

- the head loss in the exit side is calculated using equation 4.102:

$$h_2 = H\frac{\phi_2}{\phi_1 + \phi_2} = 3 \times \frac{2.3}{(1.58 + 2.3)} = 1.78\,m$$

- the flow rate is determined from equation 4.103:

$$q_l = k\frac{H}{\phi_1 + \phi_2} = k\frac{3}{(1.58 + 2.3)} = 0.773\,k \;per\;metre\;of\;perimeter$$

- the *average* hydraulic gradient is estimated from equation 4.100:

$$i_{av} = \frac{h_2}{l} = \frac{1.78}{4.5} = 0.4$$

- **on the right-hand side:**

$$b = 2.5\,m, \quad d_1/T_1 = 0.555, \quad d_2/T_2 = 0.384, \quad T_2/b = 2.6$$

Whence the form factors: $\phi_1 = 1.1$, $\phi_2 = 1.45$.

- the head loss is: $h_2 = 3 \times \dfrac{1.45}{(1.1 + 1.45)} = 1.70\,m$

- the flow rate q is: $q_r = k\dfrac{3}{(1.1 + 1.45)} = 1.176\,k \;per\;metre\;of\;perimeter$

- the average hydraulic gradient: $i_{av} = \dfrac{1.7}{2.5} = 0.68$

The total flow rate per metre length of the trench is therefore the sum of the flow rates on each side:

$$Q = q_l + q_r = (0.773 + 1.176)\,k = 1.95\,k\;(m^3/s/m)$$

The different results summarised in the following, indicate the validity of both methods used above.

	flownet solution	Davidenkoff and Franke method
flow rate per metre length	1.85 k	1.95 k
exit gradient: left side	0.35	$i_{av} = 0.40$
exit gradient: right side	0.50	$i_{av} = 0.68$

Problems

4.1 Consider the sheet pile cut-off wall then use the corresponding flownet solution illustrated in figure *p*4.1 and calculate:

(*a*) the seepage forces per unit area at point *A, B, ..., G;*

(*b*) the effective stresses as well as the porewater pressures at the same points. Assume a saturated unit weight of sand of $\gamma_{sat} = 21 \, kN/m^3$.

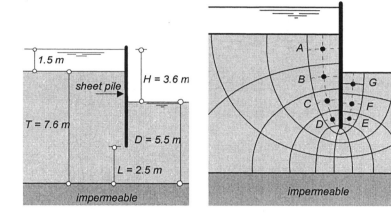

Figure p41

Ans: (*a*) *Seepage forces per unit area:*
$F_A = 1.89 \, kN/m$, $F_B = 5.49 \, kN/m$,
$F_C = 10.9 \, kN/m$, $F_D = 17.8 \, kN/m$, $F_E = -11.5 \, kN/m$,
$F_F = -8.6 \, kN/m$, $F_G = -1.8 \, kN/m$.
(*b*) *Effective stresses:* $\sigma'_A = 11.8 \, kN/m^2$, $\sigma'_B = 31.9 \, kN/m^2$
$\sigma'_C = 51.6 \, kN/m^2$, $\sigma'_D = 69.5 \, kN/m^2$, $\sigma'_E = 17.1 \, kN/m^2$
$\sigma'_F = 13.1 \, kN/m^2$, $\sigma'_G = 4.8 \, kN/m^2$.
(*c*) *Porewater pressures:* $u_A = 21.2 \, kN/m^2$, $u_B = 32.6 \, kN/m^2$
$u_C = 43 \, kN/m^2$, $u_D = 48.4 \, kN/m^2$, $u_E = 35 \, kN/m^2$,
$u_F = 22.4 \, kN/m^2$, $u_G = 7.8 \, kN/m^2$.

4.2 A small filter tank 1.6 *m* long and 0.8 *m* wide is made up of five layers of sand of equal thickness $d = 0.2 \, m$ (see figure *p*4.2), with the horizontal permeabilities of any two consecutive layers characterised by a constant ratio :
$k_{h2}/k_{h1} = k_{h3}/k_{h2} = k_{h4}/k_{h3} = k_{h5}/k_{h4} = 0.5$.

Calculate the permeability k_{h1} if the total flow quantity seeping through the sand layers is :
$Q = 8.33 \times 10^{-6}\ m^3/s$ ($\approx$ 30 *litre per hour*)

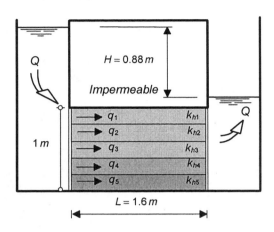

Figure p4.2

Ans: $k_{h1} = 3.91 \times 10^{-5}\ m/s.$

4.3   Calculate the vertical permeability k_{v1} in the case of the vertical flow illustrated in figure p4.3. Assume that the total flow seeping through each layer is $Q = 2.78 \times 10^{-6}\ m^3/s$ ($\approx$ 10 *l/h*), and that the ratio between consecutive permeabilities is identical to the previous case, *i.e.*
$k_{v2}/k_{v1} = k_{v3}/k_{v2} = k_{v4}/k_{v3} = k_{v5}/k_{v4} = 0.5.$

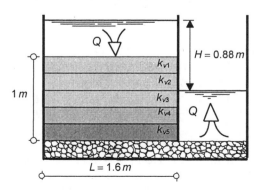

Figure p4.3

Ans: $k_{v1} = 1.53 \times 10^{-5}\ m/s.$

4.4   Assume now that the sand layers in figure p4.2 are characterised
by the respective equivalent horizontal and vertical permeabilities:
$k'_h = 1.51 \times 10^{-5}\, m/s$ and $k'_v = 2.47 \times 10^{-6}\, m/s$.

(a) Calculate the new dimensions of the tank were the five layers
of sand to be replaced by a single 1 m thick isotropic layer with a
permeability $k = \sqrt{k'_h\, k'_v}$.
(b) Estimate the corresponding quantity of vertical flow.

Ans: (a) $L' = 0.647\, m$,   (b) $Q_v = 2.78 \times 10^{-6}\, m^3/s$.

4.5   Refer to the flownet illustrated in figure p4.1 and assume that it
was sketched on a transformed section corresponding to the flow
through an anisotropic soil having a ratio of anisotropy $k_h/k_v = 2$.
Scale back the flownet in question to the natural section.

4.6   Consider the excavation in figure p4.6 in conjunction with the
confined flow conditions of example 4.2. All things being equal,
calculate the drawdown at points A, B and C.

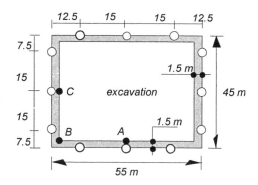

Figure p4.6

Ans: $d_A \approx 11.04\, m$, $d_B \approx 10.21\, m$, $d_C \approx 10.93\, m$.

4.7   Assume that the unconfined flow and soil conditions of example
4.3 apply, then estimate the drawdown achieved under points D, E
and F in figure p4.7.

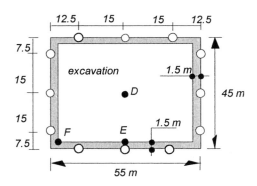

Figure p4.7

Ans: $d_D \approx 8.05\,m$, $d_E \approx 8.38\,m$, $d_F \approx 7.50\,m$.

4.8   Redraw the flownet corresponding to the unconfined flow through the earth dam of figure *p4.8* in the absence of a drainage blanket, then estimate the porewater pressure at the centre of the dam (point *A* in figure *p4.8*),

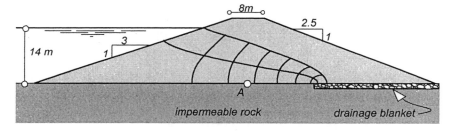

Figure p4.8

Ans: $u_A \approx 117\,kN/m^2$ *without drainage blanket, as opposed to*
$u_A \approx 85\,kN/m^2$ *in figure p4.8.*

4.9   A circular cofferdam with the dimensions indicated in figure *p4.9* is embedded 5.5 *m* into a clean sand having a saturated unit weight $\gamma_{sat} = 21\,kN/m^3$ and a permeability $k\,(m/s)$. Sketch an accurate flownet, then estimate:

(*a*) the hydraulic gradient at the most critical point of flow within the cofferdam;

(*b*) the factor of safety against localised quicksand conditions (*i.e.* piping) at the most critical point of flow;

(c) the quantity of flow in $m^3/s/m$;

(d) the profile of vertical effective stresses along each side of the pile;

(e) the porewater pressure distribution along both sides of the pile.

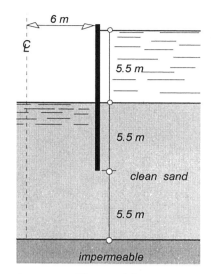

Figure p4.9

Ans: (a) $i_e \approx 0.41$, (b) $F = 2.4$, (c) $q = 1.96k\,(m^3/s/m)$

4.10 Consider the circular cofferdam of problem p4.9 above, and use *Davidenkoff and Franke* charts, based on the method of fragments, to estimate:
(a) the exit hydraulic gradient,
(b) the factor of safety against piping,
(c) the quantity of flow in $m^3/s/m$.

How can you justify the difference between these results and those calculated previously from the flownet solution ?

Ans: (a) $i_e \approx 0.75$, (b) $F = 1.33$, (c) $q = 1.85k\,(m^3/s)$.

4.11 Use *Mandel* analysis in conjunction with figure p4.11 depicting a sheet pile cut-off wall embedded in a sand, then calculate the distribution along both sides of the pile of:
(a) the porewater pressure,
(b) the hydraulic gradient,
(c) the vertical effective stresses.

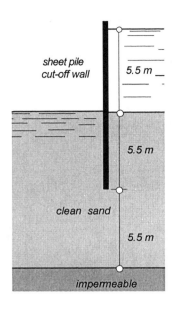

Figure p4.11

References

Bear, J. (1972) *Dynamics of Fluids in Porous Media*. Elsevier, New York.

Cedergren, H. (1990) *Seepage, Drainage and Flownets*. 3rd edn, John Wiley, New York.

Davidenkoff, R. N. and Franke, O. L. (1965) *Intersuchung der Räumlichen Sickerströmung in eine Umspundete Baugrube in Offenen Gewässern*. Die Bautechnik, 9, pp.298–307.

Davidenkoff, R. N. and Franke, O. L. (1966) *Räumliche Sickerströmung in eine Umspundete Baugrube im Grundwasser*. Die Bautechnik, 12, pp. 401–409.

Halek, V. and Svec, J. (1979) *Groundwater Hydraulics*. Elsevier, Amsterdam.

Harr, M. E. (1962) *Groundwater and Seepage*. McGraw-Hill, New York.

Hong Kong Geotechnical Engineering Office, (1993) *Review of Granular and Geotextile Filters*. Hong Kong.

Mandel, J. (1951) *Ecoulement de l'eau sous une ligne de palplanches: Abaque pour la condition de renard*. Travaux, 197, pp. 273–281.

Pavlovsky, N. N. (1933) *Motion of water under dams*. Transactions of the 1st Congress on Large Dams, Stockholm, Vol. 4.

Pavlovsky, N. N. (1956) *Collected Works*. Akad. Russia, Leningrad.

Polubarinova-Kochina, P. Ya. (1941) *Concerning Seepage in Heterogeneous (two layered) Media*. Inzhenernii Sbornik, Vol. 1 (2).

Polubarinova-Kochina, P. Ya. (1962) *Theory of Ground Water Movement*. (translated from Russian). Princeton University Press.

Somerville, S. H. (1986) *Control of Groundwater for Temporary Works*.

CIRIA Report 113, Construction Industry Research and Information Association, London.

Tomlinson, M. J. (1995) *Foundation Design and Construction.* 6th edn, Longman, London.

CHAPTER 5

Transient flow: elastic and consolidation settlements

5.1 Introduction

The basic fundamental difference between (steady) seepage and transient flows relates to the change (or the lack of it) of the volume of soil through which flow occurs. Thus, when water flows into or out of a soil mass *without* causing the volume to change, the flow is known as *seepage* (refer to chapter 3). If, on the other hand, the flow of water within a soil mass induces a volume change, then the flow is referred to as *transient*. Obviously, exception should be made for critical seepage flow conditions whereby an erosion process might take place thus causing a decrease of soil volume. The process of volume change triggered by a transient flow, known as *consolidation*, is related to the change in effective stresses within the soil matrix heralded by a surface loading (or unloading) or a variation in the water table. The *excess porewater pressure* (*i.e.* the load-induced porewater pressure) generated in both cases causes the water to be either squeezed out of the soil mass (case of a positive excess pressure) or sucked into the soil matrix (case of a negative excess pressure). This movement of water continues at a *changing rate* until all excess pressure has dissipated, and the equilibrium of stresses has been restored according to the effective stress principle.

Prior to dealing in detail with the consolidation process (*i.e.* the rate of volume change), which depends on the soil *permeability*, let us turn our attention to the final magnitude of the volume change which is related to the soil *compressibility*. In fact, the extent to which a soil deforms under the effect of an applied load depends on its stress history, that is the geological history of the soil through loading and (when applicable) unloading cycles. Thus, if at some stage during its geological history the soil has been subjected to unloading (due, for instance, to the disappearance of an ice cover or to a severe erosion), then the present pressure due to the soil weight and known as the *overburden pressure* is *smaller* than that which existed before the onset of the unloading process, and the soil is known as *overconsolidated*. If, on the other hand, the soil has not been subjected to any unloading during its entire geological history, then the present overburden pressure constitutes the largest pressure that the soil has ever experienced, and the soil is in this case referred to as *normally consolidated*. These definitions can be made easier to understand at this stage with the illustration in figure 5.1 showing a soil covered during the ice age by a thick layer of ice which has since disappeared. Obviously, at the peak of the Ice Age (*circa* 1.8 million years ago), the *maximum* vertical pressure at point A (σ_p in the figure) was due to the soil volume above A whose thickness is h_1 and to the volume of ice with a thickness h_2. However, the vertical stress σ_v has gradually decreased as the ice cover melted away, so that *at present,* σ_v corresponding to the same point is only due to the weight of soil above the point whose thickness h_1 has increased by an amount Δh due to the release of pressure.

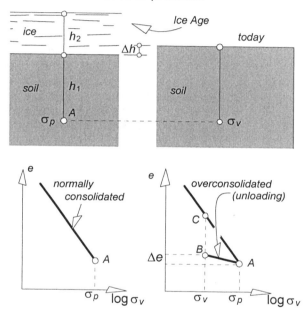

Figure 5.1: Effects of loading patterns on soil behaviour.

During the process of unloading, the soil, originally *normally consolidated* has become *overconsolidated*. The change in the void ratio Δe during overconsolidation is related to the deformation Δh (assumed to be elastic), the precise nature of the relationship being introduced in the following section. The figure shows that the change in the soil void ratio (*i.e.* the deformation) induced by the *same* pressure increment $\Delta \sigma = \sigma_p - \sigma_v$ depends on the state of soil: the deformation of the *normally consolidated soil* subjected to $\Delta \sigma$ from point C to point A is *larger* than that occurring under the same $\Delta \sigma$ between points B and A where the soil is *overconsolidated*. Though the mathematical aspects of this conclusion will be presented shortly, it is already clear that, from a practical perspective, an overconsolidated soil is less troublesome in terms of deformation and settlement than a normally consolidated one. The consolidation characteristics of saturated clays can be measured in the laboratory using the one-dimensional consolidation test (also known as the oedometer test), a brief description of which follows.

5.2 Stress–strain relationships in one-dimensional consolidation

The stress–strain relationships that will be derived in what follows are based on different consolidation parameters that can be measured from the oedometer test. The corresponding apparatus used for the test and depicted in figure 5.2, consists mainly of a stainless steel ring having an internal diameter of 75 *mm* and a height of 20 *mm*, two porous stones, a metal container and a loading hanger. The sharp end of the ring is used to cut through a bigger sample of clay, so that a clay specimen can be secured inside the ring with a minimum of disturbance. The specimen is thereafter sandwiched between the two porous stones, then placed inside the container. Note that in order to avoid any volume change of the clay sample *prior* to testing, the saturation process (*i.e.* the filling of the container with water as *per* figure 5.2) is undertaken *after* the first load increment is applied to the sample. The clay being *confined* within the ring, the *only* deformation induced by the load is *vertical* (one dimensional). The test, thus, allows for the vertical deformation of the sample to be measured as the experiment progresses under different effective stress increments $\Delta\sigma'_i$, applied successively in such a way that the soil is allowed to consolidate fully under each increment before the next increment is added.

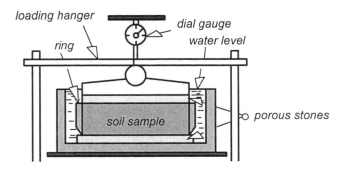

Figure 5.2: 1-D consolidation apparatus.

The deformation of the sample with time is typically as depicted in figure 5.3, where it can be seen that the higher the cumulative load, the smaller the voids between solid particles and the stiffer the soil.

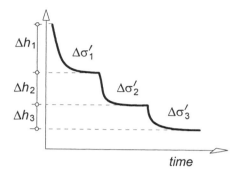

Figure 5.3: Typical results corresponding to 1-D consolidation test.

If the quantities $\Delta h_i/h$ (h being the original height of the sample) are plotted against the cumulative value of the effective vertical stress σ'_v, then a graph similar in shape to the one illustrated in figure 5.4 will ensue. The *changing* slope α of this graph is of particular interest and its use will be explained below.

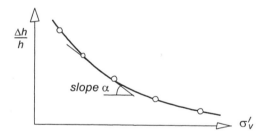

Figure 5.4: Typical 1-D consolidation test results.

In the meantime, the relationship between the variation of the void ratio and that of the sample deformation can now be established according to figure 5.5:

$$\frac{\Delta h}{h} = \frac{h_{wo} - h_{wf}}{h_s + h_{wo}} = \frac{(h_{wo}/h_s) - (h_{wf}/h_s)}{1 + (h_{wo}/h_s)} = \frac{e - e_f}{1 + e} = \frac{\Delta e}{1 + e} \qquad (5.1)$$

Giving the variation of the void ratio:

$$\Delta e = (1 + e)\frac{\Delta h}{h} \qquad (5.2)$$

Accordingly, the results of figure 5.4 can be analysed in terms of the variation of the void ratio e *versus* the effective vertical stress σ'_v. When plotted in (e, $\log \sigma'_v$) space, the shape of the corresponding curve depends on the *state* of the soil.

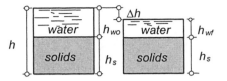

*Figure 5.5: Initial and final stages during
1-D consolidation test.*

Thus, for a *normally consolidated clay,* the curve corresponding to stress values greater than or equal to the *in situ* vertical effective stress σ'_{vo} is characterised by a slope C_c referred to as *the compression index.* For *overconsolidated clays,* the portion of the curve corresponding to vertical stresses smaller than σ'_{vo} has a different slope known as *the swelling index* C_s as depicted in figure 5.6. Note that in practice, C_s is measured from an unload–reload cycle to minimise the effects of clay disturbance.

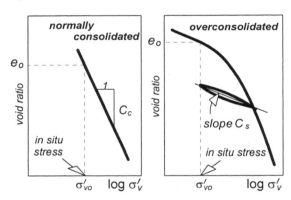

Figure 5.6: Normally consolidated and overconsolidated clays.

Meanwhile, if the *preconsolidation pressure* σ'_p is defined as being the maximum past effective overburden pressure to which the soil has been subjected during its entire geological history, then it is clear from both figures 5.1 and 5.6 that σ'_p in the case of a normally consolidated soil corresponds to the present *in situ* stress σ'_{vo}, whereas an overconsolidated soil is characterised by $\sigma'_p > \sigma'_{vo}$. In this respect, consider the layer of saturated soil with an effective unit weight $\gamma' = (\gamma_{sat} - \gamma_w)$ depicted in figure 5.7 where, through a natural process, the top layer of a thickness z_1 has since disappeared. Let us evaluate the stresses, past and present at point A situated at a depth z:

- the maximum effective vertical stress applied in the past: $\sigma'_p = \gamma'(z + z_1)$,
- the present effective vertical stress: $\sigma'_v = \gamma'z$.

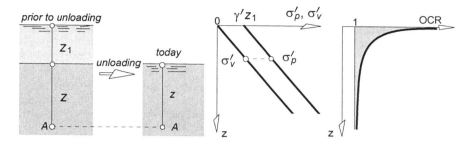

Figure 5.7: Variation with depth of the overconsolidation ratio.

Accordingly, while both preconsolidation pressure and effective vertical stress vary linearly with depth, the overconsolidation ratio OCR, defined as:

$$OCR = (\sigma'_p/\sigma'_v) = 1 + \frac{z_1}{z} \qquad (5.3)$$

is a hyperbolic function of z as indicated in figure 5.7. Clearly, as the depth increases, σ'_v increases and the OCR decreases towards its ultimate value of 1 corresponding to a normally consolidated state. In practice, the magnitude of σ'_p can be determined using one of the two following graphical procedures.

(1) The procedure due to *Casagrande* (1936) is illustrated in figure 5.8, and consists of the following steps.
 • Determine the point O on the $(e,\ \log\sigma'_v)$ graph that has the sharpest curvature (*i.e.* the smallest radius of curvature).
 • Draw the horizontal line OA.
 • Plot the tangent to the graph at O (*i.e.* OC in figure 5.8).
 • Draw the line OB that bisects the angle OAC.
 • Extend the straight line tail portion of the graph intersecting in the process the bisector OB.

The *estimated* preconsolidation pressure σ'_p of the soil corresponds to the abscissa of the point of intersection.

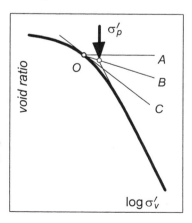

Figure 5.8: Casagrande procedure for the determination of σ'_p.

(2) The *Schmertmann* procedure (1953) was designed to minimise the effects of disturbance, represented by the shaded area in figure 5.9, due to *in situ* sampling and laboratory handling of the soil. Schmertmann suggested that the behaviour observed during a one-dimensional consolidation test does not reflect the actual soil behaviour *in situ* until the (cumulative) vertical effective stress applied to the sample reaches a magnitude corresponding to a void ratio of $0.42e_o$, where e_o is the initial void ratio corresponding to the *in situ* vertical stress σ'_{vo}. He then devised the following procedure to determine σ'_p.

(a) Apply incremental loading to the sample, including an unload–reload cycle, until point A corresponding to a void ratio of $0.42e_o$ is reached (refer to figure 4.9).

(b) Draw the line BC within the unload–reload loop.

(c) Plot point D with the co-ordinates $(e_o, \log \sigma'_{vo})$, from which the line DE is drawn parallel to BC.

(d) *Select* a point on DE (point P, for instance, in figure 5.9), thus fixing the presumed value of σ'_p.

(e) Plot the (presumed) virgin consolidation line PA.

(f) Measure the difference in void ratio Δe_p between the selected point and the actual experimental graph.

(g) Plot the point of co-ordinates $(\Delta e_p, \sigma'_p)$ in the space $(\Delta e, \log \sigma'_v)$ as shown in the figure.

(h) Repeat the procedure from step (d).

The *estimated* preconsolidation pressure of the clay, according to this method, is σ'_p which results in the most symmetrical $(\Delta e, \log \sigma'_v)$ graph.

Notice that for stiff clays, the Schmertmann method necessitates the application of very high vertical pressures in order to achieve a void ratio of $0.42e_o$. These pressure levels, which can be in excess of $20\,MN/m^2$, require the use of specially adapted laboratory equipment. However, the $(e, \log \sigma'_v)$ can be extended to $042\,e_o$ if required, without too much loss of accuracy.

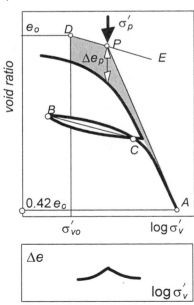

Figure 5.9: Schmertmann procedure.

5.3 One-dimensional consolidation theory

The one-dimensional consolidation test described previously simulates the behaviour of a thin layer of clay subjected to a wide surface load. Under such circumstances, the ensuing deformation, due to the expulsion of water from within the soil matrix, occurs mainly in the vertical direction, and therefore the drainage of water is predominantly vertical or one-dimensional. In the case of a transient flow, water flow is caused by a gradual change in effective stresses that leads to a continuous rearrangement of solid particles, thus effecting a volume change. Accordingly, if a volume of soil is subjected at its surface to a constant total stress increase $\Delta\sigma$ then, in accordance with the effective stress principle of equation 3.7, the changes with time of both the effective stress increment $\Delta\sigma'$ and the excess porewater pressure Δu generated by $\Delta\sigma$ are such that:

$$\frac{\partial\sigma'_v}{\partial t} = -\frac{\partial u}{\partial t}$$

(5.4)

Equation 5.4 indicates that the changes of both effective stress and porewater pressure occur at the same rate so that, for instance, the slopes at points A and B in figure 5.10 are equal and opposite.

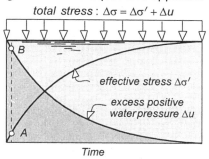

Figure 5.10: Excess water pressure dissipation with time.

On the other hand, it is clear that the behaviour exhibited in figure 5.4 can be replotted as the variation of the void ratio *versus* the effective vertical stress according to equation 5.2. Consequently, with reference to figure 5.11, an increment of stress $\delta\sigma'_v$, applied over a wide area, would generate a change in void ratio δe at the following rate:

$$m_v = -\frac{1}{(1+e)}\frac{\delta e}{\delta\sigma'_v}$$

(5.5)

m_v is known as the *coefficient of volume compressibility* of the soil, and is usually expressed in m^2/kN (notice that m_v depends on the stress increment level).

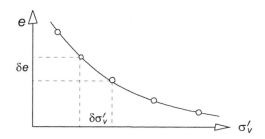

*Figure 5.11: Relationship between the void
ratio and the effective vertical stress.*

Let us now try to establish the (one-dimensional) consolidation equation. To do so, consider, first, a volume V of a *saturated* clay such as the one depicted in figure 5.12. Assuming the water flows only in the z-direction, then it is clear that the variation (*i.e.* the decrease) in time of the volume V is related to the change in velocity in the following manner:

$$-\frac{\partial V}{\partial t} = \left[v_z + \frac{\partial v_z}{\partial z} dz \right] A - v_z A = \frac{\partial v_z}{\partial z} A dz$$

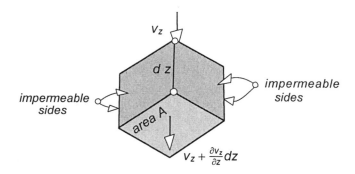

*Figure 5.12: One-dimensional flow conditions
within a saturated volume of soil.*

Since $A dz = V$ (refer to figure 5.12), it follows that:

$$-\frac{\partial V}{\partial t} = \frac{\partial v_z}{\partial z} V \qquad\qquad (5.6)$$

Moreover, a combination of equations 2.1 and 2.2 shows that:

$$V = (1 + e) V_s$$

V_s being the (constant) volume of solid particles. Thus, substituting for V in equation 5.6, it is seen that:

$$-V_s \frac{\partial e}{\partial t} = V \frac{\partial v_z}{\partial z} \tag{5.7}$$

but $V_s/V = 1/(1+e)$ and, accordingly, equation 5.7 reduces to:

$$\frac{\partial v_z}{\partial z} = -\frac{1}{(1+e)} \frac{\partial e}{\partial t} \tag{5.8}$$

Introducing Darcy's law in the form of equation 4.6, $v_z = -k_z \frac{\partial h}{\partial z}$:

$$k_z \frac{\partial^2 h}{\partial z^2} = \frac{1}{(1+e)} \frac{\partial e}{\partial t} \tag{5.9}$$

where k_z represents the permeability of the soil in the vertical direction, and the total head h is the sum of the (constant) elevation head h_e and the pressure head $h_p = u/\gamma_w$ (u being the excess porewater pressure and γ_w the unit weight of water). Hence:

$$h = h_e + \frac{u}{\gamma_w} \quad \Rightarrow \quad \frac{\partial^2 h}{\partial z^2} = \frac{1}{\gamma_w} \frac{\partial^2 u}{\partial z^2}$$

Substituting into equation 4.9, it follows that:

$$k_z \frac{1}{\gamma_w} \frac{\partial^2 u}{\partial z^2} = \frac{1}{(1+e)} \frac{\partial e}{\partial t} \tag{5.10}$$

On the other hand, the variation in time of the void ratio can be expressed as follows:

$$\frac{\partial e}{\partial t} = \frac{\partial e}{\partial \sigma'_v} \frac{\partial \sigma'_v}{\partial t} \tag{5.11}$$

Therefore, a substitution for the quantities $\partial \sigma'_v/\partial t$ and $\partial e/\partial \sigma'_v$ from equations 5.4 and 5.5 respectively into equation 5.11 yields:

$$\frac{\partial e}{\partial t} = m_v(1+e) \frac{\partial u}{\partial t} \tag{5.12}$$

Finally, introducing this quantity into equation 5.10 and rearranging, it can be seen that:

$$k_z \frac{1}{\gamma_w m_v} \frac{\partial^2 u}{\partial z^2} = \frac{\partial u}{\partial t} \tag{5.13}$$

Equation 5.13 is the differential equation for *one-dimensional consolidation* derived by Terzaghi, and is often written as follows:

$$c_v \frac{\partial^2 u}{\partial z^2} = \frac{\partial u}{\partial t} \qquad (5.14)$$

with the *coefficient of vertical consolidation*:

$$c_v = k_z \frac{1}{\gamma_w m_v} \qquad (5.15)$$

where c_v is usually expressed in $m^2/year$.

An approximate solution to the parabolic equation 5.14 can be obtained using parabolic isochrones (see for instance Schofield and Wroth (1968) or Bolton (1991)). However, an exact solution can easily be established through the use of Fourier series. Consider, for instance, a very wide area on which a uniform total stress increment $\Delta\sigma$ is applied as depicted in figure 5.13.

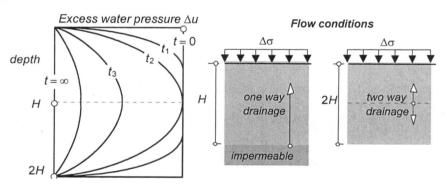

Figure 5.13: Transient flow conditions.

Assuming the soil has a very low permeability then, initially, an excess porewater pressure equal to $\Delta u_i = \Delta\sigma$ is generated within the soil mass (*i.e.* $\Delta\sigma_i' = 0$). It is accepted that under this type of uniform loading, an identical initial excess porewater pressure is generated throughout the entire depth of the soil mass, in a way that porewater pressure distribution is initially a rectangle (other types of loading generate different initial porewater pressure distributions as illustrated in figure 5.14). Under these circumstances, the boundary conditions corresponding to figure 5.13 in which H represents the longest drainage path are:

- $t = 0,\quad 0 \leq z \leq H,\quad u = u_i = \Delta\sigma$
- $0 < t < \infty,\quad z = 0,\quad u = 0$
- $0 < t < \infty,\quad z = H,\quad \dfrac{\partial u}{\partial z} = 0$ $\hspace{2cm}$ (5.16)
- $t \rightarrow \infty,\quad 0 \leq z \leq H,\quad u = 0$

Using Fourier series, together with the above boundary conditions, it can be shown (see Powrie (1997), for instance) that the exact solution to equation 5.14 in the case of a *rectangular* initial excess porewater pressure is:

$$\frac{u}{u_i} = \sum_{m=0}^{m=\infty} \frac{4}{\pi(2m+1)} \sin\left[\frac{\pi}{2}(2m+1)\frac{z}{H}\right] \exp\left[-\frac{\pi^2}{4}(2m+1)^2 T_v\right] \qquad (5.17)$$

with $\hspace{3cm} T_v = \dfrac{c_v t}{H^2} \hspace{4cm}$ (5.18)

representing a *time factor*. Notice that, depending on drainage conditions, the drainage path in figure 4.13 is either the total layer thickness if the soil is drained on one side only, or half the layer thickness were the soil to be drained on both sides. Also, in the case of one way drainage, only the upper half of the porewater pressure distribution with time applies. Because the (dimensionless) time factor T_v is time dependent, equation 4.17 yields the precise dissipation with time of excess water pressure u at any depth z. Obviously, the distribution of u with depth at any given time such as t_3 in figure 5.13 is far from being uniform. However, in practice, the *average* distribution is usually used and is estimated as follows:

$$\left(\frac{u}{u_i}\right)_{av} = \frac{1}{H} \int_0^H \frac{u}{u_i}\, dz \qquad (5.19)$$

Moreover, if the *average degree of vertical consolidation* is defined as:

$$U_v = \frac{u_i - u}{u_i} = 1 - \left(\frac{u}{u_i}\right)_{av} \qquad (5.20)$$

then, using equations 5.17 and 5.19, it is easy to show that the *average degree of vertical consolidation* in the case of a *rectangular* initial excess water pressure distribution is as follows:

$$U_v = 1 - \sum_{m=0}^{m=\infty} \frac{8}{\pi^2(2m+1)^2} \exp\left[-\frac{\pi^2}{4}(2m+1)^2 T_v\right] \qquad (5.21)$$

Equation 5.21 corresponds to graph 1 in figure 5.15, which illustrates the variation of the average degree of vertical consolidation U_v *versus* the dimensionless time factor T_v. Notice that with respect to the same figure, graph 1 (*i.e.* equation 5.21) is used in conjunction with any type of initial excess water pressure distribution as long as the soil is drained on both sides. In other words, the drainage path corresponds to half the layer thickness as indicated in figure 5.14 where the numbers in brackets correspond to the graph numbers in figure 5.15. In the case of one way drainage, the nature of dissipation of the excess pressure u_i within the soil depends on the type of loading, so that graph 1 in figure 4.15 is used if u_i were induced by a *uniform load*. Graph 2 applies when the soil is subjected to a *concentrated load,* and graph 3 corresponds to *hydraulic fills* (such as a slurry mud) which, initially, do not carry any effective stresses.

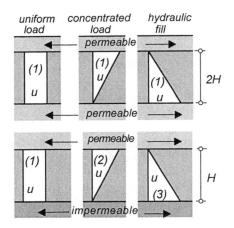

Figure 5.14: Initial porewater pressure distribution
for different drainage conditions.

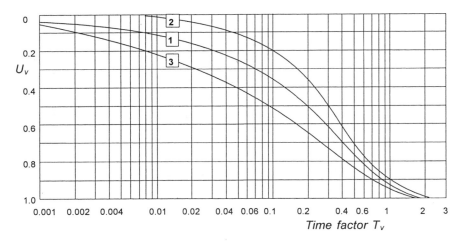

Figure 5.15: Average degree of consolidation corresponding to
initial porewater pressure distributions of figure 5.14.

It is clear that the consolidation process, represented by the rate of dissipation of the excess porewater pressure is to all intents and purposes controlled by the permeability and compressibility of the soil. Thus a sand, for instance, with a high permeability will allow any excess porewater pressure to dissipate almost as fast as it was generated. A clay, in contrast, is characterised by a very low permeability relative to a sand and, as such, any consolidation process related to a clayey soil is most likely to be very slow. Because consolidation leads to a change in volume, it is obvious that such a process will induce time dependent deformation within a clay layer. Accordingly, it is vital to remember that, while consolidation depends on the soil permeability, in other words on the ease (or the lack of it) with which water can flow out of or into the soil matrix, the magnitude of deformation generated at the end of consolidation depends on the compressibility of the soil and has very little to do with the consolidation process *per se*. Moreover, whenever a positive excess porewater pressure is generated within a clay deposit, a consolidation process is triggered during which the effective stresses increase gradually in the manner depicted in figure 5.10, thus increasing the clay density and therefore its resistance. In the meantime, the volume decreases at a rate which can be determined at any time using the graphs of figure 5.15. Ultimately, when all excess porewater pressure has dissipated, the final overall deformation better known as *settlement* can be estimated using appropriate compressibility characteristics of the clay as will be seen shortly. Consequently, both the *rate* of settlement and its final *magnitude* matter a great deal to a designer in order to ensure a safe environment on site and a sound structural design.

As already mentioned, the coefficient of consolidation c_v can be determined using the results of one-dimensional consolidation test, and in that respect, one has to go back to the one dimensional (vertical) transient flow equation 5.21. Re-plotting this equation as U_v *versus* $T_v^{1/2}$ in figure 5.16, it is seen that the corresponding graph is linear up to an approximate value $U_v \approx 0.5$. Taylor (1948) noticed that by extending the linear portion of the graph, then plotting a second line with a slope 15% less as shown in figure 5.16, the latter line intersects the graph at point A with the approximate co-ordinates ($U_v = 0.9$, $T_v^{1/2} = 0.92$). Taylor then suggested that, for a consolidation test undertaken under similar loading and drainage conditions, the graph corresponding to the variation of the (volumetric) strain $\varepsilon_v = \Delta H/H$ with the square root of time $t^{1/2}$ should be *similar* to that of figure 5.16, and therefore the time $t_{90}^{1/2}$ pertaining to 90% of consolidation can be determined in precisely the same graphical way. Now that the time factor $T_{v90} = (0.92)^2 = 0.848$ as well as the real time t_{90} are known, equation 5.18 can then be used to estimate the coefficient of vertical consolidation:

$$c_v = \frac{T_{v90}H^2}{t_{90}} = \frac{0.848H^2}{t_{90}} \qquad\qquad (5.22)$$

As mentioned earlier, the coefficient c_v is usually expressed in $m^2/year$. Conversely, for a clay deposit with a known c_v, the time needed to achieve 90% of consolidation can be estimated from equation 5.22:

$$t_{90} = 0.848\frac{H^2}{c_v} \qquad\qquad (5.23)$$

where H in equations 5.22 and 5.23 represents the length of the drainage path.

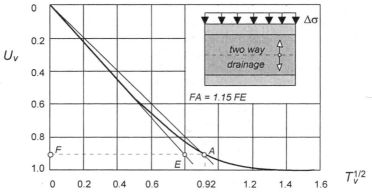

Figure 5.16: Consolidation graph (Taylor construction).

The coefficient of consolidation c_v can thus be determined from the results of a relatively simple one-dimensional consolidation test (as in figure 5.17) using equation 5.22. However, one has to be aware of the theoretical as well as the practical limitations of the method which is known to yield smaller c_v values (in some cases by more than two orders of magnitude) than those estimated from field measurements.

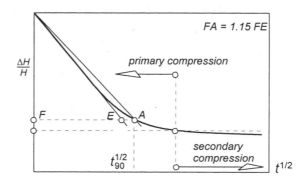

Figure 5.17: Interpretation of 1-D consolidation test results: primary and secondary consolidations.

Thus, the 1-D consolidation theory developed earlier *assumes* that c_v is constant in space and in time. According to equation 5.15, this assumption means that the ratio of vertical permeability to the coefficient of volume compressibility is constant with depth and with time. In other words, these two parameters are assumed to vary in the same proportion which may seem optimistic. However, there are instances for which the errors related to this assumption are insignificant provided that the ratio of the stress increment to the actual stress used during the test is such that $1 \leq \Delta\sigma_v'/\sigma_v' \leq 2$. In this respect, figure 5.18 shows that c_v values which correspond to different levels of effective vertical stress increments compare very favourably. The variable effective stress increments applied to the *same* natural stiff clay during several 1-D consolidation tests (Azizi and Josseaume (1988)) are such that the ratio $\Delta\sigma_v'/\sigma_v' = 1.15$. On the practical side, the determination of c_v can be markedly affected by the testing procedure which requires some detailed consideration. In particular, care must be taken so as to minimise any soil disturbance during extraction from the site, transportation, storage and sample preparation.

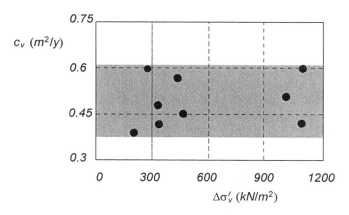

Figure 5.18: c_v values corresponding to a natural stiff clay.

More importantly (and perhaps notwithstanding the commercial pressures when applicable), the operator must have a clear procedure to follow before, during and after testing in order to ensure that high quality data are obtained. In particular, it is essential to realise that the outcome of a consolidation test can be adversely affected, to a large extent, during sample preparation. Not only are the cutting and trimming of the sample bound to disturb the soil fabric to some degree, but also, if not handled properly, the soil can be subjected to initial plastic deformation and/or a change in void ratio. The operator must therefore bear in mind that the quality of data depends almost exclusively on the stage of test that precedes the first loading, during which the very nature of the tested soil can be altered dramatically. It is well known that, once extracted from the ground, a saturated stiff clay, for instance, will be subjected to a negative porewater pressure due to the unloading process. Accordingly, once positioned inside the brass ring then trimmed, the clay sample will exhibit a tendency to expand in volume to offset the suction. However, a volume expansion can only occur if the clay has access to water and, therefore, it is fundamental to understand that *any* soil contact with water, *let alone saturation*, prior to loading must be prevented at all cost. The question that arises, then, is what load should be applied to the sample before saturation? The answer must be considered in conjunction with the entire testing procedure and, in this respect, the following logical steps are recommended:

(1) Once trimmed to the required dimensions, a dry filter paper is placed on each side of the sample as per figure 5.19.

(2) The ring containing the sample is thereafter placed on the pedestal, and a vertical stress slightly lower than the overburden pressure to which the soil was subjected *in situ* prior to its extraction is then gently applied, followed immediately by saturation of the sample and filter papers.

(3) The vertical pressure is then constantly adjusted so as to prevent any volume change (*i.e.* any axial deformation in this case) from occurring. This operation can last for up to one hour in the case of a stiff clay.

(4) Once equilibrium has been achieved, the actual incremental loading then begins. Each load increment is applied for at least 24 *h,* depending on the nature of the tested soil (for stiff clays, a duration of 48 *h* per increment might be needed). Subsequent increments must be such that the ratio of the stress increment to the current stress is within the range $1 \leq \Delta\sigma'/\sigma' \leq 2$ so as to minimise the effect of secondary compression (refer to figure 5.17).

(5) The loading is pursued until a void ratio $e \approx 0.42e_o$ is reached (where e_o is the initial void ratio as per figure 5.9), at which point an unload–reload cycle is then applied to the sample.

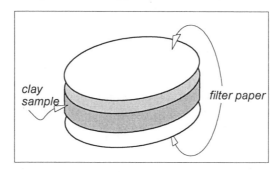

Figure 5.19: Sample preparation.

This procedure has the advantage of minimising any soil disturbance that would have otherwise occurred during testing, ensuring in the process the measurement of high quality data which can thence be used to estimate c_v values according to the Taylor procedure of figure 5.16, as well as the preconsolidation pressure σ'_p using the Schmertmann method of figure 5.9. In so doing, the operator must be aware of the fact that, for tests involving high stress levels, the measured deformation might be due partly to the deformation of the apparatus itself. The 'artificial' component of the deformation can be as high as 1.5% in some instances as depicted in figure 5.20 where a standard oedometer equipment was calibrated using a steel sample, which was subjected to the same stress path followed during a 1-D consolidation test on a natural stiff clay (Azizi and Josseaume (1988)). Clearly, any interpretation of data that does not take into account such fictitious sample deformation would be erroneous.

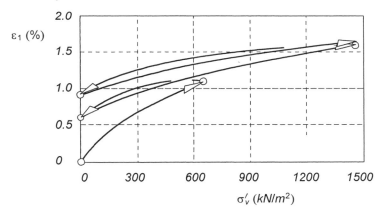

Figure 5.20: Deformation related to a standard 1-D consolidation apparatus.

Ample experimental evidence shows that standard 1-D consolidation tests yield c_v values which are *markedly smaller* than those estimated from *in situ* tests, due in part to the *size* of sample tested in the laboratory. To alleviate this problem, a Rowe cell (also known as a hydraulic compression cell (Rowe and Barden (1966)) can be used whereby samples 250 *mm* diameter and 100 *mm* thick can be tested. The cell having an impermeable base; the drainage occurs through the entire thickness of the sample within which the distribution of the porewater pressure generated by the loading is assumed to be parabolic as in figure 5.21. During the test, a back pressure can be applied to the sample (to ensure full saturation) which can then be loaded *continuously* in a variety of ways:
- constant stress rate whereby $d\sigma'/dt = $ constant,
- constant strain rate with $d\varepsilon_1/dt = $ constant,

- constant gradient so that the porewater pressure at the base of the sample remains constant.

The coefficient of (vertical) consolidation c_v can then be estimated as follows (Whitlow, 1995):

$$c_v = \frac{k}{m_v \gamma_w} \qquad (5.24)$$

with the coefficient of permeability calculated from the strain–time curve:

$$k = \frac{H_o^2 \gamma_w}{2u_b} \frac{\partial \varepsilon}{\partial t} \qquad (5.25)$$

and the coefficient of volume compressibility being estimated from the stress–strain curve:

$$m_v = \frac{1}{H_o} \frac{\partial H}{\partial \sigma'_v} \qquad (5.26)$$

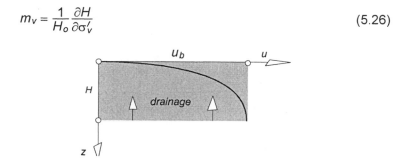

Figure 5.21: Parabolic porewater pressure distribution.

Alternatively, c_v can be estimated from the stress–time curve as follows:

$$c_v = \frac{H_o^2}{2u_b} \frac{\partial \sigma'_v}{\partial t} \qquad (5.27)$$

where ∂H represents the change in the sample thickness, H_o is the initial sample height, and u_b is the porewater pressure at the base of the sample as in figure 5.21. The c_v values calculated from equations 5.24 and 5.27 still underestimate the *in situ* values, and are affected by the *secondary consolidation* depicted in figure 5.17. This component, which is due to *creep* rather than to the expulsion of water from within the soil matrix, can develop at a very early stage of testing. In particular, the magnitude of secondary consolidation in the case of a standard oedometer test is known to increase as the ratio of the vertical stress increment to the existing vertical stress $\Delta\sigma'/\sigma'$ decreases. These creep effects which can noticeably distort c_v

values can be minimised by applying stress increments such that $1 \leq \Delta\sigma'/\sigma' \leq 2$, as suggested earlier. Notwithstanding these shortcomings, carefully undertaken consolidation tests, using either standard equipment or Rowe cells, can yield reliable information that can be used in conjunction with field measurements. It is essential to understand that the time of consolidation calculated using a c_v value estimated from a one-dimensional consolidation test is bound to be considerably greater than the *actual* time of consolidation observed in the field. This is mainly due to the fact that clay deposits are usually anisotropic with a much larger horizontal permeability than the vertical one. In order to alleviate this problem, it is advisable to follow the suggestion made by Bishop and Al-Dhahir (1970) that consists of estimating c_v as follows:

$$c_v \approx \frac{k_{h(in\,situ)}}{m_{v(lab)}\gamma_w} \qquad (5.28)$$

where $k_{h(in\,situ)}$ corresponds to the horizontal permeability of the clay measured in the field from a pumping test, and $m_{v(lab)}$ is the coefficient of volume compressibility corresponding to the same vertical stress increment applied in the field and estimated from a laboratory consolidation test according to equation 5.5.

5.4 Practical aspects of vertical consolidation

In all the relationships that have been developed previously, the pressure generating the process of consolidation is assumed to be *constant* and to have been *applied instantaneously*. However, every practising engineer would realise that the construction of any type of project is realised in a time t_c throughout which the pressure would have increased gradually. A linear increase such as that depicted in figure 5.22 can be assumed, so that the final magnitude of the pressure p can be considered to have been applied instantaneously for a period of time $t_c/2$ (refer to figure 5.22). Under these conditions, the time factor corresponding to $t_c/2$, calculated from equation 5.18, is:

$$T_v = \frac{c_v}{H^2}\frac{t_c}{2} \qquad (5.29)$$

Were the pressure to be assumed to have been applied in its entirety from the start of construction, the corresponding time factor T_v would double, resulting in an overestimate of the degree of consolidation achieved at the end of construction.

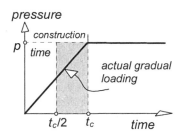

Figure 5.22: Actual and assumed pressure distribution with time.

This can be potentially unsafe as far as settlement calculations are concerned.

Example 5.1

Consider the construction of a wide, 4 *m* high embankment on top of a 5 *m* thick layer of a clay deposit with a vertical coefficient of consolidation $c_v = 1.8 \, m^2/y$. The clay is underlain by a thick layer of dense sand and, prior to placing the fill material, a thin drainage blanket of sand was applied on top of the clay deposit so as to ensure two-way drainage of the clay. If it takes 6 months to build the embankment then, assuming a linear increase of the load during that time, equation 5.29 yields:

$$T_v = \frac{1.8}{2.5^2} \times \frac{0.5}{2} = 0.072$$

using graph 1 in figure 5.15, the corresponding average degree of vertical consolidation is $U_v \approx 30\%$. If the embankment were (erroneously) assumed to have been built instantaneously then, according to equation 5.18:

$$T_v = \frac{1.8}{2.5^2} \times 0.5 = 0.144$$

thus yielding a degree of consolidation $U_v \approx 44\%$. Due allowance should therefore be made for the *delaying* effect on consolidation of the gradual increase in loading during construction.

5.5 Three-dimensional consolidation theory

The consolidation depends on the permeability of the soil. Consequently if, for whatever reason a consolidation process is generated within a semi-infinite layer of a saturated homogeneous clay, having a very low vertical permeability, then the ensuing rate of vertical consolidation is bound to be very slow, thus reflecting the clay permeability. Knowing that most natural clays are *anisotropic* as they were usually deposited in horizontal (or nearly horizontal) layers, their permeability in the horizontal direction k_h is generally much higher than that in the vertical direction k_v. Therefore, if a horizontal flow can be triggered, the overall consolidation process will occur at a much faster rate. To simulate the horizontal drainage, let us assume that perfectly cylindrical drains with radii r_w, consisting of a highly permeable material, are inserted in an arrangement such as that shown in figure 5.23. The governing two-dimensional transient flow equation can be established by considering the flow through a soil element situated at a height z and a distance r from the centre of the drain as indicated in the figure.

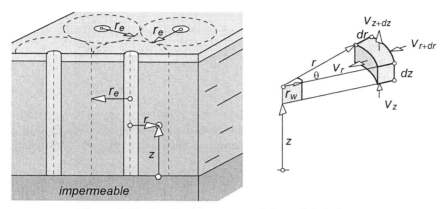

Figure 5.23: Practical arrangement for radial drainage.

Applying an approach similar to that used in the case of vertical consolidation, it can be shown that the ensuing three-dimensional consolidation equation is as follows:

$$\frac{\partial u}{\partial t} = c_v \frac{\partial^2 u}{\partial z^2} + c_h \left(\frac{\partial^2 u}{\partial r^2} + \frac{1}{r} \frac{\partial u}{\partial r} \right) \tag{5.30}$$

where u represents the excess porewater pressure, and c_h corresponds to the coefficient of *horizontal consolidation* calculated in a way similar to equation 5.15:

$$c_h = \frac{k_h}{\gamma_w m_v} \tag{5.31}$$

The average degree of *overall* consolidation U, corresponding to equation 5.30, reflects the average degree of consolidation in both vertical and radial directions. If the average degree of vertical consolidation U_v given by equation 5.21 represents the solution to the consolidation equation in the *vertical direction*, then Carrillo (1942) suggested that, provided the average degree of *radial consolidation* U_r corresponds to the solution of the following consolidation equation in the radial direction:

$$\frac{\partial u}{\partial t} = c_h \left(\frac{\partial^2 u}{\partial r^2} + \frac{1}{r} \frac{\partial u}{\partial r} \right) \tag{5.32}$$

The *overall* degree of consolidation U can then be estimated as follows:

$$(1 - U) = (1 - U_v)(1 - U_r) \tag{5.33}$$

U_v having been established earlier (refer to equation 5.21), only U_r needs to be derived to resolve equation 5.33. The details of the analytical solution to equation 5.32 were given by Barron (1948) and are outside the scope of this text. However, the corresponding graphical solution is depicted in figure 5.24 with the average degree of *radial* consolidation U_r being related to the time factor:

$$T_r = \frac{c_h t}{r_e^2} \qquad (5.34)$$

where r_e represents the radius of influence of the drain (refer to figure 5.23). The family of curves represented in figure 5.24 corresponds to different values of the ratio n reflecting the spacing of two consecutive drains:

$$n = r_e / r_w \qquad (5.35)$$

r_w being the drain radius.

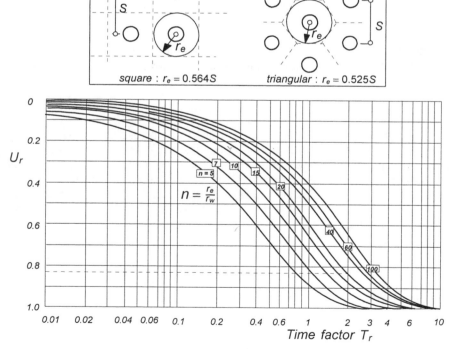

Figure 5.24: Graphical solution of equation 5.34 (Barron, 1948).
(Reproduced by permission of the ASCE.)

Notice that the spacing between drains depends on the way that they are arranged, as depicted on the top of figure 5.24.

Example 5.2

Consider the case of an 8 *m* thick layer of sand overlying a 6 *m* thick deposit of normally consolidated clay, resting on an impermeable shale. For technical reasons, the groundwater table, originally 1 *m* below the ground surface, is to be lowered permanently by 6 *m* over a wide area, causing an increase in effective vertical stresses.   To accelerate the drainage, it is proposed to install series of radial sand drains in sufficient numbers so that the time needed for 90% of overall consolidation to occur is cut to just two years. Prefabricated drains with 200 *mm* diameter are inserted throughout the clay layer in a triangular arrangement. Calculate the spacing between two consecutive drains needed to achieve the stated objective. The coefficients of horizontal and vertical consolidation of the clay are respectively: $c_h = 3\,m^2/y$, $c_v = 2.2\,m^2/y$.

First, the average degree of vertical consolidation U_v at $t = 2\,y$ can easily be found using equation 5.18 together with figure 5.15. Whence:

$$T_v = \frac{c_v t}{H^2} = \frac{2.2 \times 2}{36} = 0.122$$

Curve 1 in figure 5.15 then yields a value $U_v \approx 0.42$. On the other hand, the degree of overall consolidation, calculated from equation 5.33, must be $U = 0.90$ at $t = 2\,y$. Substituting for U and U_v in equation 5.33, it follows that:

$$(1 - 0.9) = (1 - 0.42)(1 - U_r) \quad \Rightarrow \quad U_r \approx 0.83$$

Consequently, the spacing of drains must be such that $U_r = 0.83$ at $t = 2\,y$. The drains have the same radius $r_w = 100\,mm$, so that figure 5.24 can now be used to find the appropriate spacing. The procedure consists of choosing a value n_1, in other words selecting a curve on the figure from which the quantity T_r corresponding to $U_r = 0.83$ (refer to the broken line in figure 5.24) is read. Next, use the value of T_r and a combination of equations 5.34 and 5.35 to calculate n_2:

$$n_2 = \frac{1}{r_w}\left(\frac{c_h t}{T_r}\right)^{1/2} = \frac{1}{0.1}\left(\frac{3 \times 2}{T_r}\right)^{1/2} \qquad (5.36)$$

If n_2 is different from n_1, then the same procedure is repeated using the newly calculated value of n_2 until convergence occurs. Usually, this iterative procedure converges very quickly. The results in this instance are summarised below:

n_1	T_r	n_2
20	2	17
17	1.85	18
18	1.9	18

It can be seen that, at convergence, $n = r_e/r_w = 18$, yielding a radius of influence $r_e = 1.8\,m$. Since the drains are arranged in a triangular way, their spacing S is calculated as follows (refer to figure 5.24):

$$S = \frac{1.8}{0.525} = 3.43\,m$$

Notice that the design of radial drains depends on the coefficient of horizontal consolidation c_h, whose value is usually higher than that of the coefficient of vertical consolidation. The value of c_h can be measured using a one-dimensional consolidation test during which the excess porewater pressure generated within the soil sample is dissipated *radially* through a central drain while preventing vertical drainage from occurring. The test results can then be interpreted in the same way as for vertical consolidation except that, in this case, ample experimental evidence shows that the value of $t_{90}^{1/2}$ corresponding to 90% of radial consolidation is obtained from the intersection of the graph $(\Delta h,\, t^{1/2})$ and the line with a slope 17% smaller than that of the initial linear portion of the graph (as opposed to 15% in the vertical consolidation case). The corresponding value of T_{r90}, which depends on n, is evaluated from figure 5.24, and c_h is then estimated as follows:

$$c_h = \frac{r_e^2\, T_{r90}}{t_{90}} \tag{5.37}$$

5.6 Settlement analysis

5.6.1 Nature of settlement

Any type of loading that causes the effective stress within the soil mass to change induces a transient flow, in other words a consolidation process, the effect of which was illustrated in figure 5.17. From a design perspective, the final amount of vertical deformation, referred to as *settlement,* measured at the end of this process is most relevant. The *total settlement S* has three components as shown in figure 5.25:

$$S = S_i + S_c + S_s \tag{5.38}$$

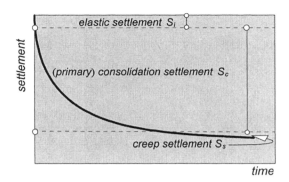

Figure 5.25: The three settlement components: S_i, S_c and S_s.

The (primary) *consolidation settlement* S_c represents by and large the major component. S_i is the (immediate) *elastic* constituent of settlement and S_s corresponds to the long term *creep settlement.* Accordingly, whenever a process of consolidation is triggered, each of these three components must be calculated in order to estimate the ensuing final total settlement. The oedometer test simulates the loading conditions applied through a *rigid foundation* in that, during the test, the increase in the vertical pressure across the sample top surface (that is the contact pressure) is almost uniform. For a *flexible foundation,* on the other hand, the contact pressure is always maximum under the foundation centre and minimum under its corners or edge. It is therefore logical to expect the least favourable design conditions, *i.e.* the maximum total settlement, to occur under the centre of a flexible foundation (were it to exist) as shown in figure 5.26. Also, a difference in the magnitude of settlement across the area of a flexible foundation is bound to occur since points at the edge will undergo a minimum settlement compared with the centre of foundation.

The total settlement beneath a *rigid foundation* is assumed to be uniform and the approach that is generally adopted in practice to estimate its magnitude consists of calculating the total settlement which would result under the centre of an equivalent *flexible foundation*, then multiplying this value by a correction factor of 0.8 to account for the effects of rigidity of the foundation.

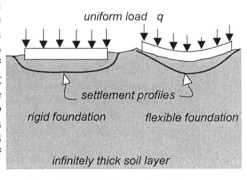

Figure 5.26: Settlement profile under rigid and flexible foundations.

5.6.2 Immediate settlement S_i

This elastic component of settlement is due to soil distortion and not to a volume change. It takes place during or immediately after construction of the structure, and can be calculated using the elasticity theory. Hence with reference to figure 5.26, assuming that the soil has a Poisson's ratio v and an undrained elasticity modulus E_u, then the immediate settlement beneath a foundation of width B, transmitting a uniform pressure q can be estimated as follows:

- settlement at the *corner* of a *flexible* foundation:

$$S_i = \frac{Bq}{E_u}(1-v^2)\frac{I_s}{2} \tag{5.39}$$

- settlement at the *centre* of a *flexible* foundation:

$$S_i = \frac{Bq}{E_u}(1-v^2)I_s \tag{5.40}$$

- settlement at the *centre or corner* of a *rigid* foundation:

$$S_i = \frac{Bq}{E_u}(1-v^2)I_r \tag{5.41}$$

The coefficients I_s and I_r depend on the ratio L/B (where L represents the foundation length and B its width), and can be read from figure 5.27 (produced from data by Giroud (1968) and Skempton (1951)).

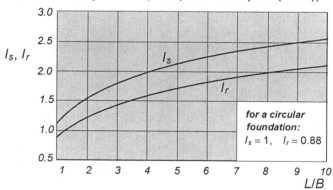

Figure 5.27: Settlement multipliers.

The derivation of the above relationships is based on the *assumption* that the soil layer beneath the foundation is infinitely thick. Consequently, the immediate settlement predictions should be interpreted cautiously. Although for a finite thickness, equations 5.39 to 5.41 yield an overestimate of S_i, leading thus to an error on the safe side. If the soil beneath the foundation consists of a layer of saturated clay of a thickness H, then the immediate settlement occurs under *undrained* conditions, corresponding to a Poisson's ratio $v = 0.5$. Under these circumstances, the average S_i value can be estimated from the following equation:

$$S_i = \alpha_1 \alpha_2 \frac{Bq}{E_u} \qquad (5.42)$$

The coefficients α_1 and α_2 are read from figure 5.28 (Christian and Carrier (1978)) in which L corresponds to the foundation length.

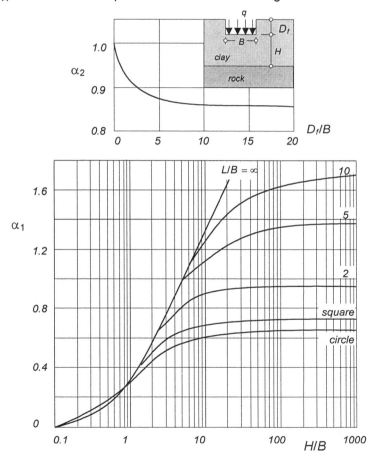

Figure 5.28: Settlement multipliers for undrained conditions.
(Reproduced by permission of the National Research Council of Canada.)

Example 5.3

Consider the case of a square foundation founded at the surface of a stiff clay layer having a thickness H, a width B and subjected to a uniform pressure q. Let us now use both previous methods to assess the average magnitude of the immediate settlement beneath the centre of foundation. Because this component of settlement is a short term phenomenon, it therefore occurs under undrained conditions for which the clay is characterised by a Poisson's ratio $\nu = 0.5$ (refer to section 7.6.1). Accordingly, equation 5.40 with a value $I_s \approx 0.9$ can be used to estimate the *average* immediate settlement at the foundation centre:

$$S_{i1} = 0.9(1 - 0.5^2)\frac{Bq}{E_u} \tag{5.43}$$

Similarly, S_{i2} can be calculated from equation 5.42 in which $\alpha_2 = 1$ since $D_f = 0$:

$$S_{i2} = \alpha_1 \frac{Bq}{E_u} \tag{5.44}$$

Obviously the *actual* settlement depends on the extent of the thickness H of the clay layer which is only taken into account in equation 5.44 *via* the coefficient α_1. The predictions of the two latter equations are plotted in figure 5.29 as the variation of the ratio S_{i1}/S_{i2} *versus* H/B. Clearly, in this case, both equations yield similar predictions for ratios $H/B > 3$.

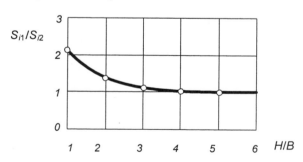

Figure 5.29: Comparison of settlement predictions for saturated clays.

5.6.3 Primary consolidation settlement

Primary consolidation (S_c in figure 5.25) represents the major component of settlement whose final magnitude is related to the *compressibility characteristics* of the soil (C_c and C_s in figure 5.6). The magnitude of the consolidation settlement S_c can be estimated in a fairly accurate way provided that representative soil parameters are used in the calculations and, most importantly, a correction factor is applied to these calculations to take into account the effect of foundation size and soil type as suggested by Skempton and Bjerrum (1957). Let us first tackle the calculations of primary consolidation using different relationships developed earlier in the case of the one-dimensional consolidation test. Consider the general case of a *saturated clay* which, after being unloaded during sampling, was subjected in the laboratory to a gradual increase in the vertical effective pressure, so that the variation of the void ratio covers phases of both overconsolidation and normal consolidation as shown in figure 5.30.

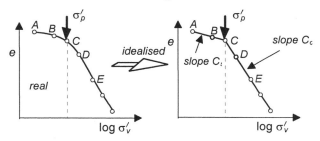

*Figure 5.30: Actual and idealised behaviours of
a saturated clay, subjected to 1-D consolidation.*

The behaviour in figure 5.30 can be assimilated to two linear portions without any significant loss of accuracy, thus allowing for both compressibility coefficients C_c and C_s to be determined. Moreover if, at any stage during the test, the clay were subjected to a pressure increment $\Delta\sigma_v$, and allowed to consolidate, then the ensuing change in the void ratio would be related to the change in the clay thickness through equation 5.2 which can be rewritten as follows:

$$\frac{\Delta e}{1+e_o} = \frac{\Delta h}{h} \tag{5.45}$$

The quantity $\Delta h/h$ (*i.e.* the vertical strain which is identical to the volumetric strain ε_v in this case) can therefore be integrated throughout the thickness of the clay H_c, yielding the consolidation settlement:

$$S_c = \int_0^{H_c} \frac{\Delta e}{1+e_o}\, dz = \frac{\Delta e}{1+e_o} H_c \tag{5.46}$$

Consequently, the consolidation settlement can be calculated at any stage of loading provided that the variation of the void ratio Δe is known. With reference to figure 5.30, three distinct cases of loading may occur, for which S_c is evaluated differently.

• **(a) Overconsolidated clays with** $\sigma'_v + \Delta\sigma' < \sigma'_p$

When the applied vertical effective stress increment $\Delta\sigma'_v$ is such that the cumulative value $\sigma'_v + \Delta\sigma'_v$ is still smaller than the preconsolidation pressure σ'_p, then the quantity Δe is calculated using the swelling index C_s as depicted in figure 5.31:

$$e_f - e_o = C_s[\log(\sigma'_v + \Delta\sigma') - \log \sigma'_v]$$

or $\qquad \Delta e = C_s \log\left(\dfrac{\sigma'_v + \Delta\sigma'}{\sigma'_v}\right)$ (5.47)

now substituting for Δe into equation 5.46, it follows that :

$$S_c = \frac{C_s H_c}{1 + e_o} \log\left(\frac{\sigma'_v + \Delta\sigma'}{\sigma'_v}\right)$$ (5.48)

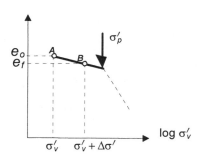

Figure 5.31: Settlement calculations: overconsolidated clays.

• **(b) Overconsolidated clays with** $\sigma'_v < \sigma'_p < \sigma'_v + \Delta\sigma'$

This case corresponds to a load increment that causes the clay behaviour to change from an overconsolidated state to a normally consolidated one as illustrated in figure 5.32. It is straightforward to establish that:

$$\Delta e = C_s\left[\log \sigma'_p - \log \sigma'_v\right] + C_c\left[\log(\sigma'_v + \Delta\sigma') - \log \sigma'_p\right]$$ (5.49)

Rearranging, then substituting for Δe into equation 5.46:

$$S_c = \frac{H_c}{1 + e_o}\left[C_s \log\left(\frac{\sigma'_p}{\sigma'_v}\right) + C_c \log \frac{\sigma'_v + \Delta\sigma'}{\sigma'_p}\right]$$ (5.50)

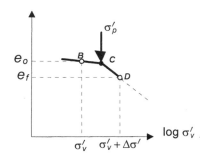

Figure 5.32: Settlement calculations: overconsolidated,
then normally consolidated clays.

• (c) Normally consolidated clays

The corresponding loading conditions are shown in figure 5.33 from which it can be seen that:

$$\Delta e = C_c \log \left(\frac{\sigma'_v + \Delta\sigma'}{\sigma'_v} \right) \qquad (5.51)$$

Substituting Δe in equation 5.46 yields:

$$S_c = \frac{C_c H_c}{1 + e_o} \log \left(\frac{\sigma'_v + \Delta\sigma'}{\sigma'_v} \right) \qquad (5.52)$$

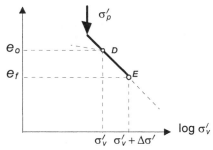

Figure 5.33: Settlement calculations: normally consolidated clays.

5.6.4 Effects of soil type and foundation size

The magnitude of consolidation settlement calculated from equations 5.48, 5.50 and 5.52 is only realistic if the dimensions of the loaded area are large in relation to the depth of the clay layer as in the case of an oedometer test (refer to figure 5.34b). However, in the majority of cases in the field, the size of the loaded area is too small compared with the thickness of the saturated clay layer as depicted in figure 5.34a. Under field conditions, the consolidation settlement is calculated by integrating the excess porewater pressure generated initially within the soil matrix by the load increment as suggested by Skempton and Bjerrum (1957) , so that for *each* individual sublayer:

$$S_{ci} = \int_0^{H_i} m_{vi} \Delta u \, dz \qquad (5.53)$$

where H_i represents the thickness of each sublayer (as in figure 5.34) having a coefficient of volume compressibility m_{vi}, and within which the initial excess porewater pressure Δu is assumed constant. Note that the limits used in conjunction with the integral sign in equation 5.53 represent the upper and lower limits of each individual sublayer.

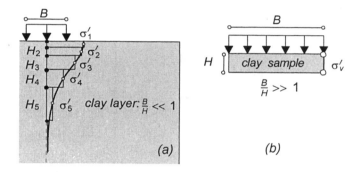

Figure 5.34: Effects of foundation size on settlement:
(a) field conditions and (b) laboratory conditions.

Moreover, the initial increase in porewater pressure can be estimated from the Skempton relationship (Skempton, 1954):

$$\Delta u = \Delta\sigma_3 + A(\Delta\sigma_1 - \Delta\sigma_3)$$

$$= \Delta\sigma_1 \left[A + \frac{\Delta\sigma_3}{\Delta\sigma_1}(1 - A) \right] \qquad (5.54)$$

where $\Delta\sigma_1 \equiv \Delta\sigma_v$ and A represents a porewater pressure coefficient, whose values are discussed in detail in section 6.3.2. Substituting for Δu in equation 5.53, it follows that:

$$S_{ci} = \int_0^{H_i} m_{vi} \Delta\sigma_1 \left[A + \frac{\Delta\sigma_3}{\Delta\sigma_1}(1 - A) \right] dz \qquad (5.55)$$

On the other hand, equation 5.46 can be expressed as follows:

$$S_{c(oed)} = \int_0^{H_i} \frac{\Delta e}{1 + e_o}\, dz = \int_0^{H_i} m_{vi} \Delta \sigma_1\, dz \qquad (5.56)$$

Comparing equations 5.55 and 5.56, it emerges that:

$$S_{ci} = \mu S_{c(oed)} \qquad (5.57)$$

with $\quad \mu = A + (1 - A)\left(\dfrac{\int_0^H \Delta \sigma_3\, dz}{\int_0^H \Delta \sigma_1\, dz}\right) \qquad (5.58)$

It is therefore essential that when the loaded area is small in dimensions compared with the thickness of the clay on which it is founded, and more importantly, when the clay is overconsolidated (*i.e.* small A values), consolidation settlement calculated from equations 5.48, 5.50 and 5.52 is corrected to make due allowance for the effects of foundation size. The correction factor μ, which depends on the value of the *pore pressure parameter A* and the ratio H/B, can be read from figure 5.35.

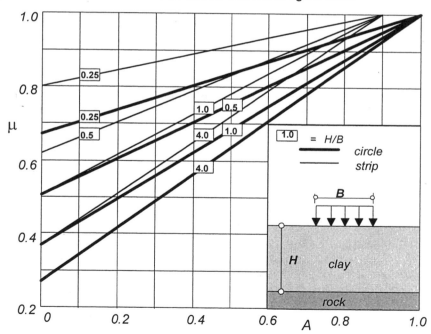

Figure 5.35: Correction factor for foundation size. (Skempton and Bjerrum, 1957). (Reproduced by permission of the Institution of Civil Engineers, London.)

The consolidation settlement of the entire clay layer corresponds to the sum of all individual contributions:

$$S_c = \sum_{i=1}^{n} S_{ci} \qquad\qquad (5.59)$$

n being the number of sublayers as illustrated in figure 5.34. Logically, the number n is related to the type of pressure distribution generated by the loaded area. With reference to figures 3.37 and 3.38 in section 3.4, it is seen that for a circular or a rectangular uniformly loaded area, the vertical pressure due to the applied uniform load decays at a depth of about $3B$ (B being the foundation width), whereas for a long strip, the clay layer is unaffected by the pressure distribution generated by the strip below a depth of around $8B$. Accordingly, the calculations of consolidation settlement are restricted to within the above limits and sublayers of equal thickness are usually used. Sublayers with a thickness varying from $B/2$ for a circular or a rectangular foundation, to B in the case of a long strip are typical.

Example 5.4

A rigid $(2 \times 2)\,m^2$ square pad foundation is founded at the top of an 8 m thick layer of a lightly overconsolidated clay, sandwiched between a 2 m thick layer of dense sand at the top and a layer of soft rock at the bottom as shown in figure 5.36. The water table is situated at a depth of 1 m below the ground surface, and a unit weight $\gamma = 19\,kN/m^3$ is assumed to apply throughout the sand layer. The clay properties are as follows:
$\gamma_s = 20\,kN/m^3$, $C_c = 0.38$, $C_s = 0.1$,

$A = 0.55$, $E_u = 8000\,kN/m^2$.

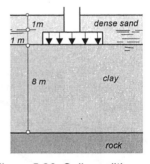

Figure 5.36: Soil conditions.

The preconsolidation pressure is assumed to vary linearly from $\sigma'_p = 140\,kN/m^2$ at the top of the clay layer to $\sigma'_p = 220\,kN/m^2$ at its bottom. The foundation will be transmitting a uniform net pressure $q = 300\,kN/m^2$, and the results of a laboratory one-dimensional consolidation test, undertaken on a clay sample extracted from a depth of 4 m below the ground surface, are as depicted in figure 5.37. The ensuing settlement includes an immediate component that can be estimated in a straightforward way using equation 5.42:

$$S_i = \alpha_1 \alpha_2 \frac{Bq}{E_u}$$

Since $H/B = 8/2 = 4$, $D_f/B = 2/2 = 1$, figure 5.28 then yields:

$\alpha_1 = 0.62$, $\alpha_2 = 0.96$

Whence:

$$S_i = 0.62 \times 0.96 \times \frac{2 \times 300}{8000} \approx 0.044 \ m$$

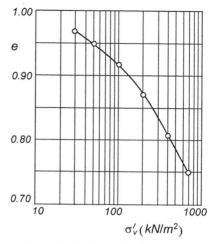

Figure 5.37: Consolidation properties of the clay.

The component of settlement due to primary consolidation depends on the stress distribution generated by the uniform load q. Because of the square shape of the foundation, the effects of stress distribution will be limited to three times the foundation width, that is 6 m. Moreover, within these 6 m of clay, six sublayers of equal thickness $H_c = B/2 = 1 \, m$ will be considered (refer to figure 5.38).

The increase in the vertical effective stress $\Delta\sigma'_v$ due to q, as well as the component σ'_{vo} due to self-weight are calculated at mid-depth, where the corresponding initial void ratio e_o is interpolated from figure 5.37. The results are summarised in the following table in which the stresses are expressed in kN/m^2, and where the depth z is taken with respect to the base of the foundation. Notice that the quantities $\Delta\sigma'_v$ are estimated from Fadum's influence chart of figure 3.23.

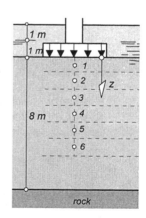

Figure 5.38: Selection of clay sublayers.

point	depth (m)	σ'_{vo}	e_o	$\Delta\sigma'_v$	$\sigma'_{vo} + \Delta\sigma'_v$	σ'_p
1	0.5	33.5	0.970	278.5	312	145
2	1.5	43.5	0.955	138	181.5	155
3	2.5	53.5	0.945	72	125.5	165
4	3.5	63.5	0.935	42	105.5	175
5	4.5	73.5	0.930	27.6	101.1	185
6	5.5	83.5	0.925	15.6	99.1	195

The clay being overconsolidated, the use of either equation 5.48 or equation 5.50 to calculate the oedometric consolidation settlement $\Delta S_{c(oed)}$ at the surface of each sublayer depends on the magnitude of the final stress level $\sigma'_{vo} + \Delta\sigma'_v$ with respect to σ'_p. Thus, with reference to the above table, it can be seen that equation 5.50 must be used in conjunction with the two top sublayers, whereas for the four remaining ones, equation 5.48 applies. It is easy to check that the calculations result in the following:

point	$\Delta S_{c(oed)}\,(m)$
1	0.115
2	0.056
3	0.019
4	0.011
5	0.007
6	0.004

Now that the consolidation settlements for different sublayers are found, their sum must be corrected for soil type and foundation size effects. The correction factor μ is read from figure 5.32 in the knowledge that the clay has a porewater pressure parameter $A = 0.55$, and the ratio $H/B = 4$. Notice that the value of μ will be read from the graph corresponding to a circle with $H/B = 4$, yielding hence $\mu \approx 0.67$. Accordingly, the *corrected* consolidation settlement at the surface of the clay layer (*i.e.* at the base of foundation) is:

$$S_c = 0.67 \sum \Delta S_{c(oed)} = 0.67 \times 0.212 = 0.142\,m$$

The immediate settlement must be added to the above value, then the sum corrected to take into account the rigidity of the foundation. Therefore, the foundation base will settle by an amount:

$$S = 0.8 \times (0.142 + 0.044) = 0.146\,m$$

5.6.5 Secondary compression settlement

At the end of the primary consolidation process when all excess porewater pressure will have dissipated, the clay continues to exhibit some deformation under constant effective stresses. This creep component, referred to as secondary consolidation settlement, occurs at a slow rate compared with primary consolidation as depicted in figure 5.39, and can be estimated during a given time increment $\Delta t = t_2 - t_1$ in the following way:

$$S_s = C_\alpha H_c \frac{1}{1 + e_o} \log \frac{t_2}{t_1} \qquad (5.60)$$

where C_α is the (constant) slope at which secondary consolidation occurs. Given that creep tests on clays are notoriously time consuming, the following empirical relationship between the slope C_α of figure 5.39 and the compression index C_c of the clay (refer to figure 5.30) can be used cautiously:

$$C_\alpha \approx 0.05 C_c \qquad (5.61)$$

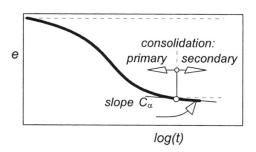

$$\log(t)$$

Figure 5.39: Creep settlement.

Accordingly, equation 5.60 can be used to evaluate the secondary consolidation settlement for each sublayer in the case of the previous example, between, say, $t_1 = 1\,y$ and $t_2 = 3\,y$. Substituting for $C_\alpha = 0.05 \times 0.38 = 0.019$ and for $H_c = 1\,m$ in equation 5.60, it follows that for each sublayer:

$$\Delta S_s = \frac{0.019}{1 + e_o} \log 3 \approx \frac{9}{1 + e_o} \times 10^{-3}\,m$$

The ensuing results are summarised in the following table.

point	e_o	ΔS_s (m)
1	0.970	4.60×10^{-3}
2	0.955	4.60×10^{-3}
3	0.945	4.60×10^{-3}
4	0.935	4.65×10^{-3}
5	0.930	4.65×10^{-3}
6	0.925	4.70×10^{-3}

The overall secondary consolidation settlement of the entire clay layer corresponds to the sum of individual contributions and thus, over two years, the base of foundation will be subjected to a creep settlement with a magnitude:

$$S_s = \Sigma \Delta S_s \approx 0.028 \, m$$

The magnitude of the creep settlement over two years is relatively small in comparison with the primary consolidation settlement calculated previously. This is due to the fact that creep deformation depends mainly on the compressibility of the clay and the logarithm of the time increment during which the deformation is estimated, whereas the extent of consolidation settlement is controlled by the stress increase due to surface loading, as well as the compressibility characteristics of the clay.

Problems

5.1 The results illustrated in figure $p5.1$ were measured on a sample of a stiff clay during an oedometer test. Apply the *Schmertmann* method and estimate the overconsolidation ratio of the clay.

Ans: $OCR \approx 4.5$

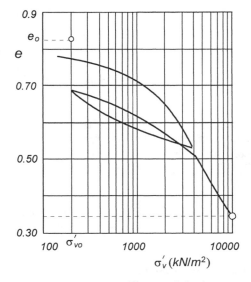

Figure p5.1

5.2   Estimate the same overconsolidation ratio using, this time, *Casagrande* method.

Ans: $OCR \approx 5.9$

5.3   The following results were measured from a one-dimensional consolidation test involving a 20 *mm* thick sample of a stiff clay, under a vertical stress $\Delta\sigma'_v = 960\,kN/m^2$ (the quantities *dh* represent the actual decrease in the sample thickness):

time	0.5 *min*	1 *min*	2 *min*	4 *min*	8 *min*	15 *min*	30 *min*	60 *min*	2 *h*	5 *h*	24 *h*
dh (*mm*)	0.61	0.67	0.72	0.79	0.89	0.99	1.14	1.25	1.31	1.33	1.35

(*a*) Plot these results according to the *Taylor* method, then estimate the coefficient of vertical consolidation c_v of the clay.

(*b*) If the test were undertaken to simulate the *in situ* behaviour of an 8 *m* thick layer of the same clay under similar loading conditions, estimate the time needed for 80% of vertical consolidation to be achieved on site. Assume that the clay layer is drained on both sides.

Ans: (*a*) $c_v \approx 0.55\,m^2/y$,   (*b*) $t_f = 15.7\,y$.

5.4   A $20 \times 20\,m^2$ raft foundation for a tall building is to be founded at the top of an 8 *m* thick layer of firm clay, sandwiched between a 2 *m* thick layer of silty sand at the top and a thick layer of dense sand at the bottom. The total net pressure transmitted to the ground can be assumed to have been increased linearly from zero at the beginning to its full magnitude of $q = 186\,kN/m^2$ ten months later. The clay is characterised by the following coefficients of vertical and horizontal consolidation respectively: $c_v = 2\,m^2/y$, $c_h = 3.1\,m^2/y$.

(*a*) Calculate the time needed for 90% of consolidation to take place if the clay is drained only vertically.

(*b*) It is suggested that 90% of the total settlement must take place by the end of the ten months construction period. For that to happen, prefabricated sand drains, 65 *mm* in diameter, need to be installed in a square arrangement. Estimate the number of drains needed, as well as their spacing.

Ans: (*a*) $t = 6.785\,y$,   (*b*) $n = 23$, $S = 1.32\,m$.

5.5 A circular flexible foundation with a diameter $D = 10\,m$ is founded 1.5 m below the ground surface on top of a 6 m thick layer of firm overconsolidated clay as depicted in figure p5.5. The clay is characterised by an undrained modulus of elasticity $E_u = 12000\,kN/m^2$, and coefficients of vertical and horizontal consolidation: $c_v = 2.1\,m^2/y$, $c_h = 3.2\,m^2/y$.

(a) If the foundation is to transmit a net pressure to the top of the clay layer of a magnitude $q = 160\,kN/m^2$, estimate the initial average elastic settlement that will ensue.

(b) Calculate the time needed for the clay layer to reach a degree of consolidation $U_v = 90\%$.

(c) If the time needed to achieve an overall degree of consolidation $U = 90\%$ is to be cut to 18 months, calculate the required number of 150 mm diameter sand drains to be installed on site in a square arrangement, as well as their spacing.

Ans: (a) $S_i = 0.024m$, (b) $t = 14.51\,y$, (c) $n = 22$, $S = 2.92\,m$.

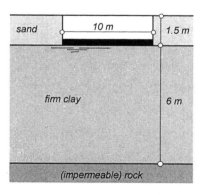

Figure p5.5

5.6 Consider the consolidation settlement of the layer of overconsolidated clay in problem p5.5, and assume that:
- the unit weight of sand is $\gamma = 19.5\,kN/m^3$,
- the clay properties are:
  $\gamma_{sat} = 20\,kN/m^3$, $C_c = 0.3$, $C_s = 0.12$, $A = 0.25$;
- the preconsolidation pressure varies linearly from $\sigma_p' = 300\,kN/m^2$ at the top of the clay layer, to $\sigma_p' = 360\,kN/m^2$ at the bottom;

- the one-dimensional results on a clay sample corresponding to a depth of 4.5 m below the ground surface are as depicted in figure $p5.6$.

(a) Estimate the amount of consolidation settlement at the top of the clay layer.

(b) Apply any correction to the consolidation settlement that you deem necessary, then calculate the total settlement (including the elastic component) at the top of the clay layer.

(c) If the clay is characterised by a creep compression index $C_\alpha = 0.015$, estimate the creep deformation at the top of the clay layer between the times $t_1 = 2\,y$ and $t_2 = 7\,y$.

Ans: (a) $S_c = 0.156\,m$,   (b) $S = 0.121m$,   (c) $S_s \approx 8.8 \times 10^{-3}\,m$.

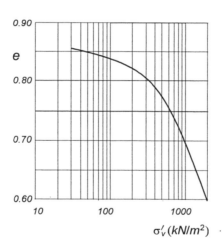

Figure p5.6

References

Azizi, F. and Josseaume, H. (1988) *Loi de comportement des sols raides: détermination de la courbe d'état limite de l'argile verte de Romainville.* Rapport des Laboratoires des Ponts et Chaussées. Série Géotechnique. GT-33.

Barron, R. A. (1948) *Consolidation of fine grained soils by drain wells.* Transactions of the *ASCE*, 113, pp. 718–742.

Bishop, A. W. and Al-Dhahir, Z. A. (1970) *Some comparisons between laboratory tests, in situ tests and full scale performance, with special reference to permeability and coefficient of consolidation.* Proceedings of the Conference on *in situ* Investigations in Soils and Rocks, ICE, London. pp. 251–264.

Bolton, M. D. (1991) *A Guide to Soil Mechanics.* M.D & K. Bolton, Cambridge.

Carrillo, N. (1942) *Simple two and three dimensional cases in the theory of consolidation of soils.* Journal of Mathematics and Physics, 21 (1), pp. 1–5.

Casagrande, A. (1936) *The determination of the preconsolidation load and its practical significance.* Proceedings of the 1st ICSM, Cambridge, Mass. Vol. 3, pp. 60–64.

Christian, J. T. and Carrier, W. D. (1978) *Janbu, Bjerrum, and Kjaernsli's Chart reinterpreted.* Canadian Geotechnical Journal, 15, pp. 124–128.

Giroud, J. P. (1968) *Settlement of a linearly loaded rectangular area.* Proceedings of the ASCE, 94, SM4, pp. 813–831

Powrie, W. (1997) *Soil Mechanics: Concepts and Applications.* E & FN Spon, London.

Rowe, P. W. and Barden, L. (1966) *A new consolidation cell.* Géotechnique, 16 (2), pp. 162–170.

Schmertmann, J. H. (1953) *Estimating the true consolidation behaviour of clay from laboratory test results.* Proceedings of the *ASCE,* 79. pp. 1–26.

Schofield, A. N. and Wroth, C. P. (1968) *Critical State Soil Mechanics.* McGraw-Hill, New York.

Skempton, A. W. (1951) *The bearing capacity of clays.* Proceedings of the Building Research Congress, London.

Skempton, A. W. (1954) *The pore pressure coefficients A and B.* Géotechnique, 4 (4). pp. 143–147.

Skempton, A. W. and Bjerrum, L. (1957) *A contribution to the settlement analysis of foundations on clay.* Géotechnique, 7 (4), pp. 168–178.

Taylor, D. W. (1948) *Fundamentals of Soil Mechanics.* John Wiley & Sons, New York.

Terzaghi, K. (1943) *Theoretical Soil Mechanics.* John Wiley & Sons, New York.

Terzaghi, K. and Peck, R. B. (1967) *Soil Mechanics in Engineering Practice.* Wiley, New York.

Whitlow, R. (1995) *Basic Soil Mechanics,* 3rd edn. Longman Scientific & Technical, England.

chapter 6

Finite Difference Modelling
of Seepage & Transient Flows

6.1 Centred finite difference formulae

Several mathematical formalisms can be used to derive a finite difference
formulation, and interested readers may wish to refer to Hoffman (1992) for
a comprehensive analyses of different methods. The finite difference
formulation developed in this chapter is based on Taylor series expansion.
Consider the case of a three dimensional mathematical function $f(x, y)$ such
as the one illustrated in figure 6.1. The shape of this function can be
determined, if only approximately, by selecting some points such as (x_1, y_1),
(x_2, y_2) & (x_3, y_3) as illustrated in the figure, and assuming a linear variation
of the graph between any two consecutive points. It is evident that the
closer the points to one another, the more accurate the graph, and the
smaller the difference between approximate and actual graphs.

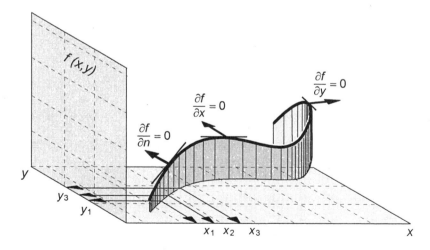

Figure 6.1: Linear approximation between selected points.

If the case of a two dimensional function as illustrated in figure 6.2, it is
seen that for equally spaced points, the smaller the distance Δx, the closer
the linear variation between points to the actual curve. Furthermore, the
same principle can be applied in conjunction with derivatives of a function.

There are several mathematical tools to formulate derivatives of a function using this principle, and Taylor's series expansion is particularly useful to the formulation of finite difference equations.

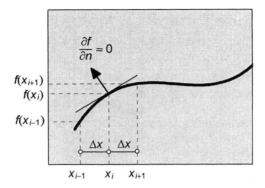

Figure 6.2: Linear approximation for finite difference formulation.

Using the first three terms of Taylor's series expansion about the central point x_i in figure 6.2, it follows that:

$$f(x_{i+1}) = f(x_i) + \frac{\Delta x}{1!}f'(x_i) + \frac{(\Delta x)^2}{2!}f''(x_i) + \cdots \qquad (6.1)$$

$$f(x_{i-1}) = f(x_i) - \frac{\Delta x}{1!}f'(x_i) + \frac{(\Delta x)^2}{2!}f''(x_i) - \cdots \qquad (6.2)$$

Thus, subtracting, one obtains:

$$f(x_{i+1}) - f(x_{i-1}) = 2\Delta x.f'(x_i) + 0\left[(\Delta x)^3\right] \qquad (6.3)$$

On rearranging equation 6.3, the expression of the first derivative at x_i can then be established:

$$f'(x_i) = \frac{f(x_{i+1}) - f(x_{i-1})}{2\Delta x} + 0\left[(\Delta x)^2\right] \qquad (6.4)$$

Similarly, adding equations 6.1 & 6.2, and rearranging, the expression of the second derivative at x_i can readily be derived:

$$f''(x_i) = \frac{f(x_{i+1}) - 2f(x_i) + f(x_{i+1})}{(\Delta x)^2} + 0\left[(\Delta x)^2\right] \qquad (6.5)$$

Equations 6.4 & 6.5 represent numerical expressions of the first and second derivatives of a function respectively about a central point x_i, at equidistance Δx from the surrounding two points x_{i-1} & x_{i+1}. Accordingly, both equations are known as *centred difference formulae*. The error resulting from the use of only the three first terms in Taylor series expansion is, in both equations, of the order $(\Delta x)^2$. In most cases of interest in geotechnical engineering, this truncation error is too small to affect the accuracy of calculations in any significant way. Furthermore, the numerical expressions of the second and first derivatives of a function (around a central point), can be substituted for second and first order differential equations for instance. In particular, these expressions can be applied to previously introduced problems such as seepage under confined or unconfined flow (Laplace equations, chapter 4), and dissipation-dispersion problems (consolidation equation, chapter 5).

6.2 Centred finite difference formulation applied to Laplace equation

The elliptic equation established earlier in the case of seepage under confined flow conditions is better known as Laplace equation:

$$\frac{\partial^2 h}{\partial x^2} + \frac{\partial^2 h}{\partial y^2} = 0 \qquad (6.6)$$

This two dimensional partial differential elliptic equation can be written in the form of equation 6.5 about a central point $x_{i,j}$ (note the use of two indices: i in the x-direction, and j in the y-direction) in a grid to which the flow domain is subdivided as in figure 6.3:

$$\left(\frac{\partial^2 h}{\partial x^2} + \frac{\partial^2 h}{\partial y^2}\right)_{i,j} = \frac{h_{i-1,j} - 2h_{i,j} + h_{i+1,j}}{\Delta x^2} + \frac{h_{i,j-1} - 2h_{i,j} + h_{i,j+1}}{\Delta y^2} \qquad (6.7)$$

The grid being formed of equal size elements (a prerequisite for this formulation) with sides $\Delta x = C \Delta y$, where C is a constant. Hence substituting for Δx into equation 6.7, it follows that:

$$\left(\frac{\partial^2 h}{\partial x^2} + \frac{\partial^2 h}{\partial y^2}\right)_{i,j} = 0 \quad \Rightarrow$$

$$\frac{1}{C^2(\Delta y)^2}(h_{i-1,j} - 2h_{i,j} + h_{i+1,j}) + \frac{1}{(\Delta y^2)}(h_{i,j-1} - 2h_{i,j} + h_{i,j+1}) = 0$$

Rearranging:

$$h_{i-1,j} - 2(1 + C^2)h_{i,j} + h_{i+1,j} + C^2 h_{i,j-1} + C^2 h_{i,j+1} = 0 \qquad (6.8)$$

Equation 6.8 represents the basic central finite difference formulation of elliptic equations such as Laplace equation. From a numerical analysis view point, the same equation is usually written as the following computational molecule:

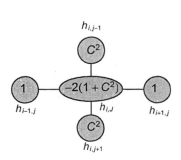

General form of computational molecule for rectangular elements
$C = (\Delta x/\Delta y)$

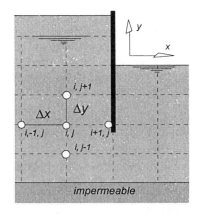

Figure 6.3: Computational molecule of finite difference formulation

According to figure 6.3, equation 6.8 implies that the total head at a selected central node (i, j) affects (and is affected by) the magnitude of the total head in the four surrounding nodes (2 in each direction of the space). It is noticeable that when $\Delta x = \Delta y$ (*i.e.* a mesh with square elements in figure 6.3), then $C = \Delta x/\Delta y = 1$, and the above computational molecule reduces to:

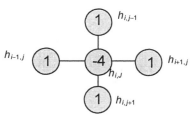

Computational molecule for a mesh with square elements

6.3 Boundary conditions

There are three types of boundary conditions relating to steady state problems in geotechnical engineering (*i.e.* problems independent of time):

- *Dirichlet* boundary condition for which the value of the function *f* is specified on the boundary
- *Neumann* boundary condition where the value of the derivative

normal to the boundary $\partial f/\partial n$ is specified
- *mixed* boundary where both the function and its normal derivative are specified on the boundary.

Referring to figure 6.3, one can see that either side of the sheet-pile represents a flow line since water cannot go through the pile. Therefore the total head function along the sheet-pile must always be normal to the flow line which happens to be the surface of the sheet-pile in this instance. In other words, the first derivative (that is the slope) of the total head function at any node along the pile surface, such as node $(i+1, j)$, is horizontal:

$\partial h/\partial x = 0$.

Similarly, the top of the impermeable surface is a (horizontal) flow line since water cannot seep through it. The total head function must thence meet this flow line at right angle, implying that the slope of the head function along the impermeable line is vertical:

$\partial h/\partial y = 0$.

Making use of the expression of the first derivative of a function in the form of equation 6.4, the following conditions must therefore be satisfied at any node where the slope of the total head function is either horizontal or vertical, respectively:

$$\left(\frac{\partial h}{\partial x}\right)_{i,j} = 0 \quad \Rightarrow \quad \frac{h_{i+1,j} - h_{i-1,j}}{2\Delta x} = 0 \quad \Rightarrow \quad h_{i+1,j} = h_{i-1,j} \qquad (6.9a)$$

$$\left(\frac{\partial h}{\partial y}\right)_{i,j} = 0 \quad \Rightarrow \quad \frac{h_{i,j+1} - h_{i,j-1}}{2\Delta y} = 0 \quad \Rightarrow \quad h_{i,j+1} = h_{i,j-1} \qquad (6.9b)$$

The stage is now set for the finite difference modelling of seepage problems represented by Laplace equation (*i.e.* confined & unconfined flow cases).

6.4 Laplace equation: case of confined flow

6.4.1 Seepage around a sheet-pile structure

Consider the excavation illustrated in figure 6.4, where the centre line implies that only half the structure is represented because of symmetry. Prior to attempting to calculate numerically the total heads, let us consider the boundary conditions of the problem:

1- in this particular case, all heads are expressed with respect to the (arbitrary) datum at the bottom of excavation. The total head at the bottom of excavation is therefore zero

2- on the upstream side (behind the sheet pile), the water level is at the ground surface, along which the total head h is constant

3- the top of the impermeable layer is a flow line (water cannot seep through this layer). Hence, the total head function intersects this line at right angle; or in mathematical terms $\partial h/\partial y = 0$ along the top surface of the impermeable layer

4- either side of the sheet pile is a flow line (water cannot flow through the sheet pile). Equally, the centre line of excavation is a flow line since water is seeping around the sheet pile into the excavation with equal flow from either side (note once more that, due to symmetry, only half the excavation is represented in the figure). Consequently, the total head intersects these (vertical) flow lines at right angle, and thus $\partial h/\partial x = 0$ along these lines.

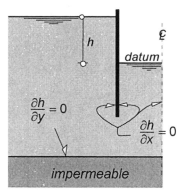

Figure 6.4: Seepage into an excavation

Having these boundary conditions in mind, a finite difference mesh can now be set. Although there are no rules *per se* on how to choose the number (and therefore the size) of elements, it is useful to bear in mind that in a finite difference model, as the size of elements is made smaller, the truncation error due to the numerical approximation of the partial derivative equations decreases. In the meantime, a smaller element size generates more equations, leading to more computations, thus increasing the round off error. The total error is illustrated in figure 6.5. The extent of the meshed area on the other hand is rather a matter of experience. The most overriding priority is for the mesh to cover *all* the area within which seepage occurs, and this can be achieved at the expense of including some border areas where water is virtually static (*i.e.* no seepage effect).

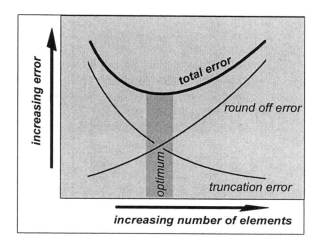

Figure 6.5: Effects of truncation and roundoff errors

Example 6.1: seepage around a sheet-pile

Consider the excavation in the previous figure with the appropriate dimensions and boundary conditions illustrated in figure 6.6. Since this example is used to explain the working of finite difference modelling, the corresponding mesh illustrated in figure 6.7 is adopted.

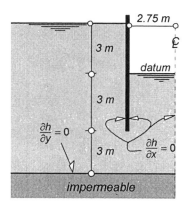

Figure 6.6: Excavation dimensions

The mesh is composed of 40 nodes, with only one degree of freedom per node (*i.e.* the total head in every node is the only unknown variable). Consequently, 40 linear equations will be generated, and would require to be solved simultaneously.

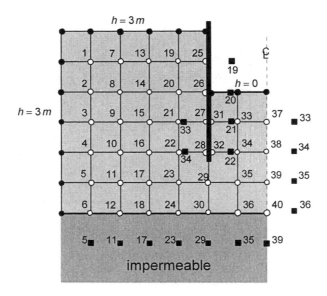

Figure 6.7: Finite difference mesh corresponding to figure 6.6

Using the dimensions in figure 6.6, the equal size elements of the mesh are such that:

$$\Delta x = 1.375\,m, \quad \Delta y = 1.5\,m \quad \Rightarrow \quad C^2 = (\Delta x/\Delta y)^2 = 0.84$$

Hence the following computational molecule calculated from the general molecule form in figure 6.3:

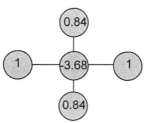

The meshed area in figure 6.7 is limited on the right hand side by the centre line (due to the symmetry of the problem). On the left hand side, the mesh extends to $1.375 \times 5 = 6.875\,m$ from the sheet pile; a distance beyond which it is assumed (or expected) that seepage effects will be marginal. The validity of this assumption will be analysed once the total heads are computed. The boundary conditions are essential to solving this problem, and must therefore be correctly implemented. Starting with the *Dirichlet*-type boundary conditions, it is seen that:

- along the bottom of excavation (where the datum was chosen), the head is zero. Hence, all three nodes represented by solid circles at the bottom of excavation have a zero total head.

- along the ground surface on the upstream side of the pile, the head with respect to the chosen datum is constant. Therefore, all corresponding six nodes represented by solid circles have a total head $h = 3\,m$

- the edge of the meshed area on the left hand side of the pile is chosen such that there would not be any seepage along it (*i.e.* the water would remain static). Accordingly, all seven nodes represented by solid circles on that edge (the top seventh node is actually a common node to the horizontal ground surface on the upstream side) have a total head $h = 3\,m$

Next, the *Neumann*-type boundary condition $\partial h/\partial y = 0$ along the top of the impermeable layer should be implemented. Accordingly, equation 6.9*b* must be applied to all nodes along this boundary: $h_{i,j+1} = h_{i,j-1}$ (note that the index i applies in the horizontal direction, and j in the vertical direction). The two nodes above and below node 6, for instance, in figure 6.7, must be identical. This is simply achieved by mirroring the node above (node 5 in this case). Whence nodes 5, 11, 17, 23, 29, 35 & 39, represented by solid squares, are mirror images of the same nodes with respect to the impermeable boundary. Similarly, the derivative boundary condition $\partial h/\partial x = 0$ along both sides of the sheet pile, as well as the centre line, has to be implemented in the form of equation 6.9*a*: $h_{i+1,j} = h_{i-1,j}$. As a result, nodes preceding and following node 20 for example must be identical (node 19 is mirrored in this instance). Hence nodes 19, 20 , 21, 22 represented by solid squares on the right hand side of the pile are mirror images of the same nodes with respect to the left hand side surface of the pile. Equally, nodes 33 and 34 represented by solid squares on the left hand side of the pile are mirror images of the same nodes with respect to the right hand side surface of the pile. Lastly, the same boundary condition must apply to nodes 37, 38, 39, 40 along the centre line. Hence the mirrored nodes 33, 34, 35, 36 represented by solid squares on the right hand side of the centre line.

The stage is now set for establishing the system of simultaneous equations according to the already established computational molecule for this problem, which is perhaps the easiest of tasks. For every node represented by an open circle on the mesh, the procedure consists of placing the centre of the molecule on the node, and then writing the corresponding equation in terms of the unknown total heads. Placing the centre of molecule on node 1 generates the first equation:

- *node 1:* $(-3.68 \times h_1) + (1 \times 3) + (1 \times h_7) + (0.84 \times 3) + (0.84 \times h_2) = 0$

This equation takes into account the boundary conditions implemented earlier, in that the total head at the nodes above and to the left of node 1 are equal to 3 *m* (hence the terms (1×3) and (0.84×3) in the equation. Similarly, applying the molecule to node 6 yields:

- *node 6:* $(-3.68 \times h_6) + (1 \times 3) + (1 \times h_{12}) + (0.84 \times h_5) + (0.84 \times h_5)$

The reader may wish to check that the equations at say, nodes 15, 19 and 27 are as follows:

- *node 15:* $-3.68\,h_{15} + h_9 + h_{21} + 0.84\,h_{14} + 0.84\,h_{16} = 0$

- *node 19:* $-3.68\,h_{19} + h_{13} + h_{25} + 0.84\,h_{20} + (0.84 \times 3) = 0$

- *node 27:* $-3.68\,h_{27} + h_{21} + h_{21} + 0.84\,h_{26} + 0.84\,h_{28} = 0$

Equally, both nodes 31 (which is totally independent from node 27) and 37 include a zero boundary condition (refer to the mesh in figure 6.7):

- *node 31:* $-3.68\,h_{31} + h_{33} + h_{33} + 0.84\,h_{32} + (0.84 \times 0) = 0$

- *node 37:* $-3.68\,h_{37} + h_{33} + h_{33} + 0.84\,h_{38} + (0.84 \times 0) = 0$

Node 29 in particular needs a special attention: on placing the centre of molecule on this node, a question arises as to which of the two nodes 28 or 32 (see figure 6.7) should be used in the corresponding equation? Water flows in a downward direction at node 28, and in an upward direction at node 32. However, the total head decreases gradually as one moves from upstream towards downstream and accordingly, the head at node 28 is higher than that at node 32. This implies that both nodes should be included in the equation with different weighting to reflect their contribution to the head at the central node 29. Once more there are no rules *per se* to quantify the weighting to be applied and, as in the case of flownet solutions, experience plays an important part when it comes to making an *à priori* decision based on engineering judgement. In this particular case, it would be logical to allocate a one third weighting to node 32, and two thirds to node 28. Whence the equation at node 29:

- *node 29:* $-3.68\,h_{29} + h_{23} + h_{35} + 0.84\left(\frac{2}{3}h_{28} + \frac{1}{3}h_{32}\right) + 0.84\,h_{30} = 0$

The task of establishing the equations is somewhat mechanical, and writing what remains of the 40 equations constitutes an excellent exercise of concentration for those who are somewhat unfamiliar with the method.

Obviously, the few equations established above were carefully selected and meticulously written so as to cover all types of boundary conditions, and to show all derivation details. In practice, every equation is arranged so that all unknown heads are written in ascending order on the left hand side, while all constants are transferred to the right hand side. Thus, the eight previous equations can be rearranged in a fairly straightforward manner as follows:

- *node 01:* $3.68\,h_1 - 0.84\,h_2 - h_7 = 5.52$
- *node 06:* $1.68\,h_5 - 3.68\,h_6 + h_{12} = -3$
- *node 15:* $h_9 + 0.84\,h_{14} - 3.68\,h_{15} + 0.84\,h_{16} + h_{21} = 0$
- *node 19:* $h_{13} - 3.68\,h_{19} + 0.84\,h_{20} + h_{25} = -2.52$
- *node 27:* $2\,h_{21} + 0.84\,h_{26} - 3.68\,h_{27} + 0.84\,h_{28} = 0$
- *node 29:* $h_{23} + 0.56\,h_{28} - 3.68\,h_{29} + 0.84\,h_{30} + 0.28\,h_{32} + h_{35} = 0$
- *node 31:* $3.68\,h_{31} - 0.84\,h_{32} - 2\,h_{33} = 0$
- *node 37:* $2\,h_{33} - 3.68\,h_{37} + 0.84\,h_{38} = 0$

On establishing the 40 equations and writing them as above, one ends up with a system of 40 simultaneous equations with 40 unknowns (these are the total heads at different nodes). The task of solving this system is greatly simplified by using matrix computation. First, the system of equations needs to be expressed in a matrix form. This is achieved using what is known in the jargon of numerical analysis as *assemblage of the global matrix*. In essence, all 40 equations in the case of this particular problem are expanded so that they are expressed in terms of all 40 nodal unknowns (h_1 to h_{40}). For instance, equation 1 (that is the equation at node 1) is expanded as follows:

$$-3.68\,h_1 + 0.84\,h_2 + 0h_3 + 0h_4 + 0h_5 + 0h_6 + h_7 + 0h_8 + \ldots + 0h_{40} = -5.52$$

On expansion, the system of simultaneous equations can then be written in a matrix form:

$$[K]\{h\} = \{c\} \tag{6.10}$$

in which [K] is a (40×40) square matrix generated from the coefficients in the equations attached to the nodal unknowns $\{h\}$, and the vector $\{c\}$ is constituted of the constants in each equation (*i.e.* the right hand side of the equal sign). The complete form of equation 6.10 is shown in figure 6.8. The reader may wish to check the content of the matrix [K] by establishing independently the system of simultaneous equations based on the mesh in figure 6.7, and its corresponding computing molecule.

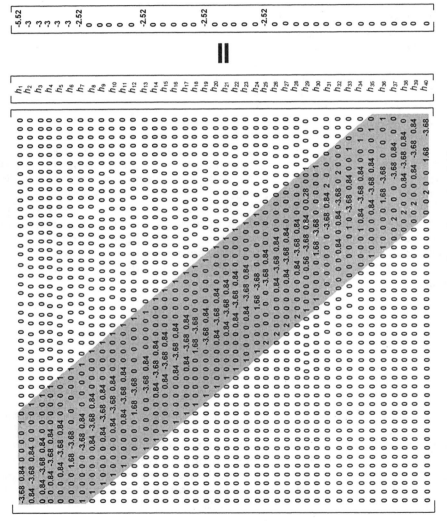

Figure 6.8: Matrix form of equation 6.10

Notice that the matrix [K] in figure 6.8 has a banded structure, since only the shaded area contains non-zero coefficients. The width of the band is of great importance as will be emphasised later in relation to finite element analysis (whose mathematical formalism is entirely different and somewhat more complex than finite differences). Though the matrix in figure 6.8 seems to be large in size (the problem of figure 6.7 is meant to be an example whereby all details of calculations are exposed for maximum understanding), one has to bear in mind that in practice such matrices are generated automatically. The size though may cause storage problems even for the most powerful of computers (for instance, finite element simulation of the head of a tunnel boring machine may yield in excess of 80,000 equations, generating a matrix of more than 64×10^8 [that is 6.4 billion] elements). Hence the importance of minimising the width of the band, because in computing practice, only non-zero elements are stored and retrieved at will when needed. This digression is somewhat relevant, in that one may wish to think about how best to minimise the band width of the K-matrix. Every finite element code has an optimisation pre-processor that generates the mesh and allocates the node (and element) numbers. Though these numbers may seem to be allocated at random, they are in fact carefully generated so as to have the minimum band width of the K-matrix .

The solution to equation 6.10 consists of inverting the K-matrix so that the nodal heads are calculated as follows:

$$\{h\} = [K]^{-1}\{c\} \tag{6.11}$$

A variety of commercial software packages for matrix inversion are available. In particular, MATLAB is very useful since it is specifically developed to handle matrix calculations. The outcome of the computation is first presented in table 6.1.

Table 6.1: Computed heads corresponding to the mesh in figure 6.7

node	1	2	3	4	5	6	7	8	9	10
head (m)	2.9738	2.9463	2.9171	2.8882	2.8655	2.8572	2.9488	2.8940	2.8339	2.7713

node	11	12	13	14	15	16	17	18	19	20
head (m)	2.7191	2.7003	2.9267	2.8462	2.7527	2.6457	2.5444	2.5119	2.9106	2.8095

node	21	22	23	24	25	26	27	28	29	30
head (m)	2.6828	2.5154	2.3121	2.2687	2.9044	2.7941	2.6472	2.4153	1.9452	1.9529

node	31	32	33	34	35	36	37	38	39	40
head (m)	0.5518	1.1461	0.5340	1.0601	1.5325	1.6498	0.5228	1.0191	1.4179	1.5439

These heads can then be used to determine the variation of porewater pressure throughout the meshed area. One has to keep in mind that all the total head values in the previous table were calculated with respect to the chosen datum in figure 6.6. This is essential for the calculation of porewater pressure at different nodes using Bernoulli's equation, in which the elevation head h_e is always measured from a fixed datum:

$$u = \gamma_w(h - h_e) \tag{6.12}$$

For example, the elevation heads at nodes 25 & 31 are $(+1.5\,m)$ and $(-1.5\,m)$ respectively, whence:

$$u_{(25)} = 10 \times (2.9044 - 1.5) = 14.044\,kN/m^2$$

$$u_{(33)} = 10 \times (0.5340 + 1.5) = 20.34\,kN/m^2$$

The numerical values of porewater pressures are indicated on the mesh in figure 6.8, so that the variation can be seen at a glance.

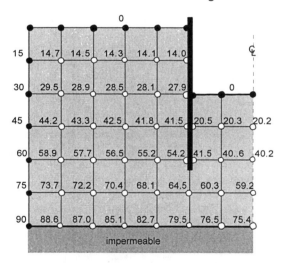

Figure 6.8: Computed porewater pressure (kN/m^2)

When the area of flow was meshed, it was assumed that seepage effects on the vertical boundary to the left hand side of the pile were marginal; whence the constant head of 3 m allocated throughout this boundary in figure 6.7. The computation validates this assumption, since the calculated porewater pressures at the nodes nearest to the boundary show slight decrease from the static values at the boundary.

Example 6.2: seepage under a concrete dam

Consider the case of seepage flow under a concrete dam structure as illustrated in figure 6.9. The area of flow is meshed into equal size squares such that $\Delta x = \Delta y = 1\,m$. Consequently, $C = (\Delta x / \Delta y) = 1$, and the corresponding computational molecule is in this case:

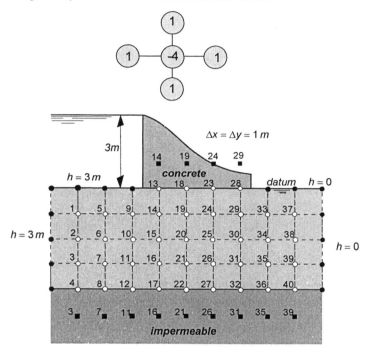

Figure 6.9: seepage under a concrete dam: finite difference mesh

The *Dirichlet* boundary conditions (expressed with respect to the chosen datum) are such that:
- the head on the edges of the meshed area on the downstream side (represented by solid circles in figure 6.9) is zero
- on the upstream side, the head at the ground surface is $h = 3\,m$. Also, the same head $h = 3\,m$ is assumed to apply along the vertical edge of the mesh (solid circles in the figure)

The *Neumann* boundary condition $\partial h/\partial y = 0$ applies at:
- the top of the underlying impermeable layer; whence the mirrored nodes represented by solid squares in the figure (nodes 3, 7, 11, 16, 21, 26, 31, 35 & 39)
- the (impermeable) base of the dam (mirrored nodes 14, 19, 24 & 29).

As in the case of the previous example, the same procedure applies to establish the system of 40 simultaneous equations (that both examples have the same number of nodes is purely coincidental). The centre of molecule is placed on top of each node, and the corresponding equation is written in an expanded form (*i.e.* expressed in terms of all 40 nodal unknowns). This in turn results in the familiar matrix form $[K]\{h\} = \{u\}$, which is then inverted as per equation 6.11 to yield the heads at different nodes throughout the mesh. It is left to reader's initiative to implement carefully these steps, referring to the detailed explanations in the previous example when needed. The outcome of such calculation is summarised in the table 6.2.

Table 6.2: Computed heads corresponding to the mesh in figure 6.9

node	1	2	3	4	5	6	7	8	9	10
head (m)	2.9070	2.8418	2.8059	2.7946	2.7861	2.6544	2.5871	2.5667	2.5830	2.4025

node	11	12	13	14	15	16	17	18	19	20
head (m)	2.3216	2.2980	2.2500	2.1433	2.0510	1.9986	1.9821	1.7133	1.6893	1.6596

node	21	22	23	24	25	26	27	28	29	30
head (m)	1.6398	1.6331	1.2245	1.2411	1.2583	1.2679	1.2708	0.7023	0.7924	0.8647

node	31	32	33	34	35	36	37	38	39	40
head (m)	0.9028	0.9142	0.3614	0.5052	0.5642	0.5805	0.1479	0.2304	0.2685	0.2794

Next, the porewater pressures are calculated at each node using Bernoulli equation 6.12, resulting in the values indicated in figure 6.10.

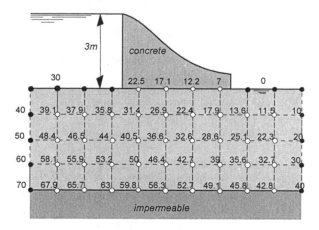

Figure 6.10: Computed porewater pressures (kN/m²)

6.5 Laplace equation: case of unconfined flow

The case of flow through an earth dam is referred to as unconfined since at least one flow boundary is unknown *a priori*. The properties of this inclined boundary were established earlier in section 4.4.3. In particular, it was shown that along the phreatic surface, the total heads h were identical to the elevation heads h_e. Furthermore, the free surface is a flow line, implying that the head function is normal to this boundary. Accordingly, the phreatic surface is a mixed boundary along which the following two conditions apply:

$$h = h_e \qquad\qquad\qquad (6.13a)$$

$$\partial h/\partial n = 0 \qquad\qquad\qquad (6.13b)$$

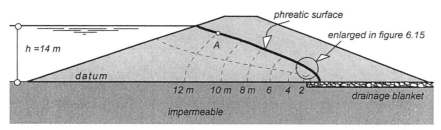

Figure 6.11: Mixed boundary conditions across an unconfined boundary.

Figure 6.11 illustrates how the boundary conditions of equations 6.13 were implemented in a previous worked example using a flownet solution (see figure 4.33, chapter 3). It is clear that the total head intersects the unconfined boundary (or phreatic surface) at right angle, and is everywhere along this surface identical to the elevation head. Point A in figure 6.11 for instance has a total head of 12 m (determined from the flownet). The reader may wish to check that the same point has an elevation head of precisely 12 m with respect to the shown datum. Although this type of flow is mathematically represented by Laplace equation, its finite difference modelling is somewhat more complex than in the previous case of confined flow; the inclined boundary being the main reason. In fact the problems related to this boundary are threefold:

- the free (or phreatic) surface being inclined, the area that needs to be meshed is no longer a parallelogram. Accordingly, barring perfect symmetry of the area, it is no longer possible to have a mesh of equal elements' size. The finite difference formulation developed previously in equations 6.8 & 6.9 is therefore no longer valid, and a new approximation must be adopted

- the implementation of the derivative boundary condition along the inclined free surface needs a special mathematical treatment, the details of which will be explained shortly

- the position of the free surface being unknown *à priori*, an initial surface must be assumed, delimiting in the process the area to be meshed. On solving for the total heads, one must check that for every node on the free surface, the computed head is equal to the elevation head. This condition is highly unlikely to be achieved at the outset of the first calculation. Therefore, an iterative procedure is required, in which the position of the nodes of the assumed free surface is adjusted so that the calculated heads at these nodes become their new elevation heads. This, in turn, leads to a new free surface, and hence a different area, requiring a new mesh. The procedure is then repeated until the calculated head at every node on the free surface coincides with the corresponding assumed elevation head.

Consider the general case of a mesh where the nodes are not uniformly spaced as per the following figure 6.12. The slopes between nodes 2 & 1 and 1 & 4 are respectively:

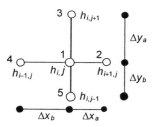

$$\frac{h_{i+1,j} - h_{i,j}}{\Delta x_a}$$

and

$$\frac{h_{i,j} - h_{i-1,j}}{\Delta x_b}$$

Figure 6.12: Unequally spaced nodes

It follows that:

$$\left(\frac{\partial^2 h}{\partial x^2}\right)_{i,j} = \frac{1}{\frac{1}{2}(\Delta x_a + \Delta x_b)}\left[\frac{h_{i+1,j} - h_{i,j}}{\Delta x_a} - \frac{h_{i,j} - h_{i-1,j}}{\Delta x_b}\right]$$

A similar derivation in the *y*-direction of space yields:

$$\left(\frac{\partial^2 h}{\partial y^2}\right)_{i,j} = \frac{2}{(\Delta y_a + \Delta y_b)}\left[\frac{h_{i,j+1} - h_{i,j}}{\Delta y_a} - \frac{h_{i,j} - h_{i,j-1}}{\Delta y_b}\right]$$

Substituting for these quantities into Laplace equation and rearranging:

$$\left(\frac{\partial^2 h}{\partial x^2} + \frac{\partial^2 h}{\partial y^2}\right)_{i,j} = 0 \quad \Rightarrow$$

$$\alpha_1 h_{i-1,j} + \alpha_2 h_{i+1,j} - \beta h_{i,j} + \alpha_3 h_{i,j-1} + \alpha_4 h_{i,j+1} = 0 \qquad (6.14)$$

with: $\alpha_1 = \dfrac{(\Delta y_a + \Delta y_b)}{\Delta x_b}$, $\alpha_2 = \dfrac{(\Delta y_a + \Delta y_b)}{\Delta x_a}$, $\alpha_3 = \dfrac{(\Delta x_a + \Delta x_b)}{\Delta y_b}$

$\alpha_4 = \dfrac{(\Delta x_a + \Delta x_b)}{\Delta y_a}$, $\beta = (\alpha_1 + \alpha_2 + \alpha_3 + \alpha_4)$

Whence the computational molecule corresponding to equation 6.14:

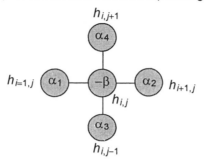

Figure 6.13: Computational molecule for non-uniformly spaced nodes

Next, the derivative boundary condition on the inclined boundary needs to be implemented. Figure 6.14 illustrates a group of unequally spaced nodes, whose centre is placed on a boundary inclined at an angle δ with respect to the horizontal. Prior to applying the molecule of figure 6.13, the mixed boundary condition at the centre node must be properly implemented. The unconfined nature of flow means that an initial position of the inclined boundary must be assumed. It is therefore highly likely that at the end of the first calculation, the position of such a boundary needs to be adjusted.

The adjustment is achieved by adopting the calculated heads as the new elevation heads for every node on the inclined boundary. This implies that the position of the nodes on the boundary, such as the centre node (i, j) in figure 6.14, must be moved up or down (not sideways). This detail is all the more important since it affects the way in which the mixed boundary condition is satisfied.

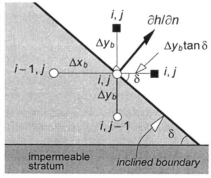

Figure 6.14: Mixed boundary condition on an inclined flow boundary

Concentrating on node (i, j) in figure 6.14, it can be seen from the geometry that:

$$\left(\frac{\partial h}{\partial n}\right)_{i,j} = 0 \implies \left(\frac{\partial h}{\partial x}\right)_{i,j} \cos\delta + \left(\frac{\partial h}{\partial y}\right)_{i,j} \sin\delta = 0$$

Rearranging: $\quad\left(\frac{\partial h}{\partial x}\right)_{i,j} = -\left(\frac{\partial h}{\partial y}\right)_{i,j} \tan\delta$ (6.15)

Figure 6.14 also shows that by using mirror images of the centre node to its left and top, the head derivatives in both directions of space are automatically satisfied:

$$\left(\frac{\partial h}{\partial x}\right)_{i,j} = \frac{h_{i,j} - h_{i,J}}{\Delta x_a} = 0 \quad \text{and} \quad \left(\frac{\partial h}{\partial y}\right)_{i,j} = \frac{h_{i,j} - h_{i,j}}{\Delta y_a} = 0$$

Now the precise spacing between different nodes is required for the molecule in figure 6.13 to be used. As mentioned earlier, the position of any node on the boundary can only be adjusted upward or downward, and accordingly the spacing between the centre node and its top mirror image is assumed to be identical to that between the nodes (i, j) and $(i, j-1)$. The remaining spacing between the centre node and its right mirror image is thereafter calculated from equation 6.15, in which the minus sign is dropped since only the absolute distance between nodes is needed in the computational molecule in figure 6.13.

For a curved inclined boundary (as opposed to a linear boundary in figure 6.14), the angle δ must be estimated for every node on the boundary as per figure 6.15, all other aspects of analysis being equal.

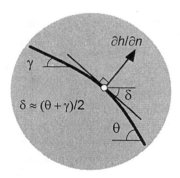

Figure 6.15: Geometry relating to a curved boundary

Example 6.3: Flow through an earth dam

A compacted clay dam with the dimensions indicated in figure 6.16 is retaining a 5m head of water. A drainage blanket is used on the downstream side in order to manage any water seeping through the clay, once a steady state seepage regime is established. The structural integrity of the dam is linked to the effective stresses within the soil matrix, which are dependent on the porewater pressure level in the clay. The water pressure distribution can be calculated from Bernouilli equation 6.12, which requires the prior knowledge of both total and elevation heads.

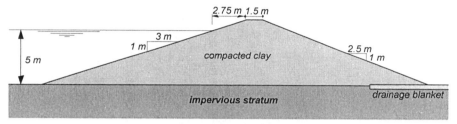

Figure 6.16: Seepage through a clay dam

Let's now use the finite difference formulation established earlier to calculate the porewater pressure distribution within the soil matrix. The first step consist of meshing the volume of compacted clay so as to calculate the total heads at different nodes of the mesh. Given the unconfined nature of flow, the free surface on the downstream side is not known *à priori* and its position is approximated by a straight line linking the highest water position on the upstream side to the deepest corner of the drainage blanket as illustrated in figure 6.17. Obviously the exact position of the free surface will be markedly different from this assumed line, and therefore an iterative procedure of calculation is required until the assumed position coincides with (or is as near to) the calculated one. What is more, every time the assumed position of the free surface changes, a new mesh is redrawn as will be seen shortly.

Referring to the first mesh of figure 6.17, it is seen that:

- while all nodes are separated vertically by a distance of 1 m the horizontal distance is not constant throughout the meshed area. For instance, nodes 10 & 15 are 3m apart whereas nodes 15 & 20 are only 2.75m apart. The mesh therefore does not consist of equal elements size

- the assumed free (or phreatic) surface is linear with a slope $\tan \delta = 1/2.75 = 0.3636$

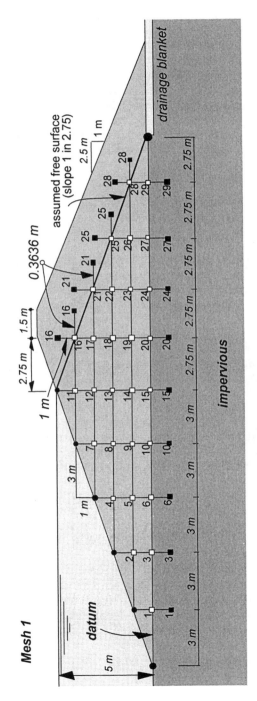

Figure 6.17: Finite difference mesh in the case of seepage flow through an earth dam

- The datum is being arbitrarily chosen at the top of the impervious layer, and accordingly all the nodes represented by solid circles on the upstream side have a constant total head $h = 5\,m$. Similarly, the node represented by a solid circle at the corner of the drainage blanket has a total head $h = 0$

- The top surface of the impervious stratum is a flow line, and therefore the boundary condition $\partial h/\partial y = 0$ applies to nodes 1, 3, 6, 10, 15, 20, 24, 27, and 29. This boundary condition is satisfied by mirroring these nodes as per figure 6.17

- Similarly the inclined linear free surface is also a flow line, and a mixed boundary condition of the type corresponding to figure 6.14 must apply to nodes 16, 21, 25, and 28. This delicate operation consists of mirroring each one of these nodes in a way that the spacing between each node and its top mirror is identical to the dimension between the node in question and that below it. The distance between each node and its left mirror is thence calculated form equation 6.15 without the minus sign. For instance, the top mirror node 16 is situated 1 m above the centre node 16, which is precisely the distance separating nodes 16 & 17. The distance between the left mirror image and the centre node 16 is calculated from equation 6.16: $d = 1 \times \tan\delta = 1 \times 0.3636 = 0.3636\,m$. In this particular case, the assumed free surface is linear and nodes 16, 21, 25, & 28 are horizontally equidistant, the calculations relating to node 16 apply equally to the remaining nodes 21, 25 & 28 (see figure 6.17)

The last step of the first iteration consists of establishing the 29 simultaneous equations to solve for the total heads at the 29 nodal points. Each equation is determined by placing the centre of the computational molecule of figure 6.13 on each node, and then writing the corresponding equation in terms of the unknown total heads. This task is made all the more easier were the coefficients $\alpha_{1,\ldots4}$ & β to be calculated beforehand according to equation 6.14. The reader may wish to note that these coefficients are linked to the elements size (i.e. the horizontal an vertical spacing between nodes). Accordingly, the finite difference equations at say nodes 1, 13, 16, 28 and 29 (refer to the mesh in figure 6.17) are determined as follows:

- **node 01**: the constants in equation 6.14 are (see also figure 6.12):

$$\alpha_1 = \frac{(1+1)}{3} = 0.6667, \qquad \alpha_2 = \frac{(1+1)}{3} = 0.6667, \qquad \alpha_3 = \frac{(3+3)}{1} = 6,$$

$$\alpha_4 = \frac{(3+3)}{1} = 6, \qquad \beta = (0.6667 + 0.6667 + 6 + 6) = 13.3333$$

Placing the centre of the computational molecule of figure 6.13 on node 01 yields the following equation:

$$-13.333\,h_1 + 6\,h_1 + (5 \times 6) + (5 \times 0.6667) + 0.6667\,h_3 = 0$$

- **node 13**: the constants in equation 6.14 being (note the different horizontal node spacing):

$$\alpha_1 = \frac{1+1}{3} = 0.6667, \qquad \alpha_2 = \frac{1+1}{2.75} = 0.7273, \qquad \alpha_3 = \alpha_4 = \frac{3+2.75}{1} = 5.75$$

$$\beta = (0.6667 + 0.7273 + 2 \times 5.75) = 12.894$$

Thus placing the molecule of figure 6.13 on node 13 yields:

$$-12.894\,h_{13} + 0.6667\,h_8 + 0.7273\,h_{18} + 5.75\,h_{12} + 5.75\,h_{14} = 0$$

- **node 16**: the constants in equation 6.14 are:

$$\alpha_1 = \frac{1+1}{2.75} = 0.7273, \qquad \alpha_2 = \frac{1+1}{0.3636} = 5.5006$$

$$\alpha_3 = \alpha_4 = \frac{2.75 + 0.3636}{1} = 3.1136,$$

$$\beta = (2 \times 3.1136 + 5.5006 + 0.7273) = 12.455$$

and the corresponding equation (established using figure 6.13 molecule):

$$-12.455\,h_{16} + 3.1136\,h_{16} + 3.1136\,h_{17} + 0.7273\,h_{11} + 5.5006\,h_{16} = 0$$

- **node 28** whose constants are identical to node 16; thus the equation:

$$-12.455\,h_{28} + 0.7273\,h_{26} + 5.5006\,h_{28} + 3.1136\,h_{28} + 3.1136\,h_{29} = 0$$

- **node 29**, with the constants:

$$\alpha_1 = \alpha_2 = \frac{1+1}{2.75} = 0.7273, \qquad \alpha_3 = \alpha_4 = \frac{2.75 + 2.75}{1} = 5.5$$

$$\beta = (2 \times 0.7273 + 2 \times 5.5) = 12.4546$$

whence the equation (notice the zero total head at the node to the right of node 29 represented by a solid circle in figure 6.17):

$$-12.4546\,h_{29} + 5.5\,h_{28} + 5.5\,h_{29} + 0.7273\,h_{27} + (0.7273 \times 0)$$

Rearranging the equations established for these five nodes, and expressing them in terms of all 29 nodal unknowns yields the following:

- **node 01:**

$$13.333\,h_1 + 0\,h_2 - 0.6667\,h_3 + 0\,h_4 + 0\,h_5 + \ldots\ldots + 0h_{28} + 0\,h_{29} = 33.333$$

- **node 13:**

$$0.667\,h_8 + 0h_9 + 0h_{10} + 0h_{11} + 5.75h_{12} + 12.894\,h_{13} + 5.75\,h_{14} +$$
$$0\,h_{15} + 0h_{16} + 0h_{17} + 0.7273\,h_{18} + 0h_{19} + \ldots\ldots + 0h_{28} + 0h_{29} = 0$$

- **node 16:**

$$0h_1 + 0h_2 + \ldots\ldots + 0h_6 + 0.7273\,h_{11} + 0\,h_{12} + 0\,h_{13} + \ldots\ldots$$
$$0h_{15} - 3.8408\,h_{16} + 3.1136\,h_{17} + 0h_{18} + \ldots\ldots + 0h_{28} + 0h_{29} = 0$$

- **node 28:**

$$0h_1 + 0h_2 + \ldots\ldots + 0h_{25} + 0.7273\,h_{26} + 0h_{27} - 3.8408\,h_{28} + 3.1136\,h_{29} = 0$$

- **node 29:**

$$0h_1 + 0h_2 + \ldots\ldots + 0h_{26} + 0.7273\,h_{27} + 5.5\,h_{28} - 6.9546\,h_{29} = 0$$

It is left to the reader to derive the remaining 24 equations and to establish the expanded matrix formulation:

$$[K]\{h\} = \{c\} \tag{6.16}$$

in which [K] is a [29 × 29] square matrix generated from the coefficients in the equations attached to the nodal unknowns {h}, and the vector {c} is constituted of the constants in each equation (*i.e.* the right hand side of the equal sign). The solution is thereafter found by inverting equation 6.16:

$$\{h\} = [K]^{-1}\{c\}$$

with *{h}* being the vector of total heads at the 29 nodes in figure 6.17. The outcome of the first iteration are represented graphically in terms of the position of the free surface in figure 6.18. The newly calculated position of the phreatic surface (represented in bold) is contrasted with the initial (assumed) surface represented by the dashed line in the figure. Obviously, the difference in the position of the assumed and calculated surfaces are markedly different, and accordingly a new iteration needs to be undertaken, in which the new assumed free surface corresponds to that just calculated.

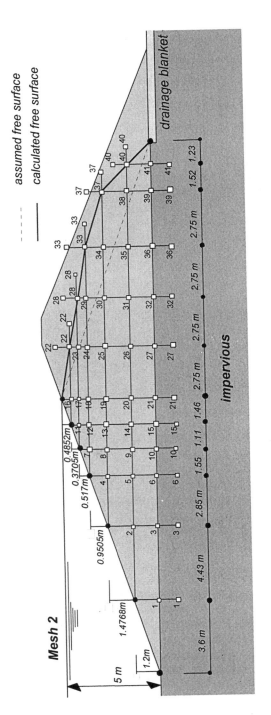

Figure 6.18: Finite difference mesh in the case of seepage flow through an earth dam

The non-linear nature of the newly assumed free surface implies that a new mesh with different size elements is adopted as per figure 6.18. Under these conditions, the task of establishing the 41 simultaneous equations for mesh 2 in figure 6.18 could be easily accomplished, though it may appear somewhat more mathematically involved to the uninitiated. All calculations are based on precisely the same procedure used for the first iteration, and apart from nodes 22, 28, 33, 37 & 40, located on the newly assumed free surface, which require some extra care as will be explained shortly, writing the equations at all other nodes should be a relatively straightforward task. Consider node 11 in figure 6.18 for instance: the total heads at the nodes represented by solid circles to the right as well as on top of node 11 are prescribed at 5m (refer to the boundary conditions elaborated in the previous iteration); the dimensions being as per figure 6.19

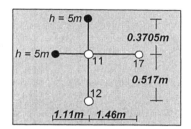

Figure 6.19: Dimensions relating to node 11, figure 6.18

The constants in equation 6.14 can now be calculated as follows:

$$\alpha_1 = \frac{(0.3705 + 0.517)}{1.11} = 0.7995, \qquad \alpha_2 = \frac{(0.3705 + 0.517)}{1.46} = 0.6079$$

$$\alpha_3 = \frac{(1.11 + 1.46)}{0.517} = 4.971, \qquad \alpha_4 = \frac{(1.11 + 1.46)}{0.3705} = 6.9365$$

$$\beta = (0.7995 + 0.6079 + 4.971 + 6.9365) = 13.3149$$

Placing thence the centre of the computational molecule of figure 6.13 on node 11 in figure 6.18 yields the following equation:

$$-13.3149\,h_{11} + (6.9365 \times 5) + (0.7995 \times 5) + 4.971\,h_{12} + 0.6079\,h_{17} = 0$$

so that once rearranged yields:

- **node 11:** $\qquad 13.3149\,h_{11} - 4.971\,h_{12} - 0.6079\,h_{17} = 38.68$

As far as the equations relating to nodes 22, 28, 33, 37 & 40, the effects of non-linearity of the free surface require some careful consideration. The angles γ, θ and δ for each of these five nodes are required for the calculation of the constants in equation 6.14. In the case of node 37 for instance, the total head (which is incidentally identical to the elevation head for any node on the free surface) can easily be scaled from figure 6.18, and using figure 6.20, the reader may wish to check the following values:

$$\gamma = 19°, \quad \theta = 44.23°, \quad \text{and} \quad \delta = (\gamma + \theta)/2 = 31.6°$$

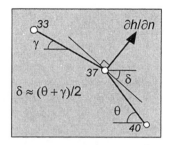

Figure 6.20: Angles relating to node 37, figure 6.18 (not to scale)

Accordingly the dimensions required for the calculation of the constants in equation 6.14 for node 37 are as per figure 21 in which the dimension $d = 0.908\,m$ is calculated using equation 6.15 (without the minus sign):

$$d = 1.4768 \times \tan 31.6 = 0.908\,m$$

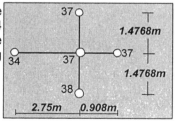

Figure 6.21: Angles relating to node 37, figure 6.18 (not to scale)

Applying a similar analysis to the remaining nodes 22, 28, 33 & 40, if follows that:

• **node 22:**

$$\gamma = 10°, \quad \theta = 7.67°,$$
$$\beta = (10 + 7.67)/2 = 8.84°$$

$$d = 0.3705 \times \tan 8.84 = 0.057\,m$$

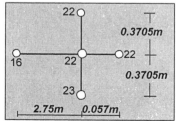

Figure 6.22: Angles relating to node 22, figure 6.18 (not to scale)

- **node 28:**

$\gamma = 8.84°$, $\theta = 10.65°$,
$\delta = (8.84 + 10.65)/2 = 9.74°$

$d = 0.517 \times \tan 9.74 = 0.089 \, m$

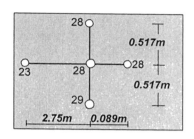

Figure 6.23: Angles relating to node 28, figure 6.18 (not to scale)

- **node 33:**

$\gamma = 10.65°$, $\theta = 19°$,
$\delta = (10.65 + 19)/2 = 14.86°$

$d = 0.9505 \times \tan 14.86 = 0.252 \, m$

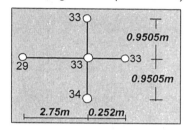

Figure 6.24: Angles relating to node 33, figure 6.18 (not to scale)

- **node 40:**

$\gamma = \theta = \delta = 44.23°$

$d = 1.2 \times \tan 44.23 = 1.168 \, m$

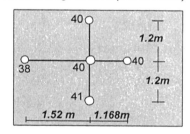

Figure 6.25: Angles relating to node 40, figure 6.18 (not to scale)

The stage is now set for establishing the finite difference equations at these nodes with the help of equation 6.14. The first step consists of calculating the constants in equation 6.14 relating to each node, whence:

- **node 22** (see figure 6.22 for dimensions):

$$\alpha_1 = \frac{(0.3705 + 0.3705)}{2.75} = 0.2694, \qquad \alpha_2 = \frac{(0.3705 + 0.3705)}{0.057} = 13$$

$$\alpha_3 = \alpha_4 = \frac{(2.75 + 0.057)}{0.3705} = 7.576, \qquad \beta = (0.2694 + 13 + 2 \times 7.576) = 28.421$$

- **node 28** (refer to figure 6.23 for dimensions):

$$\alpha_1 = \frac{(0.517 + 0.517)}{2.75} = 0.376, \qquad \alpha_2 = \frac{(0.517 + 0.517)}{0.089} = 11.618$$

$$\alpha_3 = \alpha_4 = \frac{(2.75 + 0.089)}{0.517} = 5.491, \quad \beta = (0.376 + 11.618 + 2 \times 5.491) = 23.038$$

- **node 33** (see figure 6.24 for dimensions):

$$\alpha_1 = \frac{(0.9505 + 0.9505)}{2.75} = 0.6913, \qquad \alpha_2 = \frac{(0.9505 + 0.9505)}{0.252} = 7.5436$$

$$\alpha_3 = \alpha_4 = \frac{(0.252 + 2.75)}{0.9505} = 3.1583$$

$$\beta = (0.6913 + 7.5436 + 2 \times 3.1583) = 14.5515$$

- **node 37** (see figure 6.21 for dimensions):

$$\alpha_1 = \frac{(1.4768 + 1.4768)}{2.75} = 1.074, \qquad \alpha_2 = \frac{(1.4768 + 1.4768)}{0.908} = 3.2528$$

$$\alpha_3 = \alpha_4 = \frac{(2.75 + 0.908)}{1.4768} = 2.477, \quad \beta = (1.074 + 3.2528 + 2 \times 2.477) = 9.2808$$

- **node 40** (see figure 6.25 for dimensions):

$$\alpha_1 = \frac{(1.2 + 1.2)}{1.52} = 1.5789, \qquad \alpha_2 = \frac{(1.2 + 1.2)}{1.168} = 2.0548$$

$$\alpha_3 = \alpha_4 = \frac{(1.52 + 1.168)}{1.2} = 2.24, \qquad \beta = (1.5789 + 2.0548 + 2 \times 2.24) = 8.1137$$

The next step consists of placing the centre of the computational molecule of figure 6.13 on each node and establishing the corresponding finite difference equations. It is left to the reader if he or she wishes to apply this procedure in all its intermediate steps (see the equation for node 11 developed previously), and to show that the expanded form of the simultaneous equations for these five nodes are as follows:

- **node 22:**

$$0h_1 + 0h_2 + \ldots\ldots + 0h_{15} + 0.2695h_{16} + 0h_{17} + 0h_{18} + \ldots + $$
$$0h_{21} - 7.8458h_{22} + 7.5762h_{23} + 0h_{24} + 0h_{25} + \ldots + 0h_{41} = 0$$

- **node 28:**

    $0h_1 + 0h_2 + ... + 0h_{22} + 0.376h_{23} + 0h_{24} + ... + 0h_{27} -$
    $5.8673h_{28} + 5.4913h_{29} + 0h_{30+} .... + 0h_{41} = 0$

- **node 33:**

    $0h_1 + 0h_2 + ... + 0h_{28} + 0.6913h_{29} + 0h_{30+} .... + 0h_{32} -$
    $3.8496h_{33} + 3.1583h_{34} + 0h_{35} + ... + 0h_{41} = 0$

- **node 37:**

    $0h_1 + 0h_2 + ... + 0h_{33} + 1.074h_{34} + 0h_{35} + 0h_{36} -$
    $3.551h_{37} + 2.477h_{38} + 0h_{39} + ... + 0h_{41} = 0$

- **node 40:**

    $0h_1 + 0h_2 + ... + 0h_{37} + 1.5789h_{38} + 0h_{39} - 3.8189h_{40} + 2.24h_{41} = 0$

Once again, It is left to the reader to derive the remaining equations and to establish the expanded matrix formulation similar to equation 16; the matrix [K] this time being a [41 × 41] square matrix. The total heads are calculated by inverting the matrix [K] in the usual way. Obviously in practice, the entire procedure of meshing, establishing the matrix formulation and solving for the total heads is computerised, and establishing the few previous equations in details is meant to provide the maximum clarity as to how to handle the delicate problem of inclined non-linear boundaries.

The outcome of the second iteration are represented graphically in figure 6.26 which shows interestingly a smaller difference between the positions of the newly calculated free surface (plotted in bold) and the assumed one (represented in broken line). This improvement however, is not deemed good enough and therefore at least another iteration is needed for which a new mesh is adopted to accommodate the new assumed position of the free surface (i.e. the surface represented in bold in figure 6.26). The new mesh has 41 nodes, and thus a system of 41 simultaneous equations needs to be established in precisely the same way as in the previous iteration. In this respect, notwithstanding the tedious nature of calculations, readers unfamiliar with the method are encouraged to establish all equations by hand, including intermediate steps so as to master the use of formulation.

In this particular case, five iterations with five different meshes were needed to satisfy the convergence criterion. While the results of the fourth iteration corresponding to the mesh in figure 6.27 represent a marked improvement compared to those in figure 6.26, the fifth iteration in figure 6.28 shows that both assumed and calculated position of the free surface are too close for the convergence criterion to be deemed satisfied.

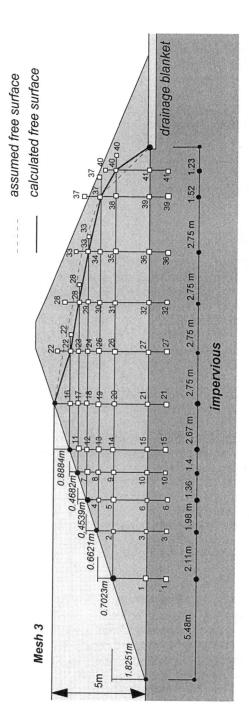

Figure 6.19: Finite difference mesh in the case of seepage flow through an earth dam

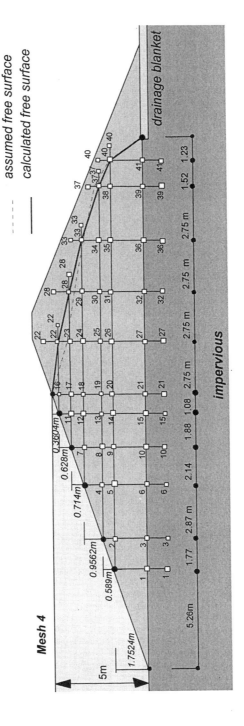

Figure 6.20: Finite difference mesh in the case of seepage flow through an earth dam

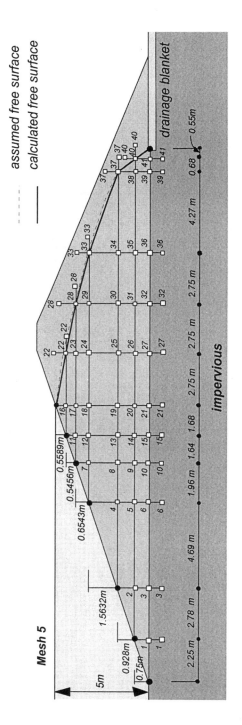

Figure 6.21: Finite difference mesh in the case of seepage flow through an earth dam

6.6 Finite difference modelling of the diffusion equation

6.6.1 Mathematical aspects of diffusion

The diffusion equation expresses the physical fact that the density of any given flux is proportional to the concentration gradient. For instance, the scent of a perfume diffuses proportionally to the scent concentration: the stronger the scent, the faster the diffusion rate. This principle applies equally to a heated radiator, which diffuses its thermal energy throughout a confined space in proportion to its thermal diffusivity. Similarly, the decay of excess porewater pressure within a soil mass diffuses in proportion to the hydraulic diffusivity of the soil (also known as permeability). In the same way, the freezing process of a soil represents a diffusion of thermal energy proportionally to the thermal diffusivity of the soil. In all cases, the 1-D form of the diffusion equation is as follows:

$$F(x, t) = -c\frac{\partial P(x, t)}{\partial x} \tag{6.17}$$

where F represents the flux density, P is the density of the physical quantity of interest such as heat or molecular concentration, and c is the proportionality constant which has various names depending on the physical quantity P. Thus, if P represents heat, c is referred to as thermal diffusivity; however when P corresponds to a molecular concentration, c is known as the coefficient of diffusion. As introduced earlier, in the specific case where P represents an excess porewater pressure within a soil matrix, c is often referred to as the coefficient of consolidation. Since it is easier to relate to (and to solve for that matter) a relationship that represents the variation of the physical quantity P in space and in time, the flux density in equation 6.17 can be eliminated in a straightforward way. In fact, the total mass density or molecular concentration $P(x, t)$ between any given boundaries a & b along the x-dimension can be written as follows:

$$M_d = \int_a^b P(x, t)dx \tag{6.18}$$

Assuming the mass density is conserved, then within the interval $[a, b] = \Delta x$, the molecular concentration can be approximated in the following way:

$$M_d = P(x, t)\Delta x \tag{6.19}$$

Moreover, any change in the number of molecules within the interval Δx is entirely due to the change of flux density:

$$\frac{\partial P(x, t)}{\partial t}\Delta x = F(x, t) - F(x + \Delta x, t) \tag{6.20}$$

Rearranging, it follows that:

$$\frac{\partial P(x,t)}{\partial t} = \frac{F(x,t) - F(x+\Delta x,t)}{\Delta x} \tag{6.21}$$

Now, using a Taylor's series expansion about x in conjunction with the right hand side of equation (6.21), it is seen that:

$$\frac{\partial P(x,t)}{\partial t} = -\frac{\partial F(x,t)}{\partial x} \tag{6.22}$$

Substituting for F from equation 6.17 into equation 6.22 yields the general 1-D form of the anisotropic diffusion equation:

$$\frac{\partial P(x,t)}{\partial t} = \frac{\partial}{\partial x}\left(c\frac{\partial P(x,t)}{\partial x}\right) \tag{6.23}$$

It can readily be shown that equation 6.22 can be expanded to a 3-D form by writing:

$$\frac{\partial P}{\partial t} = \nabla(c\nabla P) \tag{6.24}$$

with: $P \equiv P(x,y,z,t)$,

$$\nabla = \left(\frac{\partial}{\partial x} + \frac{\partial}{\partial y} + \frac{\partial}{\partial z}\right): \text{the nabla operator in a Cartesian co-ordinates}$$
$$\text{system}$$

Both equations 6.23 & 6.24 represent the anisotropic diffusion equation, for which the coefficient of diffusion c varies in space. However, were c to be constant, then $\partial c/\partial x = \partial c/\partial y = \partial c/\partial z = 0$, and equation 6.23 is written as follows:

$$\frac{\partial P}{\partial t} = c\nabla^2(P) \tag{6.25}$$

with: $P \equiv P(x,y,z,t)$,

$$\nabla^2 = \left(\frac{\partial^2}{\partial x^2} + \frac{\partial^2}{\partial y^2} + \frac{\partial^2}{\partial z^2}\right): \text{the Lapacian operator in a Cartesian}$$
$$\text{co-ordinates system.}$$

Notice finally that in radial co-ordinates system the anisotropic diffusion equation 6.25 is written as follows:

$$\frac{\partial P}{\partial t} = c_r\left(\frac{\partial^2 P}{\partial r^2} + \frac{1}{r}\frac{\partial P}{\partial r}\right) + c_v\frac{\partial^2 P}{\partial z^2} \tag{6.26}$$

with: c_r, c_v : the coefficient of diffusion in the radial and vertical
directions, respectively,

r, z: the radial and vertical dimensions, respectively.

It is clear that under isotropic diffusion conditions, a unique coefficient of diffusion c applies, and equation 6.26 reduces to:

$$\frac{1}{c}\frac{\partial P}{\partial t} = \frac{\partial^2 P}{\partial r^2} + \frac{1}{r}\frac{\partial P}{\partial r} + \frac{\partial^2 P}{\partial z^2} \qquad (6.27)$$

Equations 6.26 & 6.27 encompass all types of diffusion processes occurring within a given medium. For instance, if the quantity P represents heat T, then equation 6.27 yields the heat diffusion equation, for which the coefficient of diffusion c becomes known as the thermal diffusivity α:

$$\frac{1}{\alpha}\frac{\partial T}{\partial t} = \frac{\partial^2 T}{\partial r^2} + \frac{1}{r}\frac{\partial T}{\partial r} + \frac{\partial^2 T}{\partial z^2} \qquad (6.28)$$

If P corresponds to an excess porewater pressure u, generated by a loading process within a soil mass, then equation 6.27 yields the consolidation equation, and the coefficient of diffusion becomes known as the coefficient of consolidation:

$$\frac{1}{c}\frac{\partial u}{\partial t} = \frac{\partial^2 u}{\partial r^2} + \frac{1}{r}\frac{\partial u}{\partial r} + \frac{\partial^2 u}{\partial z^2} \qquad (6.29)$$

6.6.2 Finite difference modelling of the consolidation equation

The three dimensional form of the parabolic partial differential equation, representing the process of soil consolidation was established earlier in the form of equation 6.26 which can be rewritten as follows:

$$c_v\frac{\partial^2 u}{\partial y^2} + c_h\left(\frac{\partial^2 u}{\partial r^2} + \frac{1}{r}\frac{\partial u}{\partial r}\right) = \frac{\partial u}{\partial t} \qquad (6.30)$$

Parabolic partial differential equations govern propagation problems (such as consolidation of soils), which are initial value boundary problems in open domains. In other words, only when the function distribution along the boundary is known *à priori* at time $t = 0$ that a solution to equation 6.30 at time $t + \Delta t$ can be achieved by marching the solution at time t. Several marching methods can be used, and interested readers can refer to the work of Hoffman (1992) and Thomas (1995) for a comprehensive review of different methods. However, the following analysis is based on the so called *forward-time centered-space* (FTCS) finite difference approximation.

Referring to equation 6.30, the finite difference formulation at time t, around a central point $x_{i,j}$ (the index i applies in the radial r-direction, and j in the vertical y-direction) of this partial differential equation can be written separately as follows:

$$\left(c_v \frac{\partial^2 u}{\partial y^2}\right)_t \equiv \frac{c_v}{(\Delta y)^2}(u_{i,j-1} + 2u_{i,j} - u_{i,j+1})$$
(6.31a)

$$\left(c_h \frac{\partial^2 u}{\partial r^2}\right)_t \equiv \frac{c_h}{\frac{(\Delta r_a + \Delta r_b)}{2}}\left(\frac{u_{i+1,j} - u_{i,j}}{\Delta r_a} - \frac{u_{i,j} - u_{i-1,j}}{\Delta r_b}\right)$$
(6.31b)

$$\left(c_h \frac{1}{r}\frac{\partial u}{\partial r}\right)_t \equiv \frac{c_h}{r_i}\left(\frac{u_{i+1,j} - u_{i-1,j}}{(\Delta r_a + \Delta r_b)}\right)$$
(6.31c)

$$\frac{\partial u}{\partial t} \equiv \left(\frac{u_{(i,j),t+\Delta t} - u_{(i,j),t}}{\Delta t}\right)$$
(6.31d)

Δy is the (constant) vertical size of every element in the mesh, and Δr_a, Δr_b & r_i are as per figure 6.29.

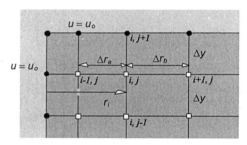

Figure 6.29: Dimensions realting to equations 6.31

Adding equations 6.31a to c, then equating to equation 6.31d yields the following three dimensional finite difference formulation of equation 6.30:

$$\frac{\left(u_{(i,j),t+\Delta t} - u_{(i,j),t}\right)}{\Delta t} = \left[\frac{c_v}{(\Delta y)^2}(u_{i,j-1} - 2u_{i,j} + u_{i,j+1})\right] +$$

$$\frac{2c_h}{(\Delta r_a + \Delta r_b)}\left(\frac{u_{i+1,j} - u_{i,j}}{\Delta r_a} - \frac{u_{i,j} - u_{i-1,j}}{\Delta r_b} + \frac{1}{2r_i}[u_{i+1,j} - u_{i-1,j}]\right)$$
(6.32)

Equation 6.32 is the time-marching algorithm for the three dimensional consolidation equation, in which the excess porewater pressure $u_{i,j}$ at time $(t+\Delta t)$ can be calculated from the value of the excess porewater pressure $u_{i,j}$ at time t. Notice that the equation has a much simpler form when $\Delta r_a = \Delta r_b = \Delta r$. The computational molecule at time t corresponding to equation 6.32 can be found by rearranging the same equation as follows:

$$(u_{i,j})_{t+\Delta t} = \lambda_1(u_{i-1,j})_t + \lambda_2(u_{i,j})_t + \lambda_3(u_{i+1,j})_t + \lambda_4\left\{(u_{i,j-1})_t + (u_{i,j+1})_t\right\} \quad (6.33)$$

where $\quad \lambda_1 = \dfrac{2\Delta t c_h}{(\Delta r_a + \Delta r_b)}\left(\dfrac{1}{\Delta r_b} - \dfrac{1}{2r_i}\right)$ $\qquad\qquad (6.34a)$

$$\lambda_2 = 1 - 2\Delta t\left(\frac{c_v}{(\Delta y)^2} + \frac{c_h}{(\Delta r_a + \Delta r_b)}\left(\frac{1}{\Delta r_a} + \frac{1}{\Delta r_b}\right)\right) \qquad (6.34b)$$

$$\lambda_3 = \frac{2\Delta t c_h}{(\Delta r_a + \Delta r_b)}\left(\frac{1}{\Delta r_a} + \frac{1}{2r_i}\right) \qquad\qquad (6.34c)$$

$$\lambda_4 = \frac{\Delta t c_v}{(\Delta y)^2} \qquad\qquad (6.34d)$$

Whence the computational molecule (at time t):

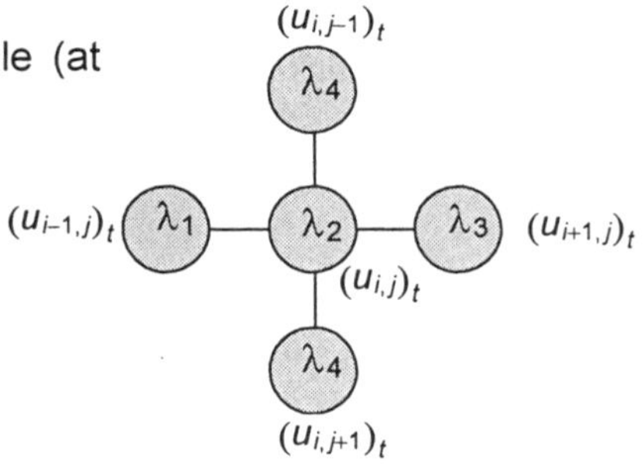

Figure 6.30: Computational molecule at time t of the three dimensional consolidation equation

Introducing initial and boundary conditions (depending on the problem to be solved) into the time dependent algorithm of figure 6.30 is no guarantee to achieving a stable (or converging) iterative solution. The stability of the solution depends on the size of the time increment Δt. To illustrate this important point, consider the one dimensional form of equation 6.32; in other words, let's assume diffusion only occurs in the vertical direction. The equation thence reduces to:

$$(u_j)_{t+\Delta t} = (u_j)_t + c_v\frac{\Delta t}{(\Delta y)^2}(u_{j-1} - 2u_j + u_{j+1})_t \qquad (6.35)$$

It can readily be shown that, for the solution of equation 6.35 to be stable (*i.e.* to converge), the time increment Δt must be such that:

$$c_v\frac{\Delta t}{(\Delta y)^2} \le \frac{1}{2} \qquad\qquad (6.36)$$

In the three dimensional case of equation 6.32, the stability condition is much more complex because of the coupling effect of both c_v & c_h on the diffusion process. The problem can be somewhat simplified by assuming that diffusion occurs predominantly in the radial direction. In which case, the following stability condition can be cautiously used, though only as an initial step:

$$c_h\frac{\Delta t}{2(\Delta r)^2} \le \frac{1}{2} \qquad\qquad (6.37)$$

The convergence rate of a stable solution can be at times painfully slow, and the time increment therefore may need to be adjusted. Furthermore, a stable solution may initially show some oscillations at one or more nodes. These oscillations, which only occur during the first few iterations, do not affect the convergence or the rate at which it occurs, and can be reduced by adjusting the size of elements or the size of time increment. Finally, the algorithm corresponding to equation 6.33 does not require inverting the now familiar [K] matrix: the iterative procedure simply necessitates the [K] matrix to be established from the system of simultaneous equations engendered by the molecule in figure 6.30, then a convergence criterion to be applied to the following iteration scheme:

$$\{u\}_{t+\Delta t} = [K]\{u\}_t \qquad\qquad (6.38)$$

Example 6.4: consolidation of a clay layer using vertical drainage

A 6 m thick saturated clay layer, underlain by a virtually impermeable strata is subjected to a uniform pre-load to simulate the pressure generated by a large building. The magnitude of the pre- load is such that an excess porewater pressure $u = 100\,kN/m^2$ would be generated within the clay layer.

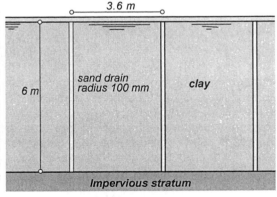

Figure 6.31: Vertical drainage system

Wick drains, equivalent to vertical sand drains with a radius $r_w = 0.1\,m$, are installed in sufficient numbers at 3.6 m centre-to-centre spacing as illustrated in figure 6.31. The clay is characterised by the respective coefficients of vertical and horizontal consolidation:

$$c_v = 2.2\,m^2/year, \quad c_h = 3\,m^2/year$$

Assuming each drain has a radius of influence $R_e = 1.8\,m$, and taking full advantage of the symmetry of the problem, only the area delimited by the drain and its radius of influence needs to be meshed. The corresponding mesh illustrated in figure 6.32 consists of 16 elements having the same vertical dimension $\Delta y = 1.5\,m$. In the radial direction however, the dimensions are chosen so that the mesh size increases logarithmically by a constant increment:

$$\Delta a = \ln r_{i+1} - \ln r_i = \text{constant} \tag{6.39a}$$

Accordingly, if the radius r_i is known, then:

$$r_{i+1} = \exp[\Delta a + \ln r_i] \tag{6.39b}$$

where r_i and r_{i+1} are the radii of any two consecutive nodes, measured from the drain axis. The mesh in figure 6.32 is composed of four radial sections, characterised by a constant logarithmic increment:

$$\Delta a = \frac{\ln R_e - \ln r_w}{4} = \frac{\ln 1.8 - \ln 0.1}{4} = 0.7226\,m$$

Using the node numbers as the radii indices, the precise radial position of nodes 1, 5, 9 & 13 in figure 6.32 are determined from equation 6.39b as follows (all radii are measured with respect to the axis of the drain):

- **node 0** (represented by a solid circle on the right hand side of node 1) has a radius:
$$r_o = r_w = 0.1\,m$$

- **node 1:** $\quad r_1 = \exp(0.7226 + \ln 0.1) = 0.206\,m$

- **node 5:** $\quad r_5 = \exp(0.7226 + \ln 0.206) = 0.4242\,m$

- **node 9:** $\quad r_9 = \exp(0.7226 + \ln 0.4242) = 0.8739\,m$

- **node 13:** $\quad r_{13} = \exp(0.7226 + \ln 0.8739) = 1.8\,m$

It is straightforward to check that, in agreement with equation 6.39a:

$$(\ln r_5 - \ln r_1) = (\ln r_9 - \ln r_5) = (\ln r_{13} - \ln r_9) = 0.7226\,m$$

Whence the dimensions indicated in figure 6.32.

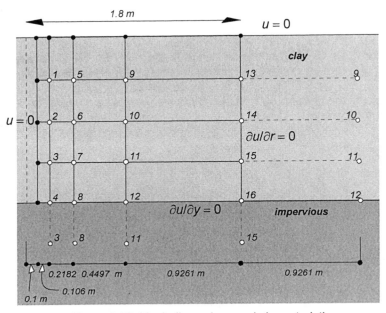

Figure 6.32: Mesh dimensions and characteristics

The implementation of both initial and boundary conditions must be considered carefully. Prior to the onset of the consolidation process (which is basically a decrease or dissipation or diffusion of the excess porewater pressure in time), the entire clay layer is assumed to be uniformly subjected to an excess porewater pressure $u = 100\,kN/m^2$. Hence the initial condition:

- $t = 0;$ $u(r, y) = 100\,kN/m^2$

Once the diffusion or consolidation process has started, the excess porewater pressure at the drained boundaries of the mesh reduces to zero. In other words, the excess porewater pressure at the nodes represented by solid circles at the top of the clay layer, as well as along the drain is zero (the vertical y-axis originates at the top of the clay layer):

- $t > 0;$ $u(r, 0) = u(r_w, y) = 0$

The bottom of the clay layer ($y = 6\,m$) is impermeable, and therefore at the onset of consolidation, the flow condition is such that:

- $t > 0;$ $\dfrac{\partial u(r, 6)}{\partial y} = 0$

Finally, the flow is normal to the vertical boundary delimited by the radius of influence $R_e = 1.8\,m$. Accordingly, along the left hand side vertical boundary of the mesh (see figure 6.32), the flow condition at the onset of consolidation is thus:

- $t > 0;$ $\dfrac{\partial u(1.8, y)}{\partial r} = 0$

These boundary conditions are then implemented in the usual way; in particular, the *Neumann* type conditions of $\partial u/\partial y = 0$ along the bottom of the clay layer and $\partial u/\partial r = 0$ along the left vertical boundary of the mesh necessitate the use of mirror image nodes as illustrated in figure 6.32. The stage is now set for the establishment of the computational molecule(s) for this problem, and the derivation of the system of simultaneous equations leading to the matrix formulation and the iterative calculation process. According to equations 6.34, the parameters λ_1 to λ_4 required to derive the molecule of figure 6.30, depend on the quantities Δt, Δr_a, Δr_b, r_i and Δy. The mesh illustrated in figure 6.32 shows that while the vertical increment $\Delta y = 1.5\,m$ is constant throughout the mesh, the radial increments Δr_a & Δr_b (see figure 6.29) as well as the radius r_i (the radial distance from the drain axis to the central node) depend on the radial position of the central node within the mesh, and consequently, four different molecules will be needed to determine the system of simultaneous equations. However, as stated earlier, the stability (or convergence) of the solution depends on the time increment Δt, which must be chosen judiciously so as to ensure a rapid rate of convergence. Although equation 6.37 can be tentatively used to select an initial time increment, one has to bear in mind the possibility of having to adjust Δt accordingly.

In this particular diffusion problem, choosing a time increment $\Delta t = 2\,days$, and using the smallest radial increment $\Delta r_a = 0.106\,m$ in conjunction with equation 6.37, it follows that:

$$3 \times \frac{(2/365)}{2 \times (0.106)^2} = 0.731 < 1$$

While this time increment seems to guarantee convergence, the rate at which the solution is achieved needs to be checked. The four computational molecules can now be determined   using equations 6.34 and the dimensions indicated at the bottom of the mesh in figure 6.32.

- **nodes 1, 2, 3 and 4:**

$\Delta r_a = 0.106\,m, \quad \Delta r_b = 0.2182\,m, \quad r_i = 0.206\,m$

$$\lambda_1 = \frac{2 \times (2/365) \times 3}{(0.106 + 0.2182)} \times \left(\frac{1}{0.2182} - \frac{1}{2 \times 0.206} \right) = 0.2186$$

$$\lambda_2 = 1 - 2 \times (2/365) \times \left(\frac{2.2}{1.5^2} + \frac{3}{0.106 + 0.2182} \times \left(\frac{1}{0.106} + \frac{1}{0.2182} \right) \right) = -0.4321$$

$$\lambda_3 = \frac{2 \times (2/365) \times 3}{(0.106 + 0.2182)} \times \left(\frac{1}{0.106} + \frac{1}{2 \times 0.206} \right) = 1.2028$$

$$\lambda_4 = \frac{(2/365) \times 2.2}{1.5^2} = 0.0054$$

Hence the molecule exclusively applicable to nodes 1, 2, 3, and 4:

The three other computational molecules are determined in precisely the same way using the appropriate radial increments. The reader may wish to check the detailed calculations.

- **nodes 5, 6, 7 and 8:** $\quad \Delta r_a = 0.2182\,m, \quad \Delta r_b = 0.4497\,m, \quad r_i = 0.4242\,m$

- **nodes 9,10, 11 and 12:** $\quad \Delta r_a = 0.4497\,m, \quad \Delta r_b = 0.9261\,m, \quad r_i = 0.8739\,m$

- **nodes 13, 14, 15, & 16:** $\Delta r_a = \Delta r_b = 0.9261\,m$, $r_i = 1.8\,m$

Notice how small the contribution of the vertical consolidation to the process of dissipation of excess porewater pressure. The magnitude of λ_4 (which is proportional to the coefficient of vertical consolidation as per equation 6.34*d*) in all four molecules is almost too small to affect the overall consolidation in any significant way. This is consistent with the fact that water can seep through a natural soil much faster in the horizontal direction than in the vertical one, due to the layered nature of soil formation. The system of 16 simultaneous equations can now be derived in a straightforward way. For instance, the equations at nodes 1, 8, 9 & 16 are:

- **-node 1** (use computational molecule 1)

$$(-0.4321\,u_1 + 0.0054\,u_2 + 1.208\,u_5)_t = (u_1)_{t+\Delta t}$$

- **node 8** (use computational molecule 2):

$$(0.0514\,u_4 + 2 \times 0.0054\,u_7 + 0.6542\,u_8 + 0.2836\,u_{12})_t = (u_8)_{t+\Delta t}$$

- **node 9** (use computational molecule 3):

$$(0.0121\,u_5 + 0.9103\,u_9 + 0.0054\,u_{10} + 0.0668\,u_{13})_t = (u_9)_{t+\Delta t}$$

- **node 16** (use computational molecule 4):

$$(2 \times 0.01423\,u_{12} + 2 \times 0.0054\,u_{15} + 0.9509\,u_{16})_t = (u_{16})_{t+\Delta t}$$

The reader may wish to establish all 16 equations using the four computational molecules as appropriate. As in the case of previous finite difference problems, these equations are expanded so that they are expressed in terms of all 16 nodal excess porewater pressures. Wence the equation at node 16, for example is rewritten as follows:

$$(0 \times u_1 + 0 \times u_2 + \cdots + 0.02846\,u_{12} + 0 \times u_{13} + 0 \times u_{14} + 0.0054\,u_{15} + 0.9509\,u_{16})$$
$$= (u_{16})_{t+\Delta t}$$

The next step is to write the system of simultaneous equations in a matrix form according to equation 6.38 as per figure 6.33.

[K] in figure 6.33 is a [16 × 16] square matrix, $\{U\}_t$ is a vector composed of the 16 nodal excess porewater pressure at time t, and $\{U\}_{t+\Delta t}$ is the vector of excess porewater pressure at time $t + 2\,days$.

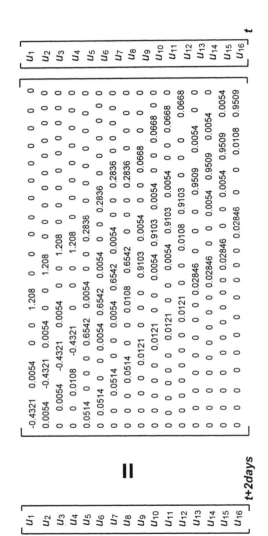

Figure 6.33: General matrix formulation of equation 6.28 algorithm

The iterative procedure of equation 6.38 algorithm starts with the initial excess porewater pressure $\{U\}_{t=0}$, which has a uniform value of $100\,kN/m^2$ throughout the clay layer. The excess porewater pressure corresponding to the first time increment is thence (see figure 6.34):

$$\{U\}_{t=2\,days} = [K]\{U\}_{t=0}$$

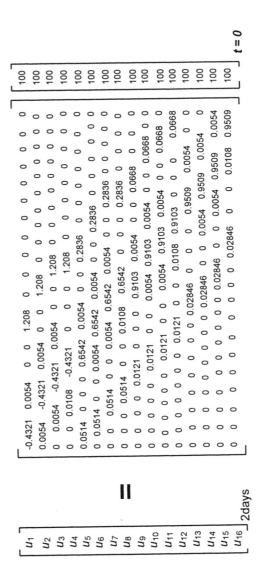

Figure 6.34: Diffusion problem - first iteration

The results at $t = 2\,days$ are then used as the starting point to calculate the excess porewater pressure corresponding to the next time increment : $\{U\}_{t=4\,days} = [K]\{U\}_{t=2\,days}$

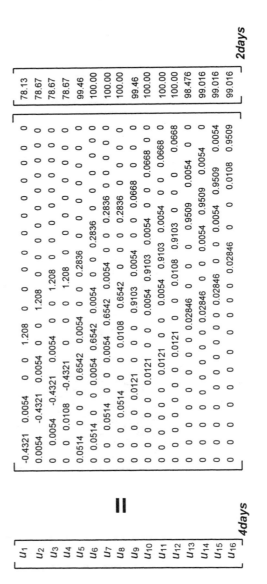

Figure 6.35: Diffusion problem - second iteration

The iterative process thus continues until the excess porewater pressure has entirely dissipated everywhere within the clay layer. The outcome of the first few calculations are tabulated below. Readers unfamiliar with Finite Difference Modelling are encouraged to go through the previous steps, re-establish the [K] matrix in figure 6.33, programme the algorithm of equation 6.38, and have a print out of all calculations. Though this task may seem somewhat tedious, it guarantees a quick and better understanding of the method, so that more complex problems can be tackled with confidence. Notice the numerical oscillations at nodes 1, 2, 3 & 4 during the first four iterations in table 6.3 . As mentioned earlier, these oscillations do not affect either the stability, or the rate at which the solution is approached.

Table 6.3: outcome of the first 8 iterations

	$t = 0$	2 days	4 days	6 days
u_1	100	78.130	86.812	81.139
u_2	100	78.670	87.653	82.539
u_3	100	78.670	87.656	82.546
u_4	100	78.670	87.656	82.546
u_5	100	99.460	97.829	97.033
u_6	100	100	98.900	98.609
u_7	100	100	98.903	98.617
u_8	100	100	98.903	98.617
u_9	100	99.460	98.860	98.195
u_{10}	100	100	99.931	99.788
u_{11}	100	100	99.934	99.797
u_{12}	100	100	99.934	99.797
u_{13}	100	98.476	96.006	95.586
u_{14}	100	99.016	98.066	97.149
u_{15}	100	99.016	98.069	97.157
u_{16}	100	99.016	98.069	97.157

8 days	10 days	12 days	14 days	16 days
82.601	80.768	80.604	79.638	79.147
84.338	82.974	83.185	82.680	82.524
84.353	82.998	83.221	82.729	82.588
84.353	82.998	83.221	82.729	82.589
96.030	95.245	94.423	93.652	92.869
98.109	97.810	97.467	97.163	96.838
98.126	97.838	97.508	97.220	96.913
98.126	97.838	97.508	97.221	96.914
97.485	96.734	95.950	95.139	94.305
99.589	99.337	99.042	98.707	98.337
99.606	99.366	99.084	98.765	98.414
99.606	99.366	99.084	98.765	98.414
94.212	92.880	91.588	90.332	89.111
96.259	95.396	94.556	93.738	92.938
96.276	95.424	94.597	93.793	93.012
96.276	95.424	94.597	93.794	93.012

The degree of consolidation of the entire clay layer at any given time can be calculated by averaging the degrees of consolidation achieved at every node throughout the mesh. For instance, it is easy to see that after 16 days, the degree of consolidation U (or excess porewater pressure dissipation) at say, nodes 1, 5 and 12 are:

- node 1: $U = (100 - 79.147) = 20.853\%$
- node 5: $U = (100 - 92.869) = 7.131\%$
- node 12: $U = (100 - 98.414) = 1.586\%$

The degree of consolidation of the entire clay layer after 16 days corresponds to the *average* degree of consolidation calculated as above at *all* nodes. It is left to the reader to check that after 16 days, the entire layer would have reached an average degree of consolidation $U \approx 8.25\%$. The following table summarises the last three iterations. The computation criterion selected for the iterative process is an excess porewater pressure smaller than $1\,kN/m^2$ at any node. The entire consolidation process in this case took $1,298\,days$ (or 3.556 *years*).

Table 6.4: outcome of the last 3 iterations

1294 days	1296 days	1298 days
0.3364	0.3339	0.3313
0.6160	0.6113	0.6067
0.7975	0.7915	0.7856
0.8599	0.8535	0.8471
0.3940	0.3910	0.3880
0.7213	0.7159	0.7105
0.9339	0.9269	0.9199
1.0070	0.9995	0.9920
0.3951	0.3921	0.3891
0.7234	0.7179	0.7125
0.9366	0.9296	0.9226
1.0099	1.0024	0.9949
0.3557	0.3530	0.3503
0.6513	0.6464	0.6415
0.8433	0.8369	0.8307
0.9093	0.9025	0.8957

These tabulated figures can be however somewhat deceptive when they are not properly analysed. In fact, were the dissipation in time of the (excess) porewater pressure to be represented graphically, a clearer picture emerges as to the significance of the computational values tabulated above. The dissipation process at nodes 13 (1.5 m below ground) to 16 (6 m below ground, see figure 6.32) is plotted in figure 6.36 at two months time intervals. These nodes were selected because they are farthest from the vertical drain, and so their rate of consolidation is an upper bound to the overall average rate of the entire clay layer. The figure shows that, one year on, more than 70% of the excess porewater pressure has dissipated. The rate of dissipation increases to 93% within 2 years, and reaches 98% in 3 years. From a practical perspective, a consolidation rate of circa 95% is good enough to consider that the soil has all but consolidated. In this particular case, this acceptable rate is achieved within 2 years, whereas the "puritan" computational criterion of less than 1% excess porewater pressure anywhere within the clay layer takes more than 3.5 years to achieve.

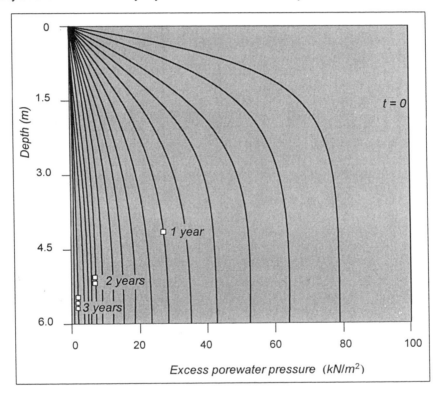

Figure 6.36: Evolution of the consolidation process in time

This pattern is repeated in figure 6.37 illustrating the entire process of consolidation at node 08 (see the mesh in figure 6.32). Hence the importance of post-calculation interpretation and analysis: *while it is important to properly model a physical problem, it is essential to be able to relate any outcome to practice, and to spot the excesses (or limitations) of a predicted behaviour.*

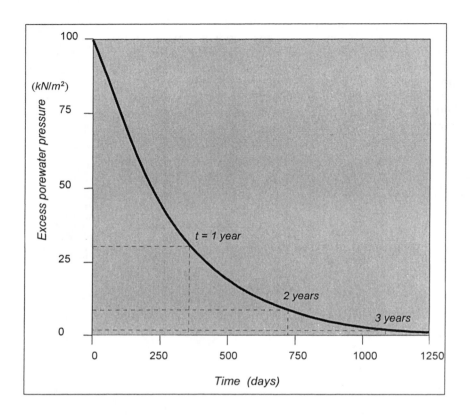

Figure 6.37: Excess porewater pressure dissipation at node 08.

• Case of one dimensional (vertical) consolidation

If radial drainage is assumed not to take place, then all excess porewater pressure diffuses in only the vertical direction. The consolidation equation then reduces to equation 6.35:

$$(u_j)_{t+\Delta t} = (u_j)_t + c_v \frac{\Delta t}{(\Delta y)^2}(u_{j-1} - 2u_j + u_{j+1})_t$$

and the corresponding computational molecule is much simpler than that in figure 6.30, since any contribution due to the horizontal diffusion is dropped, *all other things being equal* (se figure 6.38).

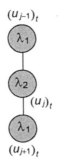

Figure 6.38: Computational molecule in 1-D diffusion case.

with: $\qquad\qquad \lambda_1 = c_v \dfrac{\Delta t}{(\Delta y)^2}$ $\qquad\qquad\qquad\qquad$ (6.40a)

$$\lambda_2 = 1 - 2c_v \dfrac{\Delta t}{(\Delta y)^2} \qquad\qquad\qquad (6.40b)$$

More importantly, the molecule in figure 6.38 applies equally to *any* set of vertical nodes, regardless of their radial dimension.

Example 6.5: Modelling of 1-D (vertical) consolidation

Assuming for instance that in the absence of wick drains in the case of example 6.4, diffusion only takes place vertically, then consolidation occurs in precisely the same way in nodes (1, 2, 3, 4) as in nodes (9, 10, 11, 12) or in nodes (13, 14, 15, 16). The time increment is selected according to the criterion of equation 6.36:

$$\Delta t \leq \frac{(\Delta y)^2}{2c_v} = \frac{(1.5)^2}{2 \times 2.2} = 0.511 \, years$$

Choosing $\Delta t = 0.25 \, y \, (\approx 3 \, months)$ yields:

$$\lambda_1 = \frac{2.2 \times 0.25}{(1.5)^2} = 0.2444,$$

$$\lambda_2 = 1 - 2\lambda_1 = 1 - 2 \times 0.2444 \doteq 0.5111$$

Hence the 1-D computational molecule:

The reader should recall that the above molecule applies to any set of vertical nodes. Positioning the centre of molecule on nodes 1, 2, 3 & 4 in turn yields the following set of four simultaneous equations (the vertical boundary conditions in figure 6.32 still hold):

node 1: $(0 \times 0.2444 + 0.5111\, u_1 + 0.244\, u_2)_t = (u_1)_{t+\Delta t}$

node 2: $(0.2444\, u_1 + 0.5111\, u_2 + 0.2444\, u_3)_t = (u_2)_{t+\Delta t}$

node 3: $(0.2444\, u_2 + 0.5111\, u_3 + 0.2444\, u_4)_t = (u_3)_{t+\Delta t}$

node 4: $(2 \times 0.2444\, u_3 + 0.5111\, u_4)_t = (u_4)_{t+\Delta t}$

or, in a matrix form:

$$
\begin{bmatrix} u_1 \\ u_2 \\ u_3 \\ u_4 \end{bmatrix}_{t+\Delta t}
=
\begin{bmatrix}
0.5111 & 0.2444 & 0 & 0 \\
0.2444 & 0.5111 & 0.2444 & 0 \\
0 & 0.2444 & 0.5111 & 0.2444 \\
0 & 0 & 0.4888 & 0.5111
\end{bmatrix}
\begin{bmatrix} u_1 \\ u_2 \\ u_3 \\ u_4 \end{bmatrix}_{t}
$$

The initial condition of the above algorithm is an excess porewater pressure $u = 100\, kN/m^2$ at all nodes. Hence the first few iterations results:

$$
\begin{bmatrix} u_1 \\ u_2 \\ u_3 \\ u_4 \end{bmatrix}
=
\begin{bmatrix} 10.00 \\ 10.00 \\ 10.00 \\ 10.00 \end{bmatrix}_{t=0}
\begin{bmatrix} 75.55 \\ 99.99 \\ 99.99 \\ 99.99 \end{bmatrix}_{0.25\,y}
\begin{bmatrix} 63.05 \\ 94.00 \\ 99.98 \\ 99.98 \end{bmatrix}_{0.5\,y}
\begin{bmatrix} 55.20 \\ 87.89 \\ 98.51 \\ 99.97 \end{bmatrix}_{0.75\,y}
\begin{bmatrix} 49.69 \\ 82.48 \\ 96.26 \\ 99.24 \end{bmatrix}_{1\,year}
$$

It is seen that one year on, the average degree of (vertical) consolidation of the entire layer (calculated by averaging the degree of consolidation at all four nodes) is a mere :

$$U = \frac{1}{4}(50.31 + 17.52 + 3.74 + 0.76) = 18.08\,\%$$

It is left to the reader to establish that under these drainage conditions, it would take more than 17 years to achieve 93% average degree of consolidation, whereas 98% average consolidation is reached after 25.5 years. The same clay layer with wick drains as per example 6.4, reached 80% of overall consolidation in one year, 93% consolidation in 2 years and

98% in 3 years. With only vertical drainage, the overall consolidation over similar periods of time decreases dramatically to 18% in one year, 32% in 2 years and only 40% in 3 years. These results are contrasted in figure 6.38.

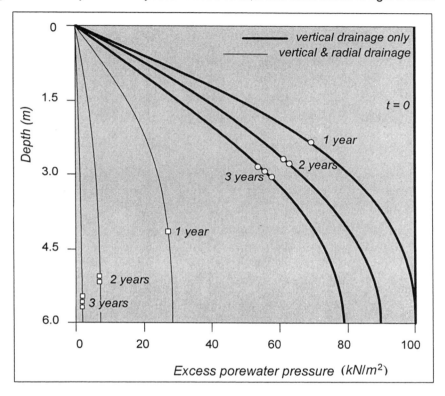

Figure 6.38: Effects of drainage type on the consolidation process

6.6.3 Practical aspects relating to soil consolidation modelling

Both examples 6.4 & 6.5 dealt with the diffusion inside a layer of clay underlain by an impermeable material, resulting in the boundary condition $\partial u/\partial y = 0$ along the bottom of the clay layer (see figure 6.32). Were a free draining soil to be substituted for the impervious material, then the boundary condition changes to $u = 0$, and flow would occur vertically at the top and at the bottom of the clay layer (as well as horizontally when applicable). The problem becomes symmetrical, and only half the clay layer thickness (*i.e.* the area between the two broken lines in figure 6.39) needs to be meshed, with the boundary conditions as per the figure. Apart from the size of the meshed area, the numerical solution of this problem is identical in nature to that of the previous two examples.

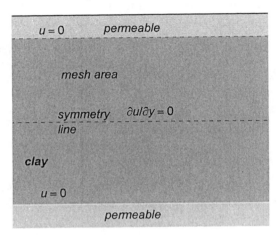

Figure 6.39: Effects of drainage conditions

Furthermore, example 6.5 dealt with solving numerically the consolidation of a clay layer in which the radius of influence of vertical drains was initially selected as per figure 6.31. The rate of dissipation in time of excess porewater pressure at different nodes was then calculated, thus yielding an accurate estimate of the overall degree of consolidation of the entire layer at any given time. In practice, such a problem is usually tackled using a slightly different approach: the computation aims at finding the number of vertical drains one needs to install within the entire layer, so that a selected overall degree of consolidation U can be achieved within a given period of time t. For instance, example 6.5 could have been formulated thus: find the number of wick drains (each equivalent to a 0.2 m diameter sand drain) that need to be installed, so that the entire clay layer would have reached an overall 80% degree of consolidation in twelve months. In which case, the numerical solution consists of the following steps:

1. select a radius of influence (*i.e.* the centre-to-centre spacing as per figure 6.31),
2. undertake the finite difference modelling as per example 6.5 (including mesh generation, computing molecules, matrix formulation of simultaneous equations as per equation 6.38)
3. use equation 6.38 algorithm to iterate up to a time $t = 1\ year$
4. use the solution at time $t = 1\ year$ to calculate the overall degree of consolidation U of the entire layer (by averaging the degrees of consolidation at all nodes)

5. the results are deemed satisfactory were U to be within 1 or 2 percentage points (on either side) of the selected value of 80%. If this is not the case, then adjust the radius of influence of the drains according to the value of U: decrease the radius if U is appreciably smaller than 80%, or increase it were U to be substantially higher than 80%
6. repeat the procedure from step 2.

Though the procedure seems to be time consuming, the reader should recall that the process can easily be automated, including mesh generation.

6.7 Limitations of finite difference modelling

Contrary to some popular belief, using a finer mesh in conjunction with finite difference modelling would not necessarily improve the accuracy of the results *per se*. As the size of elements is made smaller, the dimensions Δx & Δy decrease, and so does the truncation error due to the finite difference approximation of the partial derivatives. In the meantime, a smaller elements size generates more equations, which increases the size of the [K]-matrix, leading to more computations and therefore increasing the round off error. This trend is illustrated in figure 6.5 which shows the total error (that is the sum of truncation and round off errors) decreasing initially, before reaching a minimum then starting to increase. There is clearly an optimum number of elements linked to the minimum numerical error, and although optimisation is a theme outside the scope of this textbook, the usefulness of such graphs in figure 6.5 is highly significant, and the reader may wish to bear in mind that in engineering practice, finite difference software packages contain optimisation routines designed to keep the numerical errors to an acceptable minimum. This is all the more important in the case of diffusion problems (such as soil consolidation) where the stability of the numerical solution is linked to (the rate of) convergence. A stable solution for such problems is one that does not magnify errors arising from truncation or round off during computing (see stability criteria of equations 6.36 & 6.37).

The accuracy of finite difference modelling can be improved, in theory, by considering higher order Taylor's series, and it can readily be shown that for a regular mesh with equal size elements, the use of a fourth order centred difference formula from Taylor's series results in the general expression of the computational molecule in figure 6.40 in which $C = \Delta x/\Delta y$ (see Hoffman, 1992 for instance). In practice however, the use of such formulation results in a too cumbersome method with little benefit, since more powerful numerical tools such as the finite element method are readily available.

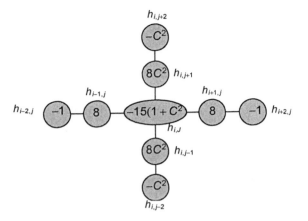

Figure 6.40: Computational molecule for a
fourth order centred difference formula

Problems

6.1   • Establish the finite difference
molecule for the seepage into
a cofferdam, through a layer
of a homogeneous isotropic
sand, illustrated in figure p6.1,
which is plotted to scale.

• Add the boundary conditions,
including the mirroring of
appropriate nodes, then
establish the (global) matrix
formulation of the problem:
$[K]\{h\} = \{c\}$.

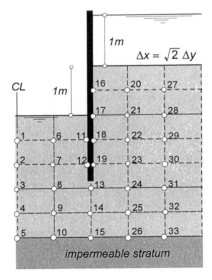

• Calculate the porewater
pressures at different nodes.

• Plot the isovalues of
porewater pressures at
$5\,kN/m^2$ intervals.

Figure p6.1

6.2   • Consider the same mesh of problem 6.1, then use a different
numbering order of the nodes as per figure p6.2.

Add the boundary conditions
as appropriate, and establish
the global [K] matrix.

- Compare the band width of
  [K] to that of the matrix
  derived for the previous
  problem 6.1.

- Calculate the nodal porewater
  pressures and compare the
  results to the solution of
  problem 6.1.

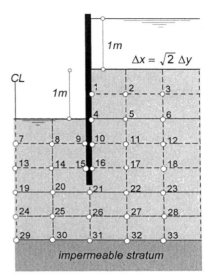

Figure p6.2

6.3 - Refer to figure p6.3 for
  the problem of seepage
  around a sheet-pile
  cut-off wall through a
  homogeneous isotropic
  sand layer, and establish
  the corresponding finite
  difference molecule (the
  mesh dimensions being
  characterised by an
  element aspect ratio
  $\Delta x / \Delta y = 2$).

- Add the node numbers,
  and all appropriate
  boundary conditions, then
  establish the (global)
  matrix formulation of the
  problem.

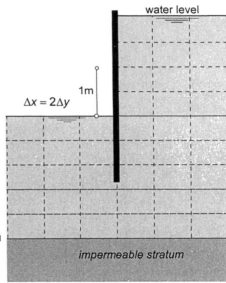

Figure p6.3

- Calculate the total heads as well
  as the porewater pressures at each node

- Plot the porewater pressure distribution
  on either side of the sheet-pile.

6.4
- The seepage problem of figure p6.4 is similar to that of figure p6.3, with the exception of the upstream seepage boundary conditions. Derive the corresponding finite difference molecule, then establish the matrix formulation of the problem.

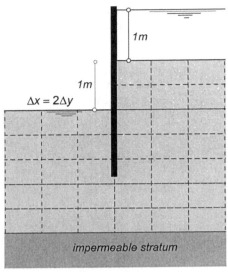

Figure p6.4

- Calculate the porewater pressures at each node, and compare the porewater pressure distribution around the sheet pile to that of the previous problem p6.3

- Calculate the exit hydraulic gradient.

6.5
- Consider the case of seepage through an isotropic homogeneous soil layer under a small concrete dam shown in figure p6.5. Establish the corresponding computational molecule, then include all boundary conditions as appropriate and derive the matrix formulation of the problem.

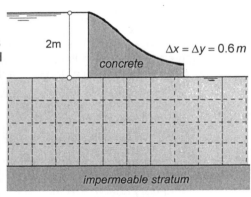

Figure p6.5

- Calculate the hydraulic uplift force exerted on the base of the dam.

6.6
- Figures p6.6 & p6.7 illustrate the same seepage problem of figure p6.5, with the addition of sheet piles to relieve the porewater pressure applied at the dam's base (one sheet pile inserted on the upstream side in the case of figure p6.6, and 2

sheet piles embedded on the upstream and downstream sides in figure p6.7). Include the boundary conditions as appropriate, then derive the corresponding matrix formulation for each problem.

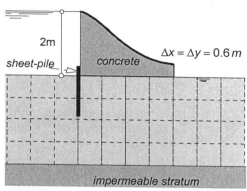

Figure p6.6

- Calculate the hydraulic uplift force exerted on the dam's base in both cases.

- Compare the hydraulic forces calculated in the three cases of seepage flow (figures p6.5 to 6.7).

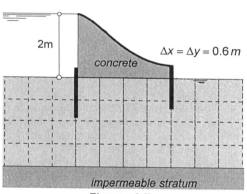

Figure p6.7

6.7   • Figure p6.8 represents a seepage flow through an anisotropic layer of clean sand into a cofferdam. The sand is characterised by a permeability ratio $k_h/k_v = 2.5$ (k_h & k_v being the horizontal and vertical permeabilities respectively). Apply the geometrical reduction as per section 4.4 to create an artificial isotropic domain of flow.

- use the artificial isotropic domain to generate a finite difference mesh, then derive the corresponding computational molecule.

- apply the boundary conditions (to the artificial domain of flow) as appropriate and establish the matrix formulation of the problem.

- Calculate the nodal porewater pressures, then expand the flow domain to its natural dimensions, and plot the variation of porewater pressure along the sheet pile.

- Contrast the results with those of problem p6.4

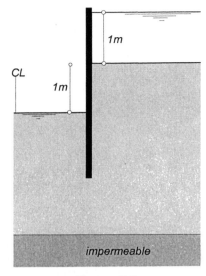

Figure p6.8

Reference:

J.W. Thomas (1995) *Numerical partial differential equations: finite difference methods*. Springer-Verlag. New York

Hoffman, J.D. (1992) *Numerical Methods for Engineers and Scientists*. McGraw-Hill, New York

CHAPTER 7

Shear strength of soils & rock masses

7.1 Peak, critical and residual strengths

The *shear strength* of a soil, that is the *maximum* resistance it can offer before the occurrence of shear failure along a specific failure plane, is intricately related to the soil *type* and *state*. Thus, the response of a granular soil to an applied load depends to a large extent on its density, whereas a fine grained overconsolidated soil exhibits markedly different behaviour to that of a normally consolidated soil as depicted in figure 7.1. In all cases, the shear strength is a quintessential design parameter on which depends the safety related to problems such as slope stability, bearing capacity and lateral thrust. Figure 7.1(a) shows that the stress–strain behaviour of a stiff clay or a dense sand exhibits a *peak* beyond which the strength of the soil decreases towards a *critical* value as the strain increases. If the *same* soils were in a different *state*, that is if the clay were normally consolidated and the sand were loose, then their strength would show a logarithmic increase, tending towards the critical value as the soil is further strained. On the other hand, when a soil is subject to very large strains (as in the case of an old land-slip for instance), then its post-peak strength decreases gradually until a *residual* value is reached as depicted in figure 7.1(b).

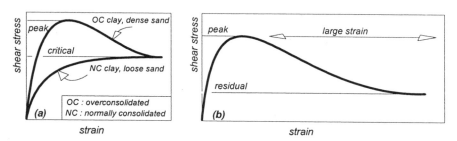

Figure 7.1: Stress–strain relationships as related to soil type and state.

From a practical perspective, the safety as well as the cost effectiveness of a design depend on how realistic are the mathematical relationships between stresses and strains. The relevance and shortcomings of an elastic analysis was highlighted in chapter 3 for the calculation of effective stress increases due to surface loading. Figure 7.2 reinforces the idea that an elastic analysis can be deemed adequate provided that the effective stress level does not far exceed the *yield stress*. This applies principally to stiff overconsolidated clays whose initial behaviour is characterised by relatively large elastic strains. Normally consolidated clays on the other hand show an elastic–plastic behaviour from the onset of loading and, consequently, the assumption of elastic behaviour for such soils, even when used in conjunction with a large factor of safety, would be grossly in error and potentially unsafe. Rather, the *stiffness* of such soils, in other words the stress–strain ratio, depends on the stress level and can be estimated either as a *tangent modulus* (see equation 3.36, figure 3.41):

$$E = \frac{\delta\sigma'}{\delta\varepsilon} \tag{7.1}$$

or as a *secant modulus* (refer to figure 7.2):

$$E = \frac{\Delta\sigma'}{\Delta\varepsilon} \tag{7.2}$$

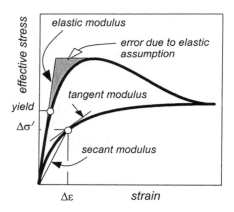

Figure 7.2: Selection of appropriate stiffness parameters.

The physical phenomena leading to soil failure under a known set of stresses are analysed in the following sections. In particular, the crucial effect of the porewater pressure on the strength of soils, with the implicit time effect, will be explored in order to dispel any confusion that may arise from the interpretation of experimental data.

7.2 Mohr's circle representation of stresses

To visualise the nature of plane stresses (*i.e.* two dimensional state of stresses), a simple method of analysis was established by Otto Mohr who suggested that the state of a sample subjected to a set of stresses can be represented graphically on a circle with a diameter corresponding to the difference between the major and minor stresses. Consider for instance the sample of cohesive soil subject to the set of principal stresses σ_1' (major stress) and σ_3' (minor stress) as depicted on the left-hand side of figure 7.3. Taking compressive stresses as well as anticlockwise shear stresses as *positive*, and considering that, under fully drained conditions, failure occurs along the plane OD at an angle α to the horizontal within the soil mass, then the same failure plane makes an angle 2α anticlockwise with respect to the horizontal in Mohr's representation. The mathematical proof of this fundamental property of Mohr's circle can be found in any textbook on stress analysis. Most importantly however, figure 7.3 can now be used to establish the expression of the shear stress τ_f and normal stress σ_n', acting on the failure plane.

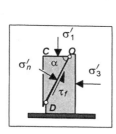
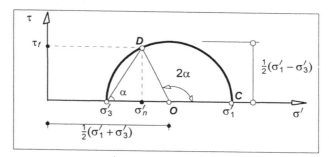

Figure 7.3: Mohr–Coulomb failure criterion for a fully drained cohesive soil.

Starting with the shear stress at failure, it is easy to see that:

$$\tau_f = OD\sin\beta = OD\sin(\pi - 2\alpha)$$
$$= \frac{1}{2}(\sigma_1' - \sigma_3')\sin 2\alpha \tag{7.3}$$

As for the normal effective stress at failure σ_n':

$$\sigma_n' = \frac{1}{2}(\sigma_1' + \sigma_3') - \frac{1}{2}(\sigma_1' - \sigma_3')\cos(\pi - 2\alpha)$$

$$= \frac{1}{2}(\sigma_1' + \sigma_3') + \frac{1}{2}(\sigma_1' - \sigma_3')\cos 2\alpha \tag{7.4}$$

Figure 7.3 also shows that the maximum shear stress occurs at an angle $\alpha = 45°$ for which the stresses corresponding to equations 7.3 and 7.4 reduce to:

$$t = \frac{1}{2}(\sigma_1' - \sigma_3') \tag{7.5a}$$

$$s' = \frac{1}{2}(\sigma_1' + \sigma_3') \tag{7.5b}$$

If, in addition, the two new stress variables, namely the *deviator stress q* and the *mean effective stress p'* are defined as follows:

$$q = (\sigma_1' - \sigma_3') \qquad\qquad (7.6a)$$

$$p' = \frac{1}{3}(\sigma_1' + 2\sigma_3') \qquad\qquad (7.6b)$$

then, by virtue of the effective stress principle $\sigma = \sigma' + u$, it is straightforward to establish that:

$$t = t', \quad q = q', \quad s = s' + u, \quad p = p' + u$$

meaning that the same equations 7.5a and 7.6a apply under effective or total stresses because water has no shear resistance. Accordingly, if Mohr's circle is represented in terms of total stresses, then the circle in figure 7.3 has simply to be shifted to the right-hand side by a distance corresponding to the porewater pressure *u*.

7.3 Stress–strain relationships at failure

7.3.1 Effective stress analysis

The behaviour exhibited in figure 7.1 is affected by the *type* and *state* of the soil. The failure stresses measured from different laboratory tests (whose details will be presented later) on the *same* natural clay are depicted in figure 7.4 (Josseaume and Azizi, 1991). It is very tempting *prima facie* to apply a linear regression analysis, so that the entire stress range at failure can be described by a unique linear equation. However, when the *state* of the clay is taken into account, a somewhat different picture emerges as shown in figure 7.5. All failure stresses corresponding to a *normal consolidation state* can be fitted with a line having a zero intercept and a slope β_c'.

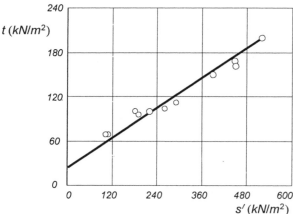

Figure 7.4: Failure stresses for a natural stiff clay.

As the clay becomes *overconsolidated* (due to the loading conditions of different tests), the relationship between stresses at failure becomes curved. For *heavily overconsolidated* samples, the behaviour at failure can be described by a linear equation with an intercept a' and a slope β'_p.

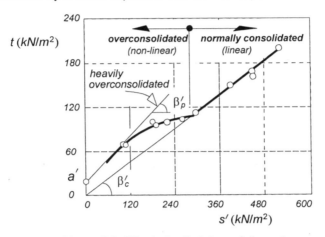

Figure 7.5: Effect of soil state on failure stresses.

Relating the behaviour depicted in figure 7.5 to that of figure 7.1, an overall picture of the shear strength associated with the state of natural soils can be drawn. Thus, for heavily overconsolidated clays, the peak shear strength can be estimated from a simple linear equation, established as early as 1776 by Charles Augustin Coulomb, who was the first to suggest that the shear strength, along a potential failure plane, of a soil subject to a normal stress σ'_n on the same plane (see figure 7.3) can be modelled with the following linear equation:

$$\tau_f = c' + \sigma'_n \tan \phi'_p \tag{7.7}$$

ϕ'_p represents the *peak angle of friction* and c', often referred to as *apparent cohesion,* was first thought to reflect the interparticle bonds otherwise known as cementation. It was not until Terzaghi established his effective stress equation (refer to section 3.1) some 150 years later that the nature of the intercept c' became clearer. In fact, experimental evidence suggests that, apart from some very sensitive soils, cementation in clays is insignificant (Bjerrum and Kenny, 1967). Rather, the apparent cohesion (that is the degree of shear strength exhibited by heavily overconsolidated clays under zero normal effective stress) is the result of curve fitting, and reflects the increase in effective stresses due to the negative porewater pressure and the suction that ensues within the clay mass. This process is tackled in detail in chapter 8.

The behaviour at failure of normally consolidated clays as well as granular soils does not exhibit any cohesion, and is therefore represented by the following simplified version of Coulomb equation 7.7:

$$\tau_f = \sigma'_n \tan \phi'_c \qquad\qquad (7.8)$$

ϕ'_c refers to the *critical angle of friction*. If the soil is subject to large deformations (refer to figure 7.1), then the behaviour at failure would be characterised by a *residual angle of friction* ϕ'_r as depicted in figure 7.6. Notice that in practice the angle ϕ'_r is usually used in conjunction with the design of slopes for which failure could be activated on an old land-slip where the soil has experienced large displacements in the past as in the case of slope stability problems. Moreover, ϕ'_r can be significantly smaller than ϕ'_c depending on the nature of the clay and its mineralogy (Lupini *et al.*, 1981). Figure 7.6 therefore represents the failure loci, better known as *failure envelopes,* for different types of soils at different states.

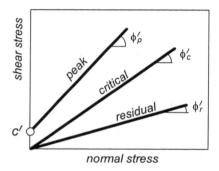

Figure 7.6: Failure envelopes.

Let us now use Mohr's circle of stresses to establish the relationships between different stresses at failure, as well as the link between the slopes β' in figure 7.5 and ϕ' in figure 7.6. Thus with reference to figure 7.7 in the case of a heavily overconsolidated clay, it is seen that:

$$\alpha = \frac{\pi}{4} + \frac{\phi'_p}{2} \qquad\qquad (7.9)$$

and therefore:

$$\sin 2\alpha = \sin\left(\frac{\pi}{2} + \phi'_p\right) = \cos \phi'_p, \qquad \cos 2\alpha = -\sin \phi'_p$$

Substituting for α in equations 7.3 and 7.4, it follows that:

$$\tau_f = \frac{1}{2}(\sigma'_1 - \sigma'_3) \cos \phi'_p \qquad\qquad (7.10)$$

$$\sigma'_n = \frac{1}{2}(\sigma'_1 + \sigma'_3) - \frac{1}{2}(\sigma'_1 - \sigma'_3)\sin\phi'_p \qquad (7.11)$$

Inserting these quantities in equation 7.7 and rearranging :

$$(\sigma'_1 - \sigma'_3) = 2c'\cos\phi'_p + (\sigma'_1 + \sigma'_3)\sin\phi'_p \qquad (7.12)$$

This equation can be further simplified, yielding thus the general relationship between effective minor and major stresses :

$$\sigma'_1 = \sigma'_3\tan^2\left(\frac{\pi}{4} + \frac{\phi'_p}{2}\right) + 2c'\tan\left(\frac{\pi}{4} + \frac{\phi'_p}{2}\right) \qquad (7.13)$$

or

$$\sigma'_3 = \sigma'_1\tan^2\left(\frac{\pi}{4} - \frac{\phi'_p}{2}\right) - 2c'\tan\left(\frac{\pi}{4} - \frac{\phi'_p}{2}\right) \qquad (7.14)$$

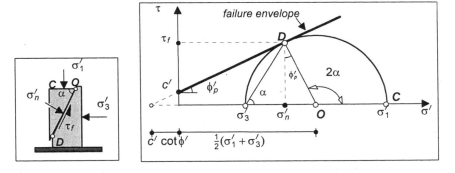

Figure 7.7: Mohr–Coulomb failure envelope for a heavily overconsolidated clay.

The relationship between the angles β'_p and ϕ'_p, as well as the intercepts a' and c' in figures 7.5 and 7.6 respectively can now be established in a straightforward way by substituting for the quantities t and s' from equations 7.5 into equation 7.12. Whence:

$$t = c'\cos\phi'_p + s'\sin\phi'_p \qquad (7.15)$$

and therefore, according to figure 7.5, it is seen that:

$$c' = \frac{a'}{\cos\phi'_p} \qquad (7.16)$$

$$\phi'_p = \sin^{-1}(\tan\beta'_p) \qquad (7.17)$$

Also, using equations 7.6, it is easy to show that:

$$(\sigma_1' + \sigma_3') = \frac{2}{3}(\sigma_1' + 2\sigma_3') + \frac{1}{3}(\sigma_1' - \sigma_3') = 2p' + \frac{q}{3} \qquad (7.18)$$

Inserting this quantity into equation 7.12 then rearranging, it follows that:

$$q = \frac{6\cos\phi'}{3 - \sin\phi'}c' + \frac{6\sin\phi'}{3 - \sin\phi'}p' \qquad (7.19)$$

Equation 7.19 indicates that, when plotted in the space (p', q), the linear stress path *at failure* is characterised by a slope:

$$M = \frac{6\sin\phi'}{3 - \sin\phi'} \qquad (7.20)$$

Both equations 7.19 and 7.20 will be used to their full potential in chapter 8.

Example 7.1

The following failure stresses were measured on three samples of an overconsolidated clay:

σ_1' (kN/m²)	250	400	645
σ_3' (kN/m²)	110	180	305

These same results are plotted in terms of the stress variables (s', t) (refer to equations 7.5) in figure 7.8, thus yielding an intercept $a' \approx 10\,kN/m^2$ and a slope $\tan\beta_p' = 0.7/2 = 0.35$.

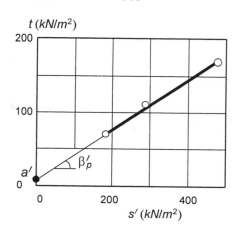

Figure 7.8: Measured results.

Making use of equations 7.16 and 7.17, it follows that:

$$\phi_p' = \sin^{-1}(0.35) = 20.5°,$$

$$c' = \frac{a'}{\cos\phi_p'} = \frac{10}{\cos 20.5} = 10.7\,kN/m^2$$

Granular soils, as well as normally consolidated clays, do not exhibit any cohesion intercept at failure, the corresponding Mohr's circle being as depicted in figure 7.9. Accordingly, equations 7.10 to 7.14 apply provided that all terms related to cohesion are dropped and that the critical angle of shearing resistance ϕ'_c is substituted for ϕ'_p.

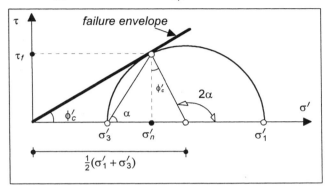

Figure 7.9: Mohr–Coulomb failure envelope for normally consolidated clays and granular soils.

7.3.2 Total stress analysis

Consider the time effect on the behaviour of a *saturated soil* subject at its surface to a *total stress increment* of magnitude $\Delta\sigma$. As soon as $\Delta\sigma$ is applied, one would expect the volume of soil to change (though it *is* possible for the stress increment to be such that it does not generate any volume change). For that to happen, water must be either expelled from within or absorbed by the soil matrix depending on the magnitude of $\Delta\sigma$ (a stress increase caused by a foundation loading, or a stress decrease generated by an excavation for instance); in other words, a *flow rate* must be established. If the soil in question is a *clay*, then the corresponding permeability is bound to be very small -bearing in mind that a permeability $k = 10^{-8}$ *m/s* corresponds to water seeping at 31.5 *cm* (roughly one foot) per year- and therefore in the *short term* (*i.e.* a few days or even a few weeks after the stress increment $\Delta\sigma$ is applied) any flow of water will be insignificant. As a result, the clay experiences virtually no volume change in the short term, meaning that the interlocking of solid particles within the clay matrix remains unchanged, and so does the effective stress. In accordance with the effective stress principle $\sigma = \sigma' + u$, it follows that in the *short term*:

$$\sigma' = \text{constant} \quad \Rightarrow \quad \Delta\sigma' = 0 \quad \Rightarrow \quad \Delta\sigma = \Delta u$$

Thus in the *short term*, any stress increase $\Delta\sigma$ applied at the surface of a *saturated* clay is transmitted to the porewater, generating an *excess porewater pressure* $\Delta u = \Delta \sigma$. It is therefore essential to realise that, in the short term, shear failure of a saturated clay occurs under a *constant volume* prior to any dissipation of the porewater pressure taking place, that is before the occurrence of any *consolidation*. As such, the behaviour of the clay is referred to as *unconsolidated undrained*. Under these circumstances, the change in effective stress is zero, and equation 7.7 reduces to the following:

$$\tau_f = c_u \tag{7.21}$$

where c_u denotes the *undrained shear strength* of the clay. Meanwhile, using the subscript u (for undrained), the shear strength of the clay can be estimated from equation 7.10:

$$c_u = \frac{1}{2}(\sigma'_1 - \sigma'_3) \cos \phi_u = t \cos \phi_u \tag{7.22}$$

Substituting for the stress variable t from equation 7.15 into the above equation, then rearranging:

$$c_u = c_u \cos^2\phi_u + s' \sin \phi_u \cos \phi_u \quad \Rightarrow \quad \phi_u = 0 \tag{7.23}$$

Therefore under *undrained conditions*, the *angle of shearing resistance* is reduced to zero (*i.e.* a horizontal failure envelope), and the shear resistance of the clay is provided by its undrained shear strength c_u as depicted in the Mohr's circle representation in figure 7.10. A thorough analysis of the undrained shear strength of clays follows in section 7.4.3.

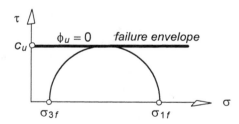

Figure 7.10: Mohr–Coulomb failure envelope for an undrained cohesive soil.

In practice, several techniques have been developed to estimate the shear strength parameters c', ϕ' and c_u, two of which are most widely used to test soils in the laboratory: the direct shear and the triaxial tests. Although both were developed to test a variety of soils, the shear box is used in the following analysis in conjunction with granular soils, whereas cohesive soils will be tested exclusively in a triaxial apparatus.

7.4 Shear strength of coarse-grained soils: direct shear test

Granular soils such as sands derive their shear strength from friction between solid particles, and the shear box test is well suited for such types of soils. The apparatus is depicted schematically in figure 7.11, and the test procedure consists basically of shearing a sand sample while subjecting it to a constant vertical pressure. The sample itself is confined in a metal box split horizontally so that the lower and upper halves can move relative to each other. Because of the relatively high permeability of granular soils, the test is undertaken at a relatively high pace so that a horizontal speed of about1 mm/min is usually used during testing. As the test progresses, the horizontal displacement Δl and the corresponding shear force S, as well as the change in sample thickness Δh (*i.e.* the vertical movement) are measured at regular time intervals.

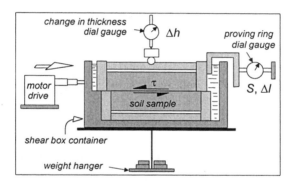

Figure 7.11: Shear box apparatus.

Knowing that the sample has a (square) cross-sectional area A, the vertical normal stress is calculated in a straightforward way:

$$\sigma = \frac{N}{A} \qquad (7.24)$$

where N is the normal force, applied through a weight hanger (refer to figure 7.11), that takes into account any lever arm effect. In calculating the shear stress, however, care must be taken to divide the measured shear force by the corresponding (decreasing) cross-sectional area:

$$\tau = \frac{S}{A^*} \qquad (7.25)$$

with : $\qquad A^* = A\left(1 - \frac{\Delta l}{\sqrt{A}}\right) \qquad (7.26)$

The behaviour of a sand during a direct shear test depends on its state, in other words on its initial density. Thus, a sample of *dense sand* has a large degree of interlocking between solid particles so that, at the onset of a shear test, the sand has to go through a looser state prior to the occurrence of shear failure as depicted schematically in figure 7.12. This behaviour, known as *dilation*, implies therefore an increase in volume and hence a decrease in density. The shear stress reaches its peak at a relatively low strain on the corresponding stress–strain curve, then a strain softening ensues, leading eventually to a *critical shear strength* τ_c as shown in figure 7.13.

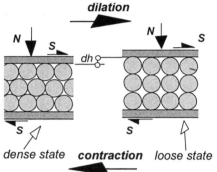

Figure 7.12: Loose and dense states for sands.

This *critical* value τ_c is linked to the rate of dilation represented by the angle υ in the figure. It is seen that, for a dense sand, dilation increases initially to reach a maximum υ_{max} under the peak shear stress τ_{max}, then decreases subsequently. For a *loose sand* on the other hand, the normal stress applied during shear causes the sand to become denser at the beginning of test, thus heralding a decrease in volume. The corresponding *negative* angle of dilation eventually reaches a maximum value $\upsilon_{max} = 0$ when the shear stress on the stress–strain curve tends towards the maximum asymptotic value τ_c depicted in figure 7.13. Because sands are deprived of cohesion, the corresponding effective angle of friction ϕ' varies in proportion to the shear stress τ. Accordingly, when the shear stress reaches the critical value τ_c, equations 7.8, 7.15 and 7.19 apply:

$$\tau_c = \sigma'_n \tan \phi'_c \tag{7.27}$$

$$t = s' \sin \phi'_c \tag{7.28}$$

$$q = Mp' \tag{7.29}$$

M being the slope given by equation 7.20.

Consequently, if several shear tests were carried out on the same sand, each under a different but constant normal stress σ'_n, then the corresponding set of stresses at failure can easily be determined from graphs similar to those in figure 7.13, so that the measured values of τ_c can be plotted against the corresponding values of σ'_n; similarly, all τ_{max} values can be plotted in the same figure yielding thus a value ϕ'_{max} of the effective angle of friction as depicted in figure 7.14 from which it is seen that:

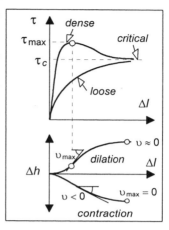

$$\phi'_{max} = \phi'_c + \upsilon_{max} \qquad (7.30)$$

Figure 7.13: Contraction and dilation of sands.

Figure 7.14 shows that, for loose sands, $\upsilon_{max} = 0$ and the maximum angle of friction ϕ'_{max} in this case corresponds to the critical angle ϕ'_c. Accordingly, the maximum shear stress of a sand can be calculated as follows:

$$\tau_{max} = \sigma'_n \tan \phi'_{max} \qquad (7..31)$$

and the relationship between the *critical* and *maximum* shear stresses can then be established by combining equations 7.27, 7.30 and 7.31. Whence:

$$\tau_c = \frac{\tau_{max} - \sigma' \tan \upsilon_{max}}{\frac{\tau_{max}}{\sigma'} \tan \upsilon_{max} + 1} \qquad (7.32)$$

The latter relationship indicates that for a *loose sand*, $\upsilon_{max} = 0$ and thus $\tau_c = \tau_{max}$.

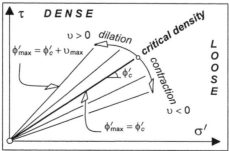

Figure 7.14: Critical density of a sand.

Typical values of the critical friction angle ϕ'_c, as well as the maximum dilation angle υ_{max} of some of the granular soils are listed below:

type of soil	$\phi'_c (°)$	$\upsilon_{max} (°)$
silt	28	3–4
silty sand	30	3–5
uniform sand	28	5–7
well graded sand	33	10–12
sandy gravel	35	12–15

7.5 Shear strength of saturated fine-grained soils: the triaxial test

7.5.1 The triaxial apparatus

The triaxial test is a sophisticated experiment that needs to be undertaken with great care if the measured results are to have any physical meaning. Contrary to what the name might imply, the test is not truly *triaxial* since only two sets of stresses can be applied to a soil sample, namely a vertical stress $\sigma_v = \sigma_1$ and a horizontal stress $\sigma_h = \sigma_3$. However, it is easy to see that, were σ_1 and σ_3 to be *principal stresses* (*i.e.* assuming that no shear stress develops at each end of the sample), then the intermediate stress σ_2 becomes irrelevant as far as the *shear strength* of the soil is concerned. The essential details of a triaxial apparatus are depicted in figure 7.15, where a cylindrical sample with a length to diameter ratio of 2, insulated by a rubber membrane, can be subjected to a chosen set of principal stresses $(\sigma_1, \sigma_2 = \sigma_3)$, under *controlled drainage conditions.* The all-round cell pressure σ_3 is applied hydraulically through a cell fluid, whereas the vertical stress σ_1 is applied mechanically through a piston. Because the contact between the piston and the top end of the sample is assumed to be reduced to a point contact, using the vertical load P applied through the piston and the known cross-sectional area of the sample A, the vertical stress σ_1 can be calculated in a straightforward way:

$$\sigma_1 = \sigma_3 + \frac{P}{A} \qquad (7.33)$$

More importantly, the deviator stress, defined in equation 7.6*a*, can now be calculated at any stage of loading from equation 7.33:

$$q = (\sigma_1 - \sigma_3) = \frac{P}{A} \qquad (7.34)$$

The quantity q can be expressed equally in terms of total or effective stresses. Also, in what follows, the stresses σ_v and σ_1 are used interchangeably, and so are σ_h and σ_3. Tests corresponding to various *stress paths* (such as the one depicted in figure 7.5) can therefore be undertaken under *undrained* or *drained* conditions, simulating both *short term* and *long term* behaviours of the tested soil. Several of these stress paths will be presented in detail shortly, some of which will be subjected to a more rigorous theoretical analysis in chapter 6. However, before any scrutiny, it is essential to examine the difficulties related to soil sampling and sample preparation in the laboratory prior to testing. In this respect, it is useful to mention that, although it can accommodate different types of soils including sands, the triaxial apparatus will be used exclusively in what follows to test cohesive soils, mainly *saturated clays*.

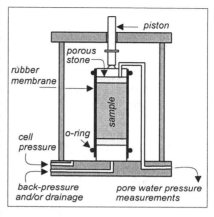

Figure 7.15: Triaxial apparatus.

7.5.2 State of a clay sample prior to testing

Consider the case of an element of a saturated clay located at a depth *z* as illustrated in figure 7.16. The corresponding state of *in situ* total stresses are such that:

$$\sigma_v = \sigma'_{vo} + u_o \tag{7.35}$$

$$\sigma_h = K_o\,\sigma'_{vo} + u_o \tag{7.36}$$

with : $$K_o = \frac{\sigma'_h}{\sigma'_v} \tag{7.37}$$

where σ'_{vo} represents the effective vertical stress *in situ*, u_o the porewater pressure at depth *z*, and K_o is known as the *coefficient of earth pressure at rest* and corresponds to the ratio of horizontal to vertical effective stresses *in situ*.

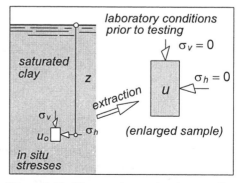

Figure 7.16: Stress release due to sampling.

As such, K_o depends on the type of soil, on its mode of deposition and especially on its stress history. Hence, for a *normally consolidated* clay, K_o can be estimated as follows (Jaky, 1944):

$$K_o = \left(1 + \frac{2}{3}\sin\phi'\right)\tan^2\left(\frac{\pi}{4} + \frac{\phi'}{2}\right) \approx 1 - \sin\phi' \qquad (7.38a)$$

For overconsolidated clays, K_o is related to the overconsolidation ratio OCR of the soil and can be evaluated using the following (Mayne and Kulhawy, 1982):

$$K_o = (1 - \sin\phi')\, OCR^{\sin\phi'} \qquad (7.38b)$$

It is clear from equations 7.38 that K_o varies from around 0.5 to 0.6 for normally consolidated clays, to well in excess of 1 in the case of heavily overconsolidated clays as indicated in figure 7.17. The clay becomes overconsolidated during the unloading process from point A to point B, and the corresponding K_o increases gradually with increasing OCR.

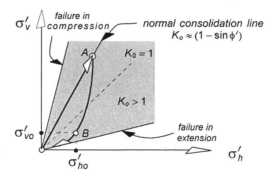

Figure 7.17: Variation of the coefficient K_o with the OCR of a soil.

Referring back to figure 7.16, it is seen that on extraction from the ground, the sample is relieved of the total stresses, so that the applied stress increments at the end of the extraction process are:

$$\Delta\sigma_v = -(\sigma'_{vo} + u_o) \qquad (7.39)$$

$$\Delta\sigma_h = -(K_o\sigma'_{vo} + u_o) \qquad (7.40)$$

At the end of this process of unloading, the clay sample *can* become overconsolidated, and consequently its volume can potentially increase (*i.e.* expand). However, any volume expansion can only occur physically if the clay has access to water. Failing that, the porewater pressure inside the sample becomes negative:

$$u = u_o + \Delta u < 0 \qquad (7.41)$$

The porewater pressure increment Δu generated by the unloading can be estimated from the Skempton (1954) relationship:

$$\Delta u = B[\Delta\sigma_h + A(\Delta\sigma_v - \Delta\sigma_h)] \qquad (7.42)$$

where A and B are porewater pressure parameters. In particular, B has a maximum value of one for *saturated* soils. A on the other hand, depends on the state of the clay, on the stress path, as well as on the magnitude of deformation. Figure 7.18 shows typical variations of parameter A with the axial deformation during an undrained triaxial test on a saturated sample of a lightly overconsolidated clay.

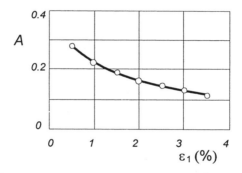

Figure 7.18: Typical variations of A with deformation.

There is ample experimental evidence to suggest that, at failure, the porewater pressure parameter A_f is related to the overconsolidation ratio of the clay. In general, $A_f \geq 0$ for normally consolidated to lightly overconsolidated clays, and $A_f < 0$ for heavily overconsolidated clays; the following limits being typical:

normally consolidated clays	$0.6 < A_f < 1.3$
lightly overconsolidated clays	$0 < A_f < 0.6$
heavily overconsolidated clays	$-0.5 < A_f < 0$

Thus, for a sample of a saturated clay (*i.e.* $B = 1$), a substitution for the quantities $\Delta\sigma_v$ and $\Delta\sigma_h$ from equations 7.39 and 7.40 into equation 7.42, then an insertion of the ensuing quantity Δu into equation 7.41 yields the expression of the (negative) porewater pressure within the clay mass after extraction from the ground:

$$u = -\sigma'_{vo}[K_o(1 - A_s) + A_s] \tag{7.43}$$

where A_s represents the porewater pressure parameter of the soil after extraction from the ground, whose value is *different* from that of A_f at failure. Equation 7.43 indicates that, while the total stresses after extraction are zero, the corresponding effective stresses are somewhat different from those applied *in situ* prior to extraction, in that the new assumed isotropic set of effective stresses generated by the unloading process is:

$$\sigma'_v = \sigma'_h = -u = \sigma'_{vo}[K_o(1 - A_s) + A_s] \tag{7.44}$$

Equally important, equation 7.43 suggests that a *suction* of water develops within the clay sample, creating in the process a gradient of moisture content from the periphery of the sample towards its centre. In some instances, this gradient can cause the moisture content in the inner part of the sample to be higher than that in the outer limits by as much as *4 percentage points* (see for instance Bjerrum (1973)), mainly because the soil is more disturbed at the periphery of the sample. This fact presents the engineer with the following dilemma: prior to any testing, the clay sample should ideally have both stress and moisture conditions similar to that *in situ*. However in practice, it is not physically possible to restore these two variables jointly to their field values since applying *in situ* stresses to the sample *will* cause the clay to have a moisture content different from the one in the field and *vice versa*. Nonetheless, given that the soil behaviour is very sensitive to the stress history, it is advisable in this case to restore the *in situ* stress conditions at the expense of having an initial moisture content slightly different from that in the field.

7.5.3 Undrained shear strength of saturated clays

If a clay layer is subjected to a total stress increase $\Delta\sigma$ at its surface, then, because of the low permeability of such type of soils, the immediate (short term) effect is manifested as a rise in porewater pressure of a magnitude $\Delta u = \Delta\sigma$; the effective stresses remaining unaltered. Under these circumstances, the clay resistance to the applied pressure is entirely provided by the *undrained shear strength* c_u. Accordingly, a simulation of the short term behaviour of a clay in a triaxial apparatus consists of preventing any drainage from taking place during testing, the corresponding triaxial test being known as *unconsolidated, undrained test*. The behaviour thus exhibited by a clay sample in the laboratory is representative of that of a saturated clay layer subject to a stress change lasting for a short period of time. For instance, the time needed to undertake an excavation or to build a foundation in a clay is relatively short, of the order of few weeks perhaps, during which the behaviour of the clay is virtually *undrained,* since the corresponding low permeability prevents any excess porewater pressure dissipation from occurring within this short time span. The unconsolidated, undrained triaxial test consists of applying a confining pressure σ_3 around the clay sample, which is then sheared immediately under constant volume conditions; in other words, without allowing any drainage to take place. The state of stresses throughout the test can be summarised as follows.

• ***Phase 1*** - the sample is placed in the triaxial apparatus: both vertical and horizontal total stresses are nil, the values of the negative porewater pressure, as well as the (isotropic) effective stresses being given by equations 7.43 and 7.44 respectively:

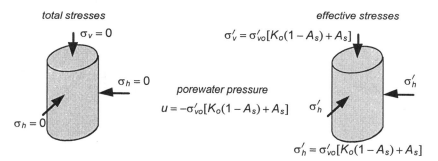

• ***Phase 2*** - a confining pressure of a magnitude σ_3 is applied around the sample, no drainage is allowed: the effective stresses therefore remain constant and the confining pressure is transferred entirely to the porewater pressure. Hence the ensuing stresses:

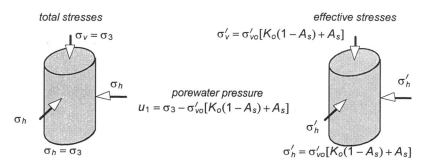

• ***Phase 3*** - the sample is immediately sheared under constant volume (*i.e.* no drainage allowed) until the occurrence of failure. The corresponding stresses *at failure* are σ_{vf}, σ_{hf} and u_f.

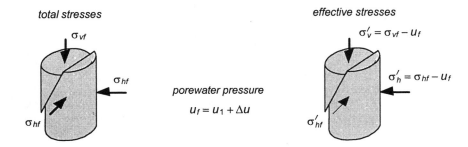

total stresses

σ_{vf}

σ_{hf}

σ_{hf}

effective stresses

$\sigma'_v = \sigma_{vf} - u_f$

$\sigma'_h = \sigma_{hf} - u_f$

σ'_{hf}

porewater pressure

$u_f = u_1 + \Delta u$

The porewater pressure increment Δu is calculated from equation 7.42 in which $B = 1$ (saturated clay) and $\Delta\sigma_3 = 0$ since the confining pressure σ_3 is maintained constant throughout the test. Accordingly, equation 7.42 reduces to the following:

$$\Delta u = A_f \Delta\sigma_1 \qquad (7.45)$$

But the quantity $\Delta\sigma_1$ represents the difference between the final (*i.e.* at failure) and initial (*i.e.* at the onset of shear) values of vertical stress:

$$\Delta\sigma_1 = \sigma_{vf} - \sigma_h \qquad (7.46)$$

Since the confining pressure is constant (*i.e.* $\sigma_3 = \sigma_h = \sigma_{hf}$), equation 7.45 can therefore be expressed as follows:

$$\Delta u = A_f(\sigma_v - \sigma_h)_f \qquad (7.47)$$

Hence the corresponding porewater pressure *at failure*:

$$u = u_1 + \Delta u$$

$$= \sigma_{hf} - \sigma'_{vo}[K_o(1 - A_f) + A_f] + A_f(\sigma_v - \sigma_h)_f \qquad (7.48)$$

The effective stresses *at failure* can now be established:

$$\sigma'_{vf} = \sigma_{vf} - u_f$$

$$= (\sigma_v - \sigma_h)_f + \sigma'_{vo}[K_o(1 - A_f) + A_f] - A_f(\sigma_v - \sigma_h)_f \qquad (7.49)$$

$$\sigma'_{hf} = \sigma_{hf} - u_f$$

$$= \sigma'_{vo}[K_o(1 - A_f) + A_f] + A_f(\sigma_v - \sigma_h)_f \qquad (7.50)$$

Moreover, the deviator stress *at failure* has already been established *via* equation 7.12:

$$(\sigma_{vf} - \sigma_{hf}) = (\sigma'_v + \sigma'_h) \sin\phi' + 2c' \cos\phi' \qquad (7.51)$$

Thus, a combination of equations 7.49, 7.50 and 7.51 yields:

$$(\sigma_v - \sigma_h)_f = \frac{2\sigma'_{vo}\,[K_o(1 - A_f) + A_f] \sin\phi' + 2c' \cos\phi'}{1 + (2A_f - 1) \sin\phi'} \qquad (7.52)$$

At the onset of shear, the effective vertical stress, given by equation 7.44, is the *same* for all samples, regardless of the magnitude of the confining pressure applied to each one of them. Consequently, all samples tested under different confining pressures possess the *same* overconsolidation ratio, and therefore have identical A_f values, so that the right-hand side of equation 7.52 corresponds to a *constant*. This, in turn, indicates that the deviator stress at failure has a *constant* value, *irrespective* of the magnitude of the confining pressure. Figure 7.19 shows that the deviator stress at failure corresponds in fact to the diameter of Mohr's circle and, accordingly, the constancy of the deviator stress during *unconsolidated undrained* triaxial tests implies that all corresponding Mohr's circles at failure have the same diameter. Under such conditions, the angle of shearing resistance of the soil is reduced to $\phi_u = 0$, and equation 7.52 then becomes:

$$(\sigma_v - \sigma_h)_f = 2c_u \qquad (7.53)$$

c_u is the undrained shear strength of the clay as shown in figure 7.19, where the quantities σ_v and σ_1 (as well as σ_h and σ_3) are used interchangeably.

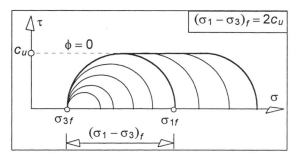

Figure 7.19: Undrained shear strength of clays.

The undrained shear strength c_u is a fundamental soil design parameter, in that it governs the clay behaviour in the short term. It will be shown (refer to section 8.5) that, for a *saturated normally consolidated clay* especially, the relationship between c_u and the moisture content w is similar to that depicted on the left-hand side of figure 7.20 where it is seen that a slight decrease in moisture content can lead to a significant increase in c_u. Accordingly, the undrained shear strength of a normally consolidated clay increases linearly with depth from a theoretical value of zero at the ground surface. However, in practice, any desiccation caused by whatever means (plant roots for instance) causes c_u to increase according to the graph shown on the right hand side of figure 7.20. Also, experimental evidence indicates that, for an *overconsolidated clay,* the variation of moisture content with depth is not as significant, and so the undrained shear strength in that case does not vary appreciably with depth.

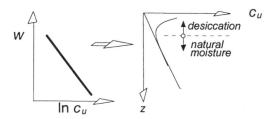

Figure 7.20: Variation of c_u with depth for a normally consolidated clay.

It should be borne in mind, however, that the undrained shear strength of a (stiff) clay, measured in the laboratory on a sample of a small size (usually 76 mm long with a diameter of 38 mm), often represents an overestimate of the actual value in the field; the reason being that a small size sample is unlikely to contain slip planes or fissures that characterise a thick stiff clay layer in situ (see Simpson et al., 1979). Skempton (1957) established the following empirical relationship between the ratio c_u/σ'_v of the undrained shear strength to the effective overburden pressure, and the plasticity index I_p, applicable exclusively to *normally consolidated clays:*

$$\frac{c_u}{\sigma'_v} \approx 0.11 + 3.7 \times 10^{-3}\, I_p \qquad\qquad (7.54)$$

The *consistency* of a clay is related to its undrained shear strength c_u, and the following table can be used as a guide

clay consistency	$c_u\ (kN/m^2)$
very soft	< 20
soft	20–40
firm to medium	40–75
stiff	75–150
very stiff	> 150

7.5.4 Drained shear strength parameters of saturated clays

The *unconsolidated undrained test* analysed previously can only yield the undrained shear strength of the clay because of the constancy of the deviator stress at failure, regardless of the magnitude of the confining pressure. Therefore a different type of test will have to be undertaken if the effective parameters (*i.e.* c' and ϕ') corresponding to the long term behaviour of the soil were to be measured. The *consolidated undrained test,* throughout which the variation of porewater pressure is measured, simulates the conditions of works extending over a period of time, long enough to assume that the excess porewater pressure induced by the loading has entirely dissipated, leading thus to a full consolidation of the clay. If, at that stage the soil is loaded rapidly, then its behaviour will be undrained, and provided that the porewater pressure is known at any stage of the undrained loading, then the effective stresses can easily be calculated, yielding in the process the drained shear strength parameters of the clay. The *consolidated undrained triaxial test with porewater pressure measurement* consists therefore of *consolidating* the clay sample under a confining pressure σ_3 (read σ_h), then shearing it under *undrained conditions* while measuring the porewater pressure until the occurrence of failure. It is important at this stage to mention that for the measurement of porewater pressure to be of any significance, the sample must be sheared at *low speed* so that the excess porewater pressure generated continuously during this phase has time to *equalise* throughout the sample (see for instance Bishop and Henkel (1962)). In this respect, a shear speed lower than 0.001 *mm/min* (just under 1.5 *mm per day*) might be needed to fulfil this requirement in the case of a stiff clay. Compared with the previous test, the state of stresses throughout a *consolidated undrained test* consists of the following phases.
- ***Phase 1*** *is identical to that of the previous unconsolidated undrained test.*

- ***Phase 2*** - A confining pressure σ_3 is applied around the sample, which is then allowed to consolidate fully. Once all excess porewater pressure has dissipated, the corresponding stresses are:

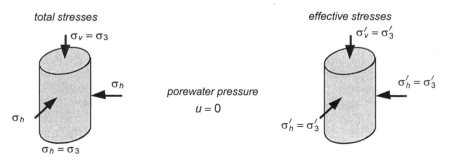

total stresses

$\sigma_v = \sigma_3$

σ_h

σ_h

$\sigma_h = \sigma_3$

porewater pressure

$u = 0$

effective stresses

$\sigma_v' = \sigma_3'$

$\sigma_h' = \sigma_3'$

$\sigma_h' = \sigma_3'$

• **Phase 3** - The sample is sheared without allowing any drainage to take place (*i.e.* the volume of the sample remains constant throughout shear). The stresses at failure are therefore:

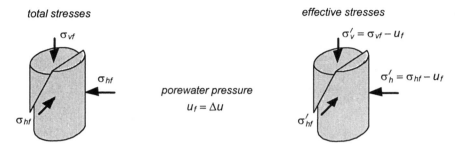

The porewater pressure at failure is identical to that given by equation 7.47:

$$u_f = \Delta u = A_f(\sigma_v - \sigma_h)_f \qquad (7.55)$$

Hence the effective stresses at failure:

$$\sigma'_{vf} = \sigma_{vf} - A_f(\sigma_v - \sigma_h)_f \qquad (7.56a)$$

$$\sigma'_{hf} = \sigma_{hf} - A_f(\sigma_v - \sigma_h)_f \qquad (7.56b)$$

Finally, a combination of equations 7.51 and 7.56 yields the deviator stress at failure:

$$(\sigma_v - \sigma_h)_f = \frac{2\sigma_3 \sin \phi' + 2c' \cos \phi'}{1 + (2A_f - 1) \sin \phi'} \qquad (7.57)$$

Significantly, equation 7.57 indicates that the deviator stress at failure (*i.e.* the diameter of Mohr's circle) depends on the magnitude of the confining pressure σ_3. This is illustrated in figure 7.21 where two samples of the same saturated clay have been consolidated under different pressures such that, at the end of consolidation, the volume of the sample subject to the lowest confining pressure has increased in a way that the clay has become *heavily overconsolidated*. The second sample, on the other hand, is in a *normally consolidated* state. At the onset of undrained shear, the porewater pressure increases gradually within both samples and, eventually, at failure, a *positive* porewater pressure is measured in connection with the normally consolidated clay sample, whilst the heavily overconsolidated one exhibits a *negative* porewater pressure. The question of how the *effective shear strength* parameters ϕ' and c' can be determined then arises once the corresponding Mohr's circles are drawn. Evidently, the *total stress* circles are of little, if any, importance since ϕ' and c' are related to effective stresses. Yet, it is still unclear how figure 7.21 can possibly be of any use to measure these two parameters. More confusing perhaps is the fact that the behaviour depicted in this figure characterises the *same* saturated clay which, when subject to a confining pressure smaller than its preconsolidation pressure σ_p' (*i.e.* the maximum effective vertical stress ever applied to the soil) becomes overconsolidated. On the other hand, the state of clay becomes normally consolidated under consolidation pressures greater than σ_p'.

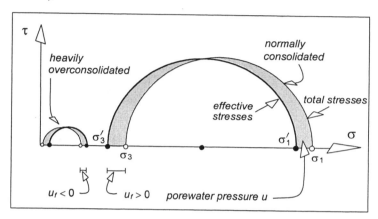

Figure 7.21: Effect of the state of a clay on its strength.

To clarify this somewhat confusing situation, let us concentrate for a moment on the *stress paths* during the undrained shear phase. In this respect, figure 7.22 depicts a typical behaviour where the variation of porewater pressure *u* clearly reflects the state of the soil: for a normally consolidated clay (*i.e.* $OCR = 1$), *u* increases continuously until the occurrence of failure, while in the case of an overconsolidated clay, the porewater pressure increases initially, only to decrease after having reached a peak, even becoming negative for heavily overconsolidated clays as the soil dilates on shearing.

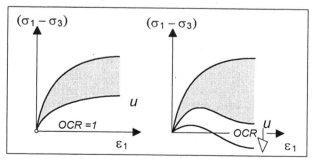

Figure 7.22: Effects of the state of a clay on the porewater pressure at failure.

These effects are better demonstrated in figure 7.23 using the stress variables *(q, p')* defined by equations 7.9 and 7.10. It will be shown in section 8.1 that the *total stress path* in the space *(q, p')* is linear with a slope of 3 as shown in the figure. The measurement of porewater pressure at the onset of shear allows *the effective stress path* to be found, and the figure further illustrates the effect of the state of clay on the shape of the effective stress path. Thus, the normally consolidated clay (consolidated under σ'_{31}) has a *positive* porewater pressure at failure. However, as the overconsolidation ratio increases, the porewater pressure at failure decreases (clay sample consolidated under σ'_{32}), only to become *negative* when the clay becomes heavily overconsolidated (sample consolidated under σ'_{33}).

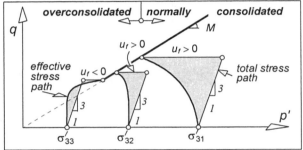

Figure 7.23: Effective and total stress paths for different states of a clay.

A clearer picture is now starting to emerge in relation to the *drained behaviour* of clays, such a picture being dominated by the *state* of the clay. Thus for a *soft normally consolidated clay*, the behaviour is characterised by an *ultimate* or a *critical* angle of shearing resistance ϕ'_c and no apparent cohesion (c' = 0) as shown in figure 7.24.

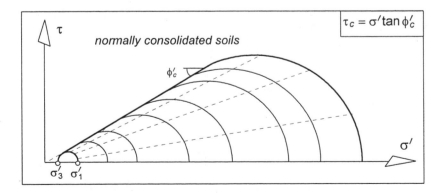

Figure 7.24: Behaviour of a normally consolidated clay.

In the absence of cohesion, equation 7.52 yields the following deviator stress at failure:

$$(\sigma_1' - \sigma_3')_f = \frac{2\sigma_3 \sin\phi_c'}{1 + (2A_f - 1)\sin\phi_c'} \qquad (7.58)$$

where σ_3' represents the (effective) consolidation pressure and A_f is the porewater pressure parameter at failure. On the other hand, the behaviour of a *stiff overconsolidated clay* is more typical of that depicted in figure 7.25. The *critical* (or ultimate) angle of shearing resistance ϕ_c' of the clay is easily measured from the linear portion of the failure envelope where the clay is normally consolidated. As soon as the clay becomes overconsolidated, that is, when the confining pressure becomes smaller than the preconsolidation pressure, the failure envelope becomes markedly non-linear, and once more the question to be answered is what values should be assigned to both the effective cohesion c' and the angle of shearing resistance ϕ' so that the entire behaviour of the clay can be represented by a unique mathematical equation:

$$\tau_f = c' + \sigma' \tan\phi' \qquad (7.59)$$

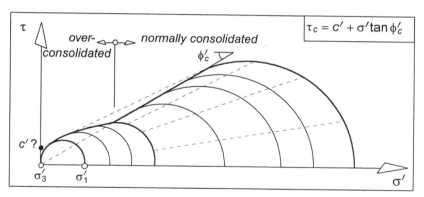

Figure 7.25: Typical behaviour of an overconsolidated clay.

The answer depends in part on the stress level to be applied in the field: if the magnitude of effective stresses is expected to cause the clay to become normally consolidated, then the ultimate critical conditions of $\phi' = \phi_c'$ and $c' = 0$ must be applied. If, however, after being loaded, the clay is still overconsolidated, then a (subjective!) engineering judgement must be made. In this respect, figure 7.25 makes it clear that neglecting the apparent cohesion might affect the shear strength of the soil, especially if the clay in question is heavily overconsolidated. Alternatively, assigning a high value to c' such as the one corresponding to the intercept of the tangent to the non-linear portion of the failure envelope (refer to figure

7.25) can be potentially dangerous, as this might increase dramatically (and artificially) the shear strength of the soil, knowing that such intercepts can be as high as $100\,kN/m^2$ in some instances. Figure 7.26 depicts results measured from consolidated undrained triaxial tests with porewater pressure measurements undertaken on a natural stiff clay (Josseaume and Azizi, 1991). The slope M of the linear portion, calculated from equation 7.20, yields an *effective critical* angle of shearing resistance $\phi_c' = 22°$. Now, there is a need to consider carefully what value might be assigned to c', if the shear strength of the clay is to be modelled by an expression similar to equation 7.19.

$$q = \frac{6\cos\phi'}{3-\sin\phi'}\,c' + \frac{6\sin\phi'}{3-\sin\phi'}\,p'$$

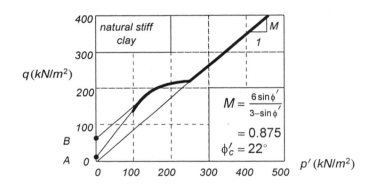

Figure 7.26: Behaviour of a natural stiff clay.

Manifestly, the somewhat contentious parameter c' is difficult to determine with sufficient accuracy because of its intricate link to the soil density and therefore to the void ratio, whose value varies with depth (*i.e.* with the effective overburden pressure) as illustrated in figure 7.27. Referring back to figure 7.26, it is seen that, were the non-linear part of the failure envelope to be prolonged as illustrated, the intersection with the q-axis at point A then yields a deviator stress $q_A \approx 10\,kN/m^2$. Alternatively, if the tangent to the curved portion is used, the ensuing deviator stress at point B will be $q_B \approx 60\,kN/m^2$. In both cases, c' is calculated from equation 7.19 in which p' is zero:

$$c' = q_{A,B}\left(\frac{3-\sin\phi_c'}{6\cos\phi_c'}\right) \qquad (7.60)$$

Hence: $c_A' = 4.7\,kN/m^2, \qquad c_B' = 28.3\,kN/m^2$

This simple example epitomises the practical difficulties that an engineer would face in selecting an appropriate value (if at all !) for c' and, in this particular instance, it is prudent to opt for the smaller of the two values.

Generally, it is advisable to limit c' to a maximum of $15\,kN/m^2$ for stiff heavily overconsolidated clays and to extend the value $c' = 0$ from normally consolidated to lightly overconsolidated clays.

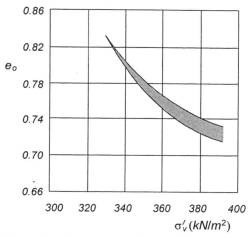

Figure 7.27: Variation of the initial void ratio with depth.

The drained shear strength parameters can also be determined from *consolidated drained triaxial tests* which consist of consolidating soil samples of the same clay under different confining pressures, then shearing them under *drained* conditions, thus allowing their volume to change. It is important to mention however that, as implied by its name, this type of test requires the sample to be sheared under drained conditions. In other words, the shear speed must be such that no build up of excess water pressure can occur during shear. To fulfil this requirement, shear speeds of as low as $5 \times 10^{-4}\,mm/min$ may be needed, implying an axial deformation of less than 1% *per day* in the case of a 76 *mm* long clay sample. Taking into account the time needed for test preparation and consolidation, it is obvious that a carefully undertaken consolidated drained test necessitates weeks rather than days to be achieved. This can deter an engineer from opting for this type of test, especially when a consolidated *undrained* triaxial test with porewater pressure measurement can be achieved comparatively quickly, and can yield similar information about the *effective* shear strength parameters as detailed previously. However, there is a need to undertake this type of *consolidated drained triaxial test* to simulate some specific stress paths. The procedure of such tests is similar in nature to that applicable to a consolidated *undrained* test, with the exception of the shear phase which must be undertaken under drained conditions. Accordingly, *at failure*, the state of stresses is as shown below. Evidently, the behaviour of the clay depends on the magnitude of the confining pressure, and therefore on the corresponding overconsolidation ratio.

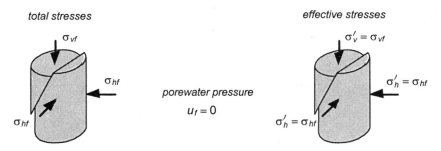

Figure 7.28 shows that a normally consolidated clay ($OCR = 1$) exhibits a behaviour characterised by a strain hardening, due to the (positive) compressive volumetric strains ε_v (*i.e. contraction* of volume). On the other hand, an overconsolidated clay initially displays a compressive volumetric strain, followed by a volume expansion that reaches a maximum when the deviator stress is at its peak.

The rate of expansion then starts to decrease, and the deviator stress tends towards its ultimate critical value q_c under which the expansion ceases. Figure 7.28 clearly indicates the link between an increasing expansion and an increasing OCR. In fact, it is well established that, as the OCR and the plasticity index increase, so does the difference between the peak shear stress q_{max} and the critical shear stress q_c. Moreover, the angle of shearing resistance associated with the critical shear stress of an overconsolidated clay is usually appreciably smaller than that corresponding to the peak shear strength.

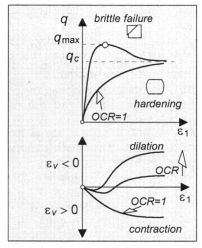

Figure 7.28: Effect of the OCR on the peak strength of a clay.

On the practical side, the *critical effective angle of friction* is an important parameter for the analysis of the stability of slopes. Although this topic is tackled in details elsewhere, it is important to mention in this respect that the use of peak shear parameters measured in the laboratory, on samples of small sizes, often leads to an overestimation of the factor of safety against shear failure (error on the unsafe side!). Several instances of slope failures reported in the literature are due precisely to this mechanical extrapolation of shear parameters measured in the laboratory to field conditions (see for example Skempton (1964), Skempton and La Rochelle (1965), Henkel (1957) and Palladino and Peck (1972)).

7.6 Quality assurance related to triaxial testing

The quality of the results measured during a triaxial test is inevitably linked to the testing procedure, especially that relating to sample preparation prior to testing. It has already been shown that sampling causes the porewater pressure in the clay to become negative, generating in the process a migration of moisture from the periphery of the sample where the soil fabric has been disturbed towards its centre. Ideally, prior to any testing taking place, each soil sample must be consolidated under stress field conditions ($\sigma_v' = \sigma_{vo}'$, $\sigma_h' = K_o\sigma_{vo}'$), where σ_{vo}' represents the effective overburden pressure and K_o is the coefficient of earth pressure at rest given by equation 7.38. In practice, however, the impediment to restoring these anisotropic stresses results from the fact that consolidation under these circumstances *must* occur under zero radial strain ($\varepsilon_r = 0$), known as K_o-condition, and refers to the fact that soils *in situ* are semi-infinite media, and as such, they do not deform radially when subjected to any type of loading. Though feasible, the stringent condition of zero lateral strain during consolidation is very difficult to maintain in the laboratory since there is a need to adjust the stress ratio, that is the coefficient K_o, almost continuously while consolidation progresses under $\varepsilon_r = 0$.

An alternative to the above procedure consists of assuming a uniform distribution of the negative porewater pressure throughout the sample, then consolidating the clay, prior to any testing, under an *isotropic* effective stress field, the magnitude of which is given by equation 7.43:

$$\sigma_v' = \sigma_h' = -u \tag{7.61}$$

Under these conditions, applying an isotropic effective stress to the clay sample amounts to measuring its isotropic swelling pressure. This can easily and accurately be achieved using the set-up depicted in figure 7.29, whereby a *nil indicator* is connected through a valve to the drainage circuit on one side and to a container filled with de-aerated water on the other side. Prior to opening the valve, an isotropic fluid pressure, with a magnitude *estimated* from equation 7.43 is applied around the sample, both ends of the drainage circuit of the nil indicator being at atmospheric pressure, hence there is an initial horizontal level of mercury.

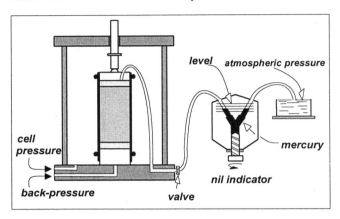

Figure 7.29: Use of a nil indicator to prevent any volume change of the sample prior to testing.

Once the valve is opened, one of three possibilities occurs:

   • **(a)** The applied pressure σ_h is such that it cancels out the negative porewater pressure, in which case the level of mercury in the nil indicator remains equalized.

   • **(b)** The porewater pressure is still negative, and consequently water is sucked into the sample making the mercury move upward in the left-hand side of the nil indicator. In this case, the pressure σ_h must be increased gradually until the mercury level is again equalized.
   • **(c)** The porewater pressure within the sample becomes positive causing water to be expelled through the drainage lead and mercury to move upward on the right-hand side of the nil indicator. Consequently, σ_h needs to be adjusted downward until a balanced mercury level is re-established.

Clearly, the first possibility above, though not impossible, is highly unlikely to occur, and the pressure σ_h almost inevitably will need to be adjusted until an equilibrium in the form of a horizontal mercury level (indicating zero porewater pressure inside the sample) is achieved. Because of the low permeability of clays, the adjustment can be a slow process, and can take several hours in the case of a stiff clay. The fluid pressure applied around the sample, under which an equilibrium is achieved is known as the *isotropic swelling pressure* σ_s of the clay. It corresponds to the limit confining (effective) pressure for which the porewater pressure within the clay is zero. Accordingly, any confining pressure smaller than σ_s will cause the porewater pressure to become negative, generating in the process a suction of water and causing the volume of the sample to expand. The task of restoring the stress conditions to as near as practically possible to those applied *in situ* can become futile if the sample is subjected to substantial disturbances during the extraction process and the subsequent transportation, storage and preparation before testing. Assuming that an appropriate sampling technique is used to extract high quality samples, which are then adequately stored in the laboratory under controlled temperature and humidity conditions so that the moisture content of the clay remains virtually unchanged, the careful preparation of every sample should then become the focus of the experimenter in order to minimise the remoulding of the clay which can affect, in a major way, the quality of the measured results during testing. Of course, every step in sample preparation can potentially lead to the clay being markedly remoulded. These steps include cutting and trimming of the sample, applying a filter paper, then a rubber membrane around the clay, and saturating then connecting the drainage circuit.

Clearly, an accumulation of differing degrees of disturbance related to these steps can be detrimental to the quality of the subsequent measured results. For instance, cutting a $38\,mm$ diameter, $76\,mm$ long sample of a soft clay is a highly delicate operation which, if not handled carefully, can easily cause the sample to have an initial deformation before being loaded, thus altering the behaviour of the clay. Also, placing a *saturated* filter paper around the sample, then connecting a *saturated* drainage circuit (including saturated porous stones on each side of the sample) will cause a stiff clay to suck water through its periphery in order to balance the negative porewater pressure existing within the soil matrix, leading to an increase in volume prior to any stresses being applied or to any measurements being made. Similarly, applying a high back pressure in a single step to a sample of a stiff clay may cause the water to flow between the membrane and the periphery of the sample, leaving the clay unsaturated. To minimise these 'side effects', the procedure detailed below, which has the advantage of not altering the volume of the sample prior to the application of a confining pressure, can be applied. Although it is more suited to stiff clays, the procedure can be used in conjunction with any type of soil, and consists of the following steps.

> ● *(a)* Once cut to the required dimensions, a *dry* filter paper, shaped in the manner depicted in figure 7.30, is carefully placed around the sample. In so doing, care must be taken to ensure that only a very small amount of water is sprayed on two points to make the

paper stick to the sample, which is then put on the pedestal of the triaxial cell on top of a *dry* porous stone overlain by a *dry* circular filter paper.

•**(b)** A rubber membrane is placed around the sample on top of which a *dry* circular filter paper and a *dry* porous stone are then laid.

•**(c)** The *empty* drainage circuit is then connected to the sample, and the triaxial cell filled with fluid under a pressure estimated from equation 7.43 (*i.e.* a cell pressure equivalent in magnitude to $-u$, where u represents the *negative* porewater pressure developed within the sample after extraction from the ground.

•**(d)** The drainage circuit is closed at one end, then the air contained within it is pumped out at the other end. This step takes about two minutes to complete.

•**(e)** The pump is carefully disconnected so as not to allow any air to re-enter the circuit, which is then immediately immersed in a bucket of de-aerated water. Because of the negative pressure inside the circuit created by pumping, water is automatically sucked in, saturating in the process the entire drainage circuit including the porous stones and filter papers. This step takes no longer than two to three minutes.

•**(f)** Once saturated, the drainage circuit is thereafter connected to a nil indicator as depicted in figure 7.29, and the adjustment of the cell pressure is undertaken in accordance with the procedure described earlier.

Once equilibrium is reached (*i.e.* a confining pressure under which the porewater pressure inside the sample is reduced to zero), a back pressure is applied to the soil *in steps* in order to ensure a very high degree of uniformity of the back pressure throughout the sample. In this respect, it is strongly advisable to apply the same pressure *simultaneously* inside and outside the sample, so that the state of effective stresses is not altered. Accordingly, a back pressure Δu, which is *per se* used to saturate the soil, is applied inside the sample through the drainage circuit, while the cell pressure σ_3 is increased at the same time by the same increment Δu. In the absence of the possibility of increasing concurrently both the back pressure and the cell pressure by the same amount, it is preferable to increase the cell pressure first, then apply the back pressure, thus eliminating the possibility, albeit remote, of the back pressure causing the water to flow between the periphery of the sample and the rubber membrane. Experimental evidence shows that in the case of stiff clays, back pressures as high as $1500\,kN/m^2$ are needed to achieve a high degree of saturation of 98% (Berre, 1981). However, these levels of back pressure can only be applied using specially adapted triaxial equipment. In fact, a standard piece of equipment (*i.e.* a Bishop triaxial cell) is designed to withstand a maximum cell pressure of $1200\,kN/m^2$ and, adopting the procedure described previously by which both back pressure and cell pressure are increased at the same time, it is clear that there is a limit to the maximum back pressure that can realistically be applied to the soil. For instance, if a stiff clay needs to be tested under an effective confining pressures as high as $800\,kN/m^2$ using standard equipment, then the maximum back pressure to which the clay can be subjected will be limited to $400\,kN/m^2$.

On the practical side, applying a back pressure of, say, $400\,kN/m^2$ to a $38\,mm$ diameter clay sample of low permeability (10^{-10} m/s for example) in one increment, may create preferential drainage paths, thus resulting in a differential consolidation of the soil. To alleviate this problem, the back pressure must be applied in gradually increasing increments, at time intervals long enough to allow the pressure throughout the sample to be as uniform as possible. An example related to the application of $400\,kN/m^2$ back pressure to a stiff clay with a permeability $k = 10^{-11}$ m/s is given in the following table. Notice the time related to each increment decreases as the back pressure increases, thus reflecting the gradual increase in saturation of the soil.

back pressure increment (kN/m^2)	application time $(days)$
50	3
50	2
100	1
200	1

The degree of saturation must be checked at the end of the last increment of back pressure. The corresponding procedure consists simply of closing the drainage circuit, then increasing the (isotropic) cell pressure by an increment $\Delta\sigma_3$ and measuring the increment of porewater pressure Δu thus generated through a pressure transducer connected to the drainage circuit. Skempton equation 7.42 can then be used to calculate the coefficient B of saturation and, because the increment of deviatoric stress is zero ($\Delta\sigma_3 = \Delta\sigma_1$), the equation takes the simpler form:

$$\Delta u = B\Delta\sigma_3 \qquad\qquad (7.62)$$

Hence, the clay is fully saturated if $B = 1$, in other words when $\Delta u = \Delta\sigma_3$. In practice, one aims at achieving a degree of saturation corresponding to a minimum of $B = 0.98$. The use of a lateral filter paper around the sample as depicted in figure 7.30 has the advantage of markedly reducing the time needed for the excess porewater pressure inside the sample either to dissipate (during a drained loading), or to become uniform (as in undrained shear, for example).

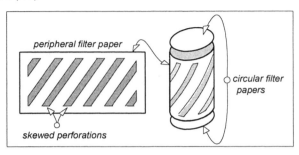

Figure 7.30: Use of peripheral filter paper during testing.

Gibson and Henkel (1954) established a relationship that yields the time t needed to achieve an average degree of consolidation U:

$$U = 1 - \frac{h^2}{\eta c_v t} \tag{7.63}$$

where h represents the length of the drainage path (half the sample length if the soil is drained on both ends), c_v corresponds to the coefficient of vertical consolidation given by equation 5.15 in section 5.3, and η is a coefficient that depends on drainage conditions, whose values are summarised in the following table.

Table 7.1: Coefficient η (from Bishop and Henkel, 1962)

drainage conditions	η
sample drained at one end	0.75
sample drained at both ends	3.0
sample drained radially	32.0
sample drained at both ends as well as radially	40.4

Equation 7.63 can be rearranged in the following way:

$$t = \frac{h^2}{(1 - U)\eta c_v} \tag{7.64}$$

The latter equation indicates that a sample of clay for which drainage occurs radially through a lateral filter paper, as well as vertically at both ends ($\eta = 40.4$) consolidates 13.5 times faster than when the sample is drained at the ends only ($\eta = 3$). Also, equation 7.64 can be used to check the adequacy of the shear speed used during undrained shear, in the knowledge that any ensuing excess porewater pressure Δu cannot be representative of the undrained behaviour unless it is distributed uniformly throughout the sample.

Example 7.2

Consider the undrained shear of a 38 *mm* diameter, 76 *mm* long sample of a stiff clay, with a coefficient $c_v = 2 \times 10^{-8}\ m^2/s$ and with drainage conditions represented by a coefficient $\eta = 40.4$ in table 7.1. Considering that, in practice, a degree of uniformity of the excess porewater pressure $U = 95\%$ is deemed satisfactory, let us, first, use equation 7.64 to calculate the corresponding time t_{95}:

$$t_{95} = \frac{38^2 \times 10^{-6}}{(1 - 0.95) \times 40.4 \times 1.2 \times 10^{-6}} = 596\ min$$

Accordingly, the sample must be sheared undrained for about 10 *hours* before the excess porewater pressure reaches a degree of uniformity of 95%, which in turn indicates that any measurement of porewater pressure taken within 10 *hours* of the onset of shear is *not* representative of the clay behaviour. Thus, it is necessary to select a shear speed that yields a minimum axial deformation, say $\varepsilon_1 = 0.005$, in 10 *hours*, leading hence to a shear speed:

$$v = \varepsilon_1 \frac{l}{t_{95}} = \frac{0.005 \times 76}{600} = 6.3 \times 10^{-4}\ mm/min$$

Adopting this speed for the entire undrained shear phase, one can then easily calculate the degree of uniformity U of the excess porewater pressure throughout the test since, for any selected time t, U can be calculated from equation 7.63, while the axial strain is determined in a straightforward way:

$$\varepsilon_1 = \frac{tv}{l}$$

with $v = 6.3 \times 10^{-4}\ mm/min$ and $l = 76\ mm$ (the sample length). The ensuing results, plotted in figure 7.31, show the extent to which the degree of uniformity U of the excess porewater pressure is below the required minimum value of 0.95. Clearly, any measurement of excess porewater pressure Δu for which U falls outside the shaded area in the figure are erroneous. In particular, Δu is not representative of the clay behaviour up to an axial deformation of 0.5% when the sample is drained radially as well as vertically (refer to the graph in bold in the figure).

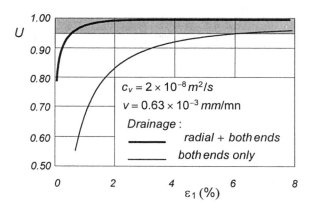

Figure 7.31: Effect of the shear speed on the degree of uniformity of excess porewater pressure.

However, were the sample to be drained only at the ends, the excess porewater pressure measured during shear will *not* be typical of the clay behaviour until the axial deformation reaches the significant value of 6.6%, which is most probably beyond failure considering the (stiff) nature of the clay in this case. It is clear therefore that a good deal of care in sample handling, preparation, saturation and consolidation is not enough to ensure results of high quality with respect to (drained or undrained) shear. In fact it would be very unfortunate if, after going through all the trouble of meticulous preparations, the experimenter overlooked the details related to the selection of an adequate shear speed during an undrained triaxial test for example. In conclusion, it is vitally important for the operator to be aware of the many pitfalls related to laboratory triaxial testing. A clear procedure that includes the means of checking the quality of measurements is therefore a necessity, without which the risk of making the wrong interpretations increases dramatically. Figure 7.32 (Azizi and Josseaume, 1988) shows results measured at the end of consolidation (*i.e.* prior to shear) for some undrained triaxial tests, carefully undertaken according to the procedure detailed previously that includes the use of a nil indicator. These results, together with those of figure 7.26 indicate that the stiff clay in question has a swelling pressure of around $250\,kN/m^2$.

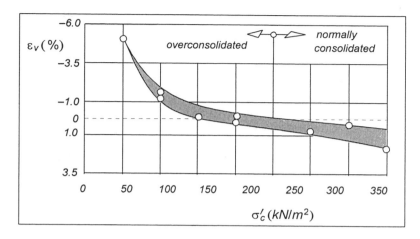

Figure 7.32: Natural stiff clay: volume change vs consolidation pressures.
(Reproduced by permission of the Laboratoire Central des Ponts et Chaussées.)

7.7 The shear vane test

However careful an operator is, soils tested in the laboratory are almost inevitably remoulded to a certain extent. To minimise the disturbance, *in situ* tests, when properly carried out, can yield high quality results which complement those obtained under laboratory conditions. The *shear vane test* is a theory-based reliable *in situ* test, specifically developed for saturated clays with undrained shear strengths of up to $100 \, kN/m^2$. The equipment, depicted schematically in figure 7.33, consists of four thin stainless rectangular blades, welded to a steel rod. The length L of the vane and its width D are typically $100 \, mm$ and $50 \, mm$ respectively, though vanes with $L = 150 \, mm$ are often used for clays with undrained shear strengths larger than $50 \, kN/m^2$. Once pushed gently into the ground to the required depth, the vane is then rotated at a rate of about $6°$*per minute* until the occurrence of failure where a maximum torque T (*i.e.* moment of resistance) is recorded. Since the test is carried out quickly, the corresponding behaviour of the clay is therefore undrained. If the clay is *anisotropic,* then its *vertical* undrained shear strength c_{uv} developed throughout the length of the vane, is distinct from its *horizontal* component c_{uh} occurring on the horizontal top and bottom sides of the vane as shown in figure 7.33. Accordingly, the maximum torque is the sum of a vertical and a horizontal components:

$$T = T_v + T_h \tag{7.65}$$

Referring to figure 7.33, the undrained shear strength c_{uv} is assumed to be fully mobilised throughout the length of the vane. Hence the corresponding torque is:

$$T_v = c_{uv}\pi DL\frac{D}{2} = c_{uv}\pi D^2\frac{L}{2} \tag{7.66}$$

On the other hand, experimental evidence (refer to Wroth (1984)) strongly suggests that the distribution of c_{uh} on the top and bottom sides of the vane is rather similar to that shown in figure 7.33. Under these circumstances, c_{uh} depends on the ratio r/R, where r represents the radial distance from the vane centre and R is the vane radius; so that in accordance with figure 7.34, the torque T_h is evaluated as follows:

$$T_h = 2\int_0^R c_{uh}\, 2\pi r^2\, (r/R)^n\, dr \tag{7.67}$$

where the value of the exponent n can be as high as 5.

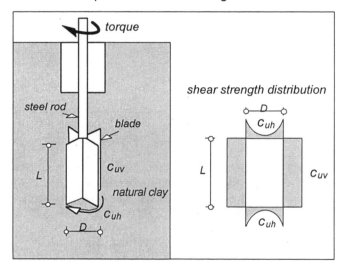

Figure 7.33: Vane shear apparatus.

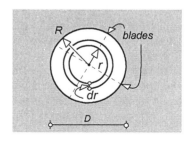

Figure 7.34: Boundary conditions

A straightforward integration of equation 7.67 then yields:

$$T_h = c_{uh}\pi\frac{D^3}{2(n+3)}$$ (7.68)

Consequently, the total moment resistance $(T_h + T_v)$ is:

$$T = \pi D^2\left[c_{uv}\frac{L}{2} + c_{uh}\frac{D}{2(n+3)}\right]$$ (7.69)

Equation 7.69 is the general expression relating the undrained shear strength of an *anisotropic clay* to the maximum torque recorded during an *in situ* shear vane test. If the conditions of isotropy can be assumed to prevail, then $c_{uv} = c_{uh} = c_u$. Moreover, if the vane is characterised by a ratio $L/D = 2$, then equation 7.69 yields an *apparent undrained shear strength* c_u:

$$c_u = \frac{T}{\pi D^3}\frac{(n+3)}{(n+3.5)}$$ (7.70)

This equation is plotted in figure 7.35 as the variation of the dimensionless quantity $\pi D^3 c_u/T$ *versus* the coefficient n. The graph shows clearly the limited effect of n on the undrained shear strength of the clay and, for all intents and purposes, a value $n = 2$ can be used in conjunction with equations 7.69 and 7.70.

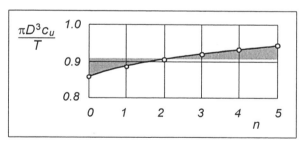

Figure 7.35: Effect of the exponent n on the undrained
shear strength of a clay.

Defining the *strength ratio* as being:

$$\xi = \frac{c_{uh}}{c_{uv}}$$ (7.71)

then using $n = 2$, the quantity c_{uv} in equation 7.69 can be calculated as follows:

$$c_{uv} = \frac{10T}{\pi D^2 (5L + \xi D)} \qquad (7.72)$$

Obviously, when $L = 2D$, the above equation reduces to:

$$c_{uv} = \frac{10T}{\pi D^3 (\xi + 10)} \qquad (7.73)$$

so that when the clay is *isotropic*, $\xi = 1$ and equation 7.73 further reduces to the following:

$$c_u = \frac{10T}{11\pi D^3} \qquad (7.74)$$

One should bear in mind that both equations 7.73 (for anisotropic clays) and 7.74 (for isotropic clays) were derived using $n = 2$ and $L = 2D$, the quantity T being the total torque measured during the test.

Example 7.3

Consider the case of two shear vane tests, carried out on a clay. The first, made using a vane with a length $L = 150\,mm$ and a diameter $D = 50\,mm$, yielded, at failure, a torque $T_1 = 57\,Nm$, while the second, undertaken at the same depth, using this time a vane characterised by the dimensions $L = D = 50\,mm$, registered at failure a torque $T_2 = 23.9\,Nm$. Let us, in the first instance, explore the clay anisotropy by calculating the strength ratio ξ using equation 7.72 for both tests. Thus:

• from test 1:

$$c_{uv} = \frac{10 \times 57 \times 10^{-3}}{\pi \times 5^2 \times 10^{-4} \times (5 \times 0.15 + 0.05\xi)} = \frac{5700}{58.9 + 3.93\xi}\,kN/m^2$$

• a similar analysis of test 2 yields:

$$c_{uv} = \frac{2390}{19.63 + 3.93\xi}\,kN/m^2$$

Whence a strength ratio $\xi = 2.22$, leading to the following components of shear strength:

$$c_{uv} = 84.3\,kN/m^2, \qquad c_{uh} = 187.1\,kN/m^2$$

The shear vane test can also be used to determine the sensitivity of a clay. Consider for example the case of a third test carried out on a clay that can be described as isotropic, using a vane with a diameter $D = 50\,mm$ and a length $L = 100\,mm$. At failure, a torque $T = 37\,Nm$ was measured, following which, the vane was rotated rapidly several times to remould the clay, yielding in the process a maximum torque $T = 9\,N.m$. In order to estimate the sensitivity of the clay, both undrained shear strengths corresponding to undisturbed and remoulded clays must be determined using equation 7.74. Hence, for the undisturbed clay:

$$c_u = \frac{10 \times 37 \times 10^{-3}}{11 \times \pi \times 5^3 \times 10^{-6}} = 85.6\,kN/m^2$$

Similarly for the remoulded soil:

$$c_u = \frac{85.6 \times 9}{37} = 20.8\,kN/m^2$$

Whence a sensitivity:

$$S = \frac{85.6}{20.8} = 4.1$$

According to the classification table in section 2.5, the clay is described as being sensitive.

7-8 Shear strength of rocks

The physical behaviour of a rock mass depends on its nature and state. The process of rock formation, including the mineral constitution was introduced earlier in section 1.4. The engineering behaviour of rock masses is essentially defined by their shear strength, which is affected by several factors, in particular:

- *Rock type:* intact crystalline rocks such as granite are much stronger than intact clastic rocks such as sandstone,
- *Rock mineralogy:* within the same type of rock, the shear strength is affected by the mineral composition of the rock structure. For example, in their intact state, the calcite-rich limestone is much more resistant than the weak, friable chalk; both being sedimentary rocks,
- *Weathering:* a chemical process that alters the structure of the rock, and can ultimately lead to its decomposition. Thus rocks such as granite, disintegrated under the effect of millions of years of weathering, become too soft and friable to the point that it can be mined for china clay using a jet of water.
- *Size and density of discontinuities:* rock masses usually contain fractures, which are classified according to their density (or spacing). These fracture vary from microfissures with an average spacing of between 1 mm and 1 cm, to joints characterised by an

average spacing of between 1 cm and 1m. Fractures with an
average spacing exceeding 1 m are defined as faults,
- *sample size:* as in the case of clays, only small in situ cored rock
samples are tested in the laboratory. These samples are unlikely
to contain enough discontinuities so as to be truly representative
of the rock mass in situ. Consequently, test results almost
invariably yield an overestimate of the actual shear strength in situ.

Moreover, the shear strength of a rock mass (which must not be confused
with the rock hardness) can be affected by the cleavage planes. In fact,
cleavage may in some instances have a major effect on the capacity of a
rock mass to withstand a pressure of whichever type (compressive or
shear). Such an effect is typically illustrated in figure 7.36, where the same
rock characterised by one main cleavage plane is used. It is seen that the
rock is least resistant when subjected to an external pressure applied at a
45° angle with respect to the cleavage plane. Unsurprisingly perhaps, the
maximum resistance of the rock is developed when the applied pressure is
normal to the cleavage plane. The intermediate resistance corresponding to
the case where the line of action of the load is parallel to the cleavage plane
reflects the mode of failure engendered by splitting (see figure 7.37). The
informative nature of the figure emphasises the importance of accurately
knowing the main cleavage planes of a rock mass prior to cutting building
blocks from a quarry for instance. Some of the building repair works to
which the palace of Westminster in London (famous for its Big Ben tower) is
often subjected relate to the fact that some limestone blocks were cut at the
wrong angle with respect to the bedding plane, and are thus being replaced
due to their steady disintegration.

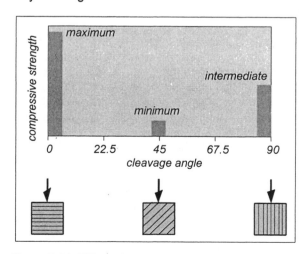

*Figure 7.36: Effect of cleavage and bedding planes on
the shear resistance of an intact rock*

The shear strength of a rock mass also depends on its saturation moisture content and the level of confining pressure. The reader should recall that the moisture content of a saturated material w_s can be expressed in terms of its void ratio e or its porosity n and specific gravity G_s in the following way (refer to equations 2.7 & 2.8, section 2.1):

$$w_s = \frac{e}{G_s} \qquad \text{or} \qquad w_s = \frac{n}{G_s(1-n)} \qquad\qquad (7.75)$$

Accordingly, intact igneous and metamorphic rocks, characterised by very low saturation moisture contents due to their low porosity, do exhibit large shear strength characteristics. Typical examples include intact granite and marble, with $w_s \approx 0.5\%$. Some sedimentary rocks on the other hand do have very high saturation moisture contents, and are thus characterised by very low shear strength. Chalk, for instance, with a typical saturation moisture content $w_s \approx 19\%$, has very poor shear resistance (refer to table 7.3). Figure 7.37 illustrates the effects of confinement and saturation on the shear strength of a rock. The maximum shear stress that can be applied to a rock structure is achieved under dry confined stress conditions. The shear resistance decreases significantly when the rock in question is subjected to a uniaxial stress field (see figure 7.38) under dry conditions, reaching a minimum value when the unconfined rock becomes saturated.

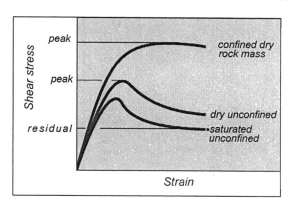

Figure 7.37: Effect of confinement pressure on the shear strength of a rock

Figure 7.37 also indicates that under confined stress conditions, rocks are ductile, in that they can withstand large elasto-plastic deformation without fracturing (refer to section 1.3 relating to the degree of rock folding). Under unconfined stress conditions, rocks usually exhibit a brittle behaviour characterised by a significant drop in shear strength beyond a peak value. Furthermore, the graphs in figure 7.37 show an initial (non-linear) elastic behaviour in all cases, regardless of the level of confinement. The elastic characteristics of rocks are best represented by the elasticity modulus E

(also defined as Young's modulus in section 1.2, equation 1.3): the smaller E, the more elastic is the material.

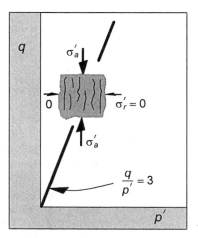

Figure 7.38: Splitting failure related to unconfined stress conditions in rocks

The following useful table 7.2 contains typical values of E for different materials, including rubber for comparison purposes. Note that E is expressed in GN/m^2 ($1\ GN/m^2 = 10^6\ kN/m^2$).

Table 7.2: Elasticity modulii of a selected number of materials

Material	$E(GN/m^2)$
Diamond (D)	1000
Nickel (Ni)	214
Iron (Fe)	196
Copper (Cu)	124
Aluminium (Al)	69
Unweathered granite	75
Unweathered marble	60
Hard limestone	30
Slate	30
Chalk	6
Dense sand	0.035 to 0.055
Loose sand	0.01 to 0.024
Stiff clay	0.01 to 0.025
Soft clay	0.002 to 0.005
Rubber	0.01 to 0.1

Although rocks are less elastic than sands or clays, they do exhibit similar behaviour in terms of stress-strain relationship as depicted in figure 7.39. Such behaviour can be (approximately) modelled using a Mohr-Coulomb type equation:

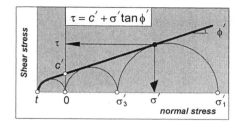

$$\tau = c' + \sigma' \tan \phi' \qquad (7.76)$$

Figure 7.39: Tensile strength of rocks

However, unlike clays or sands, rocks *do* have a tensile strength *t* depending on their degree of weathering and fracture density. Typical shear strength characteristics corresponding to different unweathered rock types are indicated in the useful figure 7.40.

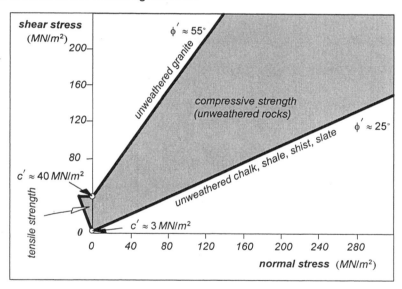

Figure 7.40: Shear strength of unweathered rocks

Notwithstanding its informative nature, the figure shows that under zero normal stress conditions, rocks exhibit shear strength ranging from a very respectable $3,000\, kN/m^2$ for unweathered chalk or slate, to a very substantial $40,000\, kN/m^2$ for unweathered granite. These values can fully be appreciated when contrasted to the drained shear strength of a stiff clay under similar zero normal stress conditions, which is usually limited to $15\, kN/m^2$. *Typical average* values of the shear strength parameters c' and ϕ' for different soils and rocks are summarised in table 7.3. Notice that in the case of clay and mud, the cohesion figures correspond to undrained loading conditions. The table, which also includes dry and saturated unit weights (γ_d and γ_{sat}) of the materials in question, is compiled using *average values* and should not be used as a substitute for measured parameters.

Table 7.3: Typical average shear strength parameters of soils and rocks

Soil type			cohesion kN/m^2	$\gamma_d - \gamma_{sat}$ kN/m^3	ϕ' (°)
Cohesionless		Loose sand — Uniform grain size		14 - 19	28-34
		Loose sand — mixed grain size		17 - 21	32-40
		Dense sand — Uniform grain size		16 - 20	34-40
		Dense sand — mixed grain size		18 - 21	38-46
		Gravel — Uniform grain size		17 - 19	34-37
		Gravel — mixed grain size		20 - 22	38-45
	Blasted-broken rocks	Basalt		17 - 22	40-50
		Chalk		10 - 13	30-40
		Granite		17 - 20	45-50
		Limestone	undrained	16 - 19	35-40
		Sandstone		13 - 17	35-45
		Shale		16 - 20	30-35
Cohesive	Mud - clay	Soft bentonite	10 - 20	6 - 13	7-13
		Very soft organic clay	10 -30	6 - 14	12-16
		Soft slightly organic clay	20 -50	10 - 16	17-22
		Soft glacial clay	30 - 70	12 - 17	22-28
		Stiff glacial clay	70 - 150	17 - 20	20-25
		Glacial till of mixed grain size	150-250	20 - 23	27-32
	Unweathered rock	Hard igneous: Granite, Basalt, Porphyry	35000 - 55000	25 - 30	35-45
		Metamorphic: Quartzite, Gneiss, Slate	20000 - 40000	25 - 28	30-40
		Sedimentary (hard): Limestone, Dolomite, Sandstone	10000 - 30000	23 - 28	35-45
		Sedimentary (soft): Sandstone, Chalk, Shale, Coal	1000 - 20000	17 - 23	25-35

7-9 Engineering properties of soils and rocks

The engineering properties of rocks are best defined by the following parameters:

- *Poison's ratio:* an elastic parameter corresponding to the ratio of lateral strain to axial strain in the direction of a given uniaxial stress change (see figure opposite):

$$\nu = -\frac{\varepsilon_r}{\varepsilon_1} \qquad (7.77)$$

(compressive strains are positive). Poisson ratio can be negative for foam material (a compressive uniaxial stress can cause a reduction in volume),

- *Elasticity modulus E* as defined earlier (see table 7.2),

- *Bulk modulus:* a parameter linking the elasticity modulus to Poison's ratio as follows:

$$K = \frac{E}{3(1-2\nu)} \qquad (7.78)$$

- *Shear modulus* reflecting the effect of shear stress and expressed as follows:

$$G = \frac{E}{2(1+\nu)} \qquad (7.79)$$

Average values of different engineering parameters of *intact rocks* are summarised in table 7.4. These values should be used cautiously so as to take into account, when applicable, any regional variations due to a loss of structural integrity of the rock mass.

The different parameters and corresponding units used in the table are as follows:

G_s : specific gravity,
w_s (%) : saturation moisture content,
ϕ' (°) : angle of shearing resistance,
c' (MN/m^2) : cohesion under zero normal stress (1 MN/m^2 = $10^3 kN/m^2$),
t(MN/m^2) : tensile strength as per figure 7.40,
E(GN/m^2) : elasticity (or Young's) modulus (1 GN/m^2 = $10^6 KN/m^2$),
K(GN/m^2) : bulk modulus,
G(GN/m^2) : shear modulus,
ν : Poisson's ratio.

Table 7.4: Average value of engineering properties of some rocks

		G_s	w_s	ϕ'	c'	t	E	K	G	ν
Igneous	granite	2.7	0.5	55	35	15	75	50	30	0.25
	basalt	2.9	1	50	40	15	90	80	34.5	0.31
Sedimentary	hard limestone	2.7	1.5	35	30	10	60	40	24	
	hard sanstone	2.8	5	45	15	5	30	20	12	0.23
	soft limestone	2.4	8	35	5	2	15	10	6	to
	soft sandstone	2.5	14	40	4	1	4	2.7	1.6	
	chalk	2.3	19	25	3	0.3	6	4	2.4	0.26
	mudstone	2.3	5	30	N/A	N/A	10	6.7	4	
	hard shale	2.3	8	25	N/A	N/A	2	1.3	0.8	
Metamorp hic	shist	2.8	1.5	25	10	3	20	17.5	7.6	0.30
	gneiss	2.8	0.5	30	30	10	45	39.5	17.2	to
	marble	2.6	0.5	35	32	10	60	52.6	22.9	0.32
	slate	2.7	0.5	25	25	10	30	26.3	11.5	

Similarly, *average values* of different engineering parameters corresponding to different types of soils are presented in table 7.5

Table 7.5: Average value of some engineering properties of soils

	$w_s(\%)$	G_s	$\phi'\,(°)$	$E\,(MN/m^2)$	ν
dense sand	15	2.6	38 to 45	35 to 55	0.3 to 0.45
medium dense	to	to	35 to 40	17 to 28	0.25 to 0.4
loose sand	30	2.7	28 to 35	10 to 24	0.2 to 0.4
silty sand	10 to 20	2.65	23 to 28	10 to 17	0.2 to 0.4
stiff clay	20	2.65	19 to 24	10 to 25	0.2
firm clay	to	to	20 to 25	5 to 10	to
soft clay	30	2.75	22 to 28	2 to 5	0.5
organic silts	40 to 80				
organic clays	50 to 100		very poor engineering properties		
peat	500 to 1000				

Problems

7.1 A series of *drained* triaxial tests were undertaken on samples of a *normally consolidated* clay. At failure, the following results were measured in terms of radial and deviator stresses :

$\sigma_3'\,(kN/m^2)$	50	100	150	200
$q\,(kN/m^2)$	64	129	193	257

Plot these results as the variation of deviator stress *versus* the mean effective stress at failure, then estimate the effective angle of shearing resistance of the clay.

Ans : $\phi' \approx 23°$

7.2 Four shear box tests were performed on a clean dense sand, under four different values of effective vertical stresses. The corresponding peak shear stresses are as follows.

$\sigma_1'\,(kN/m^2)$	30	60	90	120
$\tau_{max}\,(kN/m^2)$	28	63	96	120

Estimate the effective angle of friction at the critical density, knowing that, on average, the sand has a maximum dilation angle $\upsilon_{max} = 10°$.

Ans : $\phi_c' \approx 35°$

7.3 A drained triaxial test is to be performed on a *76 mm* long, *38 mm* diameter sample of firm clay with a coefficient of vertical consolidation $c_v = 2.7\,m^2/y$.

(*a*) Knowing that the minimum shear speed that can be generated by the testing equipment is $v_{min} = 6 \times 10^{-4}\,mm/min$, assume the sample will only be drained at both ends then check if the requirement of a minimum excess porewater pressure dissipation $U = 97\%$ beyond an initial axial deformation $\varepsilon_1 = 0.003$ can be fulfilled.

(*b*) Will the shear speed be adequate to fulfil the same requirements were the sample to be drained radially as well as vertically ?

(*c*) Plot the corresponding graphs of porewater pressure dissipation *versus* axial strain.

Ans :   (*a*) $v = 7.3 \times 10^{-5}\,mm/min\ <6 \times 10^{-4}\,mm/min$ (inadequate)
            (*b*) $v = 9.83 \times 10^{-4}\,mm/min$ (adequate)

7.4   Two samples of a normally consolidated clay were consolidated in triaxial cells under different cell pressures σ_3, then sheared under undrained conditions by gradually increasing the deviator stress q while keeping σ_3 constant. The values at failure of the measured deviator stress q_f and the porewater pressure u_f were as follows.

$\sigma_3 (kN/m^2)$	$q_f (kN/m^2)$	$u_f (kN/m^2)$
200	120	96
300	203	123

(a) Determine the shear strength parameters of the clay c' and ϕ'.
(b) Calculate the shear and effective normal stresses at failure for both tests.

Ans: (a) $c' = 0$, $\phi' = 21.4°$
(b)

$\sigma_3 (kN/m^2)$	$\tau_f (kN/m^2)$	$\sigma_f' (kN/m^2)$
200	55.9	142.5
300	94.5	241.1

7.5   Two undrained triaxial tests were carefully undertaken on two clay samples A and B, which were consolidated then sheared under the respective (constant) cell pressures $\sigma_{3A} = 80 \, kN/m^2$ and $\sigma_{3B} = 250 \, kN/m^2$. The results were measured in terms of deviator stress and porewater pressure as follows.
sample A:

$q (kN/m^2)$	0	80	112	138	145
$u (kN/m^2)$	0	16	18	5	-12

sample B:

$q (kN/m^2)$	0	100	150	180	190	195
$u (kN/m^2)$	0	30	55	88	100	105

(a) Plot the effective and total stress paths in (q,p') and (q,p) spaces.

(b) Calculate the porewater pressure parameter at failure A_f and comment on the state of the clay.

Ans: (a) Sample A: $A_f = -0.08$
(b) Sample B: $A_f = 0.54$

References

Azizi, F. and Josseaume, H. (1988) *Loi de comportement des sols raides: détermination de la courbe d'état limite de l'argile verte de Romainville.* Rapport des Laboratoires des Ponts et Chaussées, Série Géotechnique, GT-33.

Berre, T. (1981) *Triaxial Testing at the Norwegian Geotechnical Institute.* N.G.I. Publication 134, Oslo.

Bishop, A. W. and Henkel, D. J. (1962) *The Measurement of Soil Properties in the Triaxial Test, 2nd edn.* Arnold, London. In Soils and Rocks. ICE, London, pp. 251–264.

Bjerrum, L. (1973) *Problems of soil mechanics and construction on soft clays and structurally unstable soils (collapsible, expansive and others).* Proceedings of the 8th I.C.S.M.F.E, Moscow, pp. 111–160.

Bjerrum, L. and Kenny, T. C. (1967) *Effect of structure on the shear behaviour of normally consolidated quick clays.* Proceedings of the Oslo Conference on Geotechnics, Vol. 2, pp. 19–27.

Gibson, R. E. and Henkel, D. J. (1954) *Influence of duration of tests at constant rate of strain on measured drained strength.* Géotechnique (4), pp. 6–15.

Henkel, D. J. (1957) *Investigation of two long term failures in London clay slopes at Wood Green and Northolt.* Proceedings of the 4th I.C.S.M.F.E, London, pp. 315–320.

Jaky, J. (1944) *The coefficient of earth pressure at rest.* Journal of the Society of Hungarian Architects and Engineers, 78 (22), pp. 355–358.

Josseaume, H. and Azizi, F. (1991) *Détermination expérimentale de la courbe d'état limite d'une argile raide très plastique: l'argile verte du Sannoisien.* Revue Française de Géotechnique, 54, pp. 13–25.

Lupini, J. F., Skinner, A. E. and Vaughan, P. R. (1981) *The drained residual strength of cohesive soils.* Géotechnique, 31 (2), pp. 181–213.

Mayne, P. W. and Kulhawy, F. H. (1982) *Relationships in soil.* ASCE Journal, 108, GT6, pp. 851–872.

Palladino, D. J. and Peck, R. B. (1972) *Slope failures in an overconsolidated clay in Seattle, Washington.* Géotechnique, 22 (4), pp. 563–595.

Simpson, B., Calabresi, G., Sommer, H. and Wallays, M. (1979) *Design parameters for stiff clays. General report.* Proceedings of the 7th European Conference on Soil Mechanics and Foundation Engineering, Brighton, Vol. 5, pp. 91–125.

Skempton, A. W. (1954) *The pore pressure coefficients A and B.* Géotechnique, 4 (4), pp. 143–147.

Skempton, A. W. (1957) *Discussion on the Planning and Design of the New Hong Kong Airport.* Proceedings of the I.C.E, Vol. 7, pp. 305–307.

Skempton, A. W. (1964) *Long term stability of clay slopes.* Géotechnique, 14 (2), pp. 77–102.

Skempton, A. W. and Bjerrum, L. (1957) *A contribution to the settlement analysis of foundations on clay.* Géotechnique, 7 (4), pp. 168–178.

Skempton, A. W., and La Rochelle, P. (1965). *The Bradwell slip: a short term failure in London clay.* Géotechnique, 15 (3), pp. 221–242.

Wroth, C. P. (1984) *The interpretation of in situ tests.* 24th Rankine Lecture. Géotechnique, 34 (4), pp. 449–489.

CHAPTER 8

Modelling of soil behaviour: limit and critical states

8.1 Introduction

This chapter aims at linking different aspects of soil behaviour such as consolidation, shear strength, and elastic and plastic deformations through the use of a unique *predictive model*. The model combines elements of *critical state theory* that are particularly suited to normally consolidated or lightly overconsolidated clays, and Hvorslev *limit state* which applies to heavily overconsolidated clays. Such a combination yields a *state boundary surface*, the details of which are given in the following sections. It is however important to mention at this stage that the model is based on the assumptions that the soil is *isotropic* and *saturated*, and that its behaviour is represented through *global* (*i.e.* average) strain values induced by a set of *effective stresses*. The *state* of a saturated soil, which depends entirely on the magnitude of the applied effective stresses and on the density of the soil, can be defined using the three following parameters:

- *the specific volume :* $v = 1 + e$ (8.1)
- *the deviator stress :* $q = \sigma_1' - \sigma_3'$ (8.2)
- *the mean effective stress :* $p' = (\sigma_1' + 2\sigma_3') / 3$ (8.3)

Since water has no shear strength, the deviator stress can be expressed *equally* in terms of total or effective stresses. Also, both equations 8.2 and 8.3 correspond to the axisymmetric stress conditions of figure 8.1 (*i.e.* the conditions of a triaxial test whereby $\sigma_2' = \sigma_3'$). Making use of the effective stress principle $\sigma' = \sigma - u$, and combining the two equations then rearranging yield:

$$p' + u = \sigma_3 + q/3 \qquad\qquad (8.4)$$

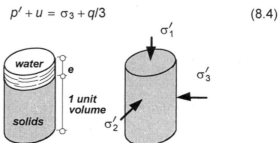

Figure 8.1: Triaxial stress field applied to a saturated soil.

Accordingly, a soil sample consolidated under a set of effective stresses $(\sigma_1', \sigma_2' = \sigma_3')$ in a triaxial cell, then sheared under a constant cell pressure $(\sigma_3 = constant)$ follows one of two possible stress paths depending on drainage conditions as follows.

- If shear occurs under *drained* conditions, then the excess porewater pressure is $u = 0$ and, according to equation 8.4, the *effective stress path* is linear with a slope of 1/3.
- If, on the other hand shear takes place under *undrained* conditions, then the excess porewater pressure u is no longer zero, and equation 8.4 indicates in this case that the *total stress path* is linear with a slope of 1/3 as depicted in figure 8.2.

Although the full implications of equation 8.4, as well as the detailed nature of different stress paths will be analysed in due course, it is important to specify a third stress path along which both principal effective stresses σ_1' and σ_3' vary at a *constant ratio:*

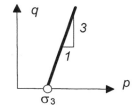

Figure 8.2: total stress path for equation 8.4.

$$\sigma_3'/\sigma_1' = K = constant \qquad (8.5)$$

In this case, it is easy to see that both equations 8.2 and 8.3 reduce to:

$$q = \sigma_1'(1 - K), \qquad p' = \sigma_1' \frac{(1 + 2K)}{3}$$

thus yielding the following relationship:

$$\frac{q}{p'} = \eta = \frac{3(1 - K)}{1 + 2K} \qquad (8.6)$$

The corresponding effective stress path is shown in figure 8.3.

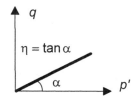

Figure 8.3: Effective stress path corresponding to equation 8.6.

8.2 Critical state theory: the modified Cam-clay model

The mathematical model known as *Cam-clay*, developed at the University of Cambridge (see for instance Schofield and Wroth (1968)), is based on the following assumptions:

- the soil is *isotropic*.
- the soil behaviour is *elasto-plastic*.
- the soil deforms as a *continuum*.
- the soil behaviour is *not affected by creep*.

The earlier version of *Cam-clay* was *modified* by Roscoe and Burland, (1968), to take into account the effect of the plastic component of the volumetric strain on the work dissipated per unit volume. The critical state *concept* is based on the consideration that, when sheared, a soil sample will eventually reach a state at which (large) shear distortions ε_s occur without any further changes in p', q or v. In other words, the onset of a critical state implies that:

$$\frac{\partial p'}{\partial \varepsilon_s} = \frac{\partial q}{\partial \varepsilon_s} = \frac{\partial v}{\partial \varepsilon_s} = 0$$

Such a *concept* has been validated experimentally, in that for a given soil, all critical states *do* form a unique line referred to as *the critical state line* (*CSL*) with the following equations in the space (p', q, v):

$$q = Mp' \tag{8.7}$$

$$v = \Gamma - \lambda \ln p' \tag{8.8}$$

where M, Γ and λ are soil constants. In particular, Γ corresponds to the specific volume when $p' = 1$ *unit*. Moreover, the plastic compression under isotropic stress conditions (*i.e.* $q = 0$) of a *normally consolidated soil* can be accurately represented by a unique line called *the normal consolidation line* (*NCL*), which has the following equations in (p', q, v) space :

$$q = 0 \tag{8.9a}$$

$$v = N - \lambda \ln p' \tag{8.9b}$$

with N corresponding to the specific volume when $p' = 1$ *unit pressure*. If at some point on the *NCL* the soil were unloaded, then it will follow a path known as the *swelling line*, represented by the equations:

$$q = 0 \tag{8.10a}$$

$$v = v_\kappa - \kappa \ln p' \tag{8.10b}$$

Using these three lines and their respective equations, an early picture of the *state* of a soil emerges (see figure 8.4). In particular, notice that:
- a soil whose state lies on the *NCL* is *normally consolidated*,
- a soil with states along the swelling line is *overconsolidated*.

On the whole, a clay in a state within the shaded area in figure 8.4 (*i.e. between* the *CSL* and the *NCL*) is *lightly overconsolidated*. This shaded area is sometimes referred to as the *wet* side of the critical state, the reason being that a clay with a state within that area will generate positive excess porewater pressure when subjected to undrained loading, expelling water once the drainage is allowed to take place, thus appearing 'wet' in the process. Prior to developing the mathematical formalism, it is worth emphasising that the critical state theory is best suited to *normally consolidated* or *lightly overconsolidated clays* (refer to Roscoe and Burland (1968)). As such, the following formulation will be limited to the shaded area in figure 8.4.

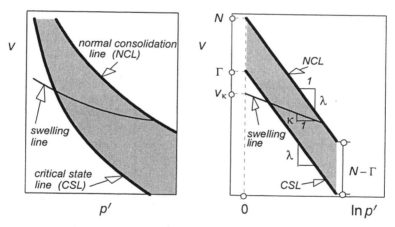

Figure 8.4: NCL, CSL and swelling lines.

Referring to the same figure, it is seen that both *CSL* and *NCL* plot parallel to each other in the space (v, ln p'). Furthermore, the spacing between the two lines in the case of the modified Cam-clay model is represented by the following equation (Wood, 1992):

$$N - \Gamma = (\lambda - \kappa) \ln 2 \qquad (8.11)$$

substituting for N in equation 8.9b, the *NCL* equation then becomes:

$$v = \Gamma + (\lambda - \kappa) \ln 2 - \lambda \ln p' \qquad (8.12)$$

Although the *CSL* and *NCL* are defined in terms of the three (known) soil constants Γ, λ and κ, the nature of the stress path, however, remains partially undefined in the (q, p') space. Consider for instance the case of figure 8.5 in which an isotropic clay sample is sheared undrained from a normally consolidated state (point *A* on the *NCL*) to failure (point *B* on the *CSL*). Knowing the initial consolidation pressure p'_A, both specific volumes v_A and v_B can be calculated from equation 8.12 and 8.9*b* respectively. Similarly, the stresses at failure p'_B and q_B are found from equations 8.8 and 8.7, in that order. Nevertheless, it is seen in the figure that, while the specific volume during the *undrained* shear remains *constant*, both mean effective stress and deviator stress *vary* throughout the test, so that at point *C*, q_C and p'_C cannot be evaluated at this stage.

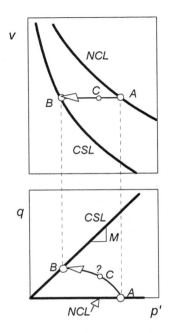

Figure 8.5: Stress path for undrained loading.

Because the clay sample is *normally consolidated*, all ensuing deformations will be *elastoplastic* since a *purely elastic* strain component occurs only in conjunction with *overconsolidated* samples that were unloaded along a swelling line prior to shearing. Consequently, the stress path lies entirely on the *boundary surface* which is yet to be defined. To define the boundary surface, Roscoe and Burland (1968) adopted the following expression for the work dissipated per unit volume:

$$\delta W = p' \left[\left(\delta \varepsilon_v^p \right)^2 + \left(M \delta \varepsilon_s^p \right)^2 \right]^{1/2} \qquad (8.13)$$

Knowing that the dissipated work done by a load (q, p') is such that:

$$\delta W = p' \, \delta \varepsilon_v^p + q \, \delta \varepsilon_s^p \qquad (8.14)$$

they then derived the *associated plastic flow* by combining these two equations:

$$\frac{\delta \varepsilon_v^p}{\delta \varepsilon_s^p} = \frac{M^2 - \eta^2}{2\eta} \qquad (8.15)$$

the quantities $\delta\varepsilon_v^p$ and $\delta\varepsilon_s^p$ being the increments of plastic volumetric strain and plastic shear strain respectively, and $\eta = q/p'$. Both equations 8.13 and 8.15 will be discussed in detail in conjunction with the calculation of plastic strains that follow. Next, Roscoe and Burland have combined the plastic flow equation 8.15 and the equations of plastic strains to derive the following expression of the *state boundary surface* (delimited by the *NCL* and the *CSL*):

$$\frac{p'}{p_e'} = \left[\frac{M^2}{M^2 + \eta^2}\right]^{\left(\frac{\lambda - \kappa}{\lambda}\right)}$$

(8.16)

p_e' being the Hvorslev *equivalent pressure* defined as the mean effective pressure on the *NCL* corresponding to the specific volume at failure. But for an undrained shear test, the specific volume remains constant (refer to figure 8.5), and thus the equivalent pressure can be found simply by rearranging equation 8.12:

$$p_e' = \exp\left[\frac{\Gamma + (\lambda - \kappa)\ln 2 - v}{\lambda}\right]$$

(8.17)

Substituting for p_e' into equation 8.16 and rearranging, yields the equation of the state boundary surface, also known as the *Roscoe surface*:

$$q = Mp'\left[2\exp\left(\frac{\Gamma - v - \lambda\ln p'}{\lambda - \kappa}\right) - 1\right]^{1/2}$$

(8.18a)

As will emerge, it is useful to express the *same* equation as follows:

$$v = \Gamma - \lambda\ln p' - (\lambda - \kappa)\ln\left|\left(\frac{q}{Mp'\sqrt{2}}\right)^2 + \frac{1}{2}\right|$$

(8.18b)

Equation 8.18 is that of the *Roscoe surface* (or the state boundary surface), depicted in figure 8.6, on which all elastoplastic deformations occur. Now consider what happens if, instead of being sheared from a normally consolidated state, the clay is first allowed to become overconsolidated by unloading it along an elastic swelling line. In that case, the onset of shear will generate *elastic strains* while the state of the clay remains *inside* the Roscoe surface, irrespective of the stress path followed during shear. As soon as the Roscoe surface is reached, the deformations become plastic. The *vertical surface* with a swelling line at its base and along which the deformations are purely elastic is known as the *elastic wall*. Because the base of this wall corresponds to a swelling line throughout which the specific volume is *not* constant, the curve resulting from the intersection of the elastic wall with the Roscoe surface, referred to as *the yield curve*, cannot be represented by equation 8.18.

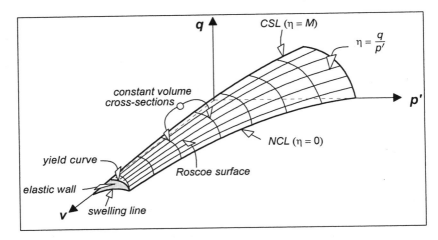

Figure 8.6: State boundary surface as per equation 8.18b.

It is however easy to establish its appropriate equations knowing that the elastic wall is a vertical surface with, at its base, a swelling line whose equation has already been established (equation 8.10*b*):

$$v = v_\kappa - \kappa \ln p'$$

On the other hand, the *NCL* equation 8.12 is:

$$v = \Gamma + (\lambda - \kappa) \ln 2 - \lambda \ln p'$$

and according to figure 8.7, both equations become identical at point *A* where the mean effective pressure is $p' = p_o$. Equating the two equations yields the intercept v_κ:

$$v_\kappa = \Gamma + (\lambda - \kappa) \ln 2 - (\lambda - \kappa) \ln p_o$$

Inserting this quantity into the swelling line equation and rearranging results in the expression of the yield curve equation in the (v, p') space:

$$v = \Gamma + (\lambda - \kappa) \ln\left(\frac{2}{p_o}\right) - \kappa \ln p' \tag{8.19}$$

In (q, p') space, the yield curve results from intersecting the elastic wall with the Roscoe surface. Thus equating equations 8.19 and 8.18*b* then rearranging gives:

$$\frac{p'}{p_o} = \frac{M^2}{M^2 + \eta^2} \tag{8.20}$$

$\eta = q/p'$. Hence, the yield curve is entirely defined by equations 8.19 and 8.20 in which the quantity p_o represents the normal consolidation pressure of the clay sample that determines the size of the yield curve. Note that p_o automatically becomes an overconsolidation pressure as soon as the clay is unloaded along a swelling line. Also, equation 8.20 is that of an *ellipse* with one axis coincident with the p' axis and, most importantly, the point where the yield curve intersects the *CSL* on which $\eta = M$ (point *C* in figure 8.9 for instance) has a mean effective stress $p' = p_o/2$.

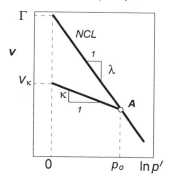

Figure 8.7: Normal consolidation and elastic lines.

8.3 Hvorslev limit state and the complete state boundary surface

The elegant critical state theory is best suited to 'wet' clays meaning normally consolidated to lightly overconsolidated clays. Heavily overconsolidated clays are characterised by a brittle behaviour and their states are on the dry side of the critical state line as depicted in figure 8.8. The loading of such clays can induce negative porewater pressures inside the sample which will then increase in volume were drainage to be allowed, appearing 'dry' in the process. This type of behaviour is best represented by Hvorslev's shear law (Hvorslev, 1937):

$$\frac{q}{p'_e} = g + h\frac{p'}{p'_e} \qquad (8.21)$$

where the equivalent pressure p'_e has been already defined through equation 8.17, and the slope h is a soil constant. The intercept g can easily be determined since, as shown in figure 8.9, point *C* is where both the Hvorslev equation and the *CSL* equation become identical. Equating equations 8.21 to 8.8 yields:

$$g = (M - h)\exp\left[\frac{(\kappa - \lambda)\ln 2}{\lambda}\right] \qquad (8.22)$$

Substituting for g from equation 8.22 and for p'_e from equation 8.17 into equation 8.21, it follows that:

$$q = (M - h) \exp\left(\frac{\Gamma - v}{\lambda}\right) + h\,p' \qquad (8.23a)$$

The same equation can be expressed differently:

$$v = \Gamma - \lambda \ln\left(\frac{q - hp'}{M - h}\right) \qquad (8.23b)$$

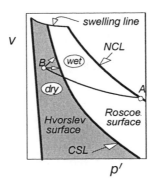

Figure 8.8: Dry and wet sides of the CSL.

Equations 8.23 define the *Hvorslev boundary surface* to the left of the *CSL* as sketched in figure 8.9. This surface is limited on its left by the *tension cut-off* since soils cannot withstand any tensile pressure, meaning that the minor stress σ'_3 cannot fall below zero. Hence at the limit, when $\sigma'_3 = 0$:

$$q = 3p' \qquad (8.24)$$

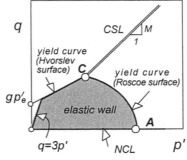

Figure 8.9: Roscoe and Hvorslev surfaces.

As for the yield curve to the left of the *CSL*, it can be established in a way similar to that used previously in conjunction with the Roscoe surface. In fact, the yield curve results from the intersection of the (vertical) elastic wall and the Hvorslev surface equation. Fortunately, the yield curve equation 8.19 established earlier is still valid on the left of the *CSL*. Thus, the second equation in (*q, p'*) space can be obtained by equating the Hvorslev surface equation 8.23*b* to that of the elastic wall (equation 8.19), resulting in the following:

$$q = h p' + \frac{(M-h)}{2} p_o \left(\frac{2 p'}{p_o} \right)^{\kappa/\lambda}$$

(8.25)

Both equations 8.19 and 8.25 represent the *yield curve* to the left of the *CSL*. The *complete state boundary surface*, with its three components, namely the *Roscoe surface*, the *Hvorslev surface* and the *tension cut-off* can now be drawn, and figure 8.10 depicts a 3-D sketch of such a surface.

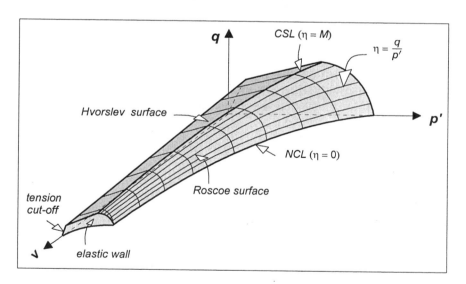

Figure 8.10: Complete state boundary surface.

It should be borne in mind that:
- the model applies to *isotropic saturated clays;*
- the Roscoe surface is used in conjunction with *normally consolidated to lightly overconsolidated clays*;
- the Hvorslev surface is used for *heavily overconsolidated clays*.

8.4 Stress paths within and on the state boundary surface during a triaxial test

Now that the mathematical formalism has been established, let us have a thorough examination of the complete state boundary surface (SBS) through the use of a numerical example. Consider a sample of an isotropic saturated clay, consolidated in a triaxial cell under an isotropic effective mean pressure $p'_A = 400\,kN/m^2$. The clay is characterised by the following constants:

$$\lambda = 0.095, \quad \kappa = 0.035, \quad \Gamma = 2.0, \quad M = 0.9, \quad h = 0.75$$

Once consolidation is complete, it is proposed to determine the precise nature of different stress paths assuming that the sample is:

1 • sheared under undrained conditions until the occurrence of failure;
2 • sheared under drained conditions until failure;
3 • unloaded along a swelling line from $p'_A = 400\,kN/m^2$
to $p'_B = 320\,kN/m^2$, allowed to consolidate then:
  • sheared under undrained conditions until failure;
  • sheared under drained conditions until failure;
4 • unloaded along a swelling line from $p'_A = 400\,kN/m^2$
to $p'_B = 100\,kN/m^2$, allowed to consolidate then:
  • subjected to undrained shear until failure;
  • subjected to drained shear until failure.

8.4.1 Normally consolidated clay: undrained shear

In the first instance, the clay sample is *normally consolidated* under the initial isotropic pressure $p_o = p'_A = 400\,kN/m^2$, $q_A = 0$. Therefore, the state of the sample is *on* the NCL whose equation 8.12 can be used to calculate the corresponding specific volume at point A:

$$v_A = \Gamma + (\lambda - \kappa)\ln 2 - \lambda \ln p'_A$$

$$= 2 + (0.095 - 0.035)\ln 2 - 0.095\ln 400 = 1.472$$

The sample is sheared under *undrained conditions,* so that failure occurs *on* the CSL at point D at a *constant specific volume* (since no drainage is allowed during shear). Whence:

$$v_D = v_A = 1.472$$

The stresses at failure can now be calculated from the CSL equations 8.8 and 8.7 respectively:

$$v_D = \Gamma - \lambda \ln p'_D \quad \Rightarrow \quad p'_D = \exp\left(\frac{\Gamma - v_D}{\lambda}\right) = \exp\left(\frac{2 - 1.472}{0.095}\right) = 259.3 \, kN/m^2$$

$$q_D = Mp'_D = 0.9 \times 259.3 = 233.3 \, kN/m^2$$

The entire stress path is sketched in figure 8.11 which indicates that the sample undergoes an undrained shear under constant volume from A (on the *NCL*) to D on the *CSL*.

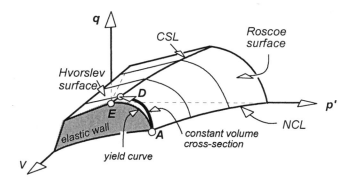

Figure 8.11: Normally consolidated clay; 3-D undrained stress path.

Also, the figure shows that the clay is on the *Roscoe surface* from the onset of shear and, therefore, the stress path AD in (q, p') space can be determined using the Roscoe surface equation 8.18a. Because of the *undrained* shear, the volume remains constant, hence the projection in a straight line from A to D in (v, p') space. If the sample were unloaded from A prior to shear, then it would follow a swelling line which forms the basis of the elastic wall. The curve AE represents the intersection between the Roscoe surface and the elastic wall, and can be calculated using the yield curve equations 8.19 and 8.20. Thus, in (v, p') space, AE is calculated as follows:

$$v = \Gamma + (\lambda - \kappa) \ln(2/p_o) - \kappa \ln p'$$

$$= 2 + (0.095 - 0.035) \ln(2/400) - 0.035 \ln p'$$

$$= 1.628 - 0.035 \ln p'$$

Now, equation 8.20 is used to calculate the stress path AE in (q, p') space. Knowing that $\eta = q/p'$, the equation can easily be rearranged as follows:

$$\frac{p'}{p_o} = \frac{M^2}{M^2 + \eta^2} \quad \Rightarrow \quad q = Mp'\left(\frac{p_o}{p'} - 1\right)^{1/2}$$

The corresponding stress path is depicted in figure 8.12. With regard to the *excess porewater pressure* generated during the undrained shear, the precise nature of its distribution can be calculated from equation 8.4 in which the quantity σ_3 is replaced by $p'_A = 400\,kN/m^2$. Rearranging this equation:

$$u = (400 - p') + \frac{1}{3}q$$

Accordingly, the porewater pressure can be calculated at any stage of the undrained shear, and in particular at points A and D:

$$u_A = (400 - p'_A) + \frac{1}{3}q_A = 0$$

$$u_D = (400 - p'_D) + \frac{q_D}{3} = (400 - 259.3) + \frac{233.3}{3}$$

$$= 218.5\,kN/m^2$$

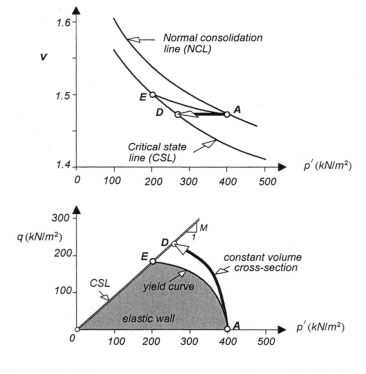

Figure 8.12: Undrained stress path for normally consolidated clay.

The variation of the porewater pressure during shear is illustrated by the shaded area in figure 8.13.

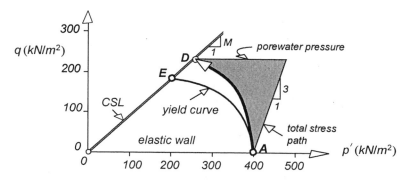

Figure 8.13: Variation of the porewater pressure during undrained loading.

8.4.2 Normally consolidated clay: drained shear

Now the clay is being sheared under *drained conditions* from point *A*, therefore, the initial *state* of the sample is identical to that calculated in the previous case:

$$v_A = 1.472, \ p'_A = 400 \, kN/m^2, \ q_A = 0.$$

When the clay fails at point *D*, the *CSL* equation 8.7 applies $q_D = Mp'_D$. Moreover, because of the drained shear, there is no excess water pressure $(u = 0)$ and equation 8.4 reduces to:

$$p'_D = p'_A + \frac{q_D}{3}$$

Combining this equation with that of the *CSL* yields the mean effective stress at failure:

$$p'_D = \frac{3p'_A}{3-M} = \frac{3 \times 400}{3-0.9} = 571.4 \, kN/m^2$$

and
$$q_D = Mp'_D = 0.9 \times 571.4 = 514.3 \, kN/m^2$$

the corresponding specific volume is calculated from the *CSL* equation 8.8:

$$v_D = \Gamma - \lambda \ln p'_D = 2 - 0.095 \ln 571.4 = 1.397$$

The 3-D nature of the stress path for this drained loading is illustrated in figure 8.14 which shows that the entire stress path lies on the Roscoe surface from the onset of shear.

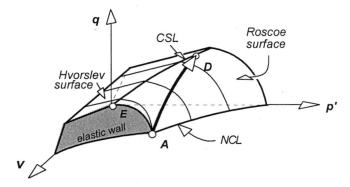

Figure 8.14: Normally consolidated clay; 3-D drained stress path.

Consequently, the Roscoe surface equation 8.18b:

$$v = \Gamma - \lambda \ln p' - \ln \left[\left(\frac{q}{Mp'\sqrt{2}} \right)^2 + \frac{1}{2} \right]^{(\lambda-\kappa)}$$

is used in conjunction with the effective stress path equation 8.4, which is rearranged as follows:

$$q = 3(p' - p'_A) = 3(p' - 400)$$

in order to calculate precisely the stress path *AD* represented in figure 8.15. Notice that since there is no generation of water pressure during the drained shear, both effective and total stress paths are *identical*.

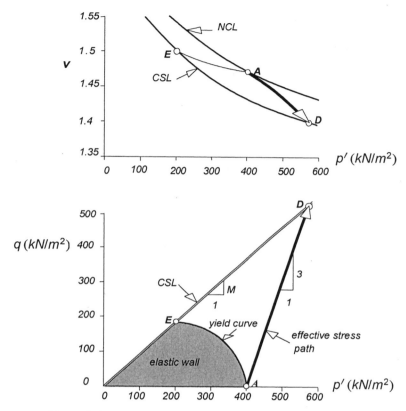

Figure 8.15: Drained stress path for a normally consolidated clay.

8.4.3 Lightly overconsolidated clay: undrained shear

In this case the clay sample is allowed to increase in volume, becoming in the process lightly overconsolidated; the overconsolidation ratio (OCR) being $OCR = 400/320 = 1.25$. The initial state having already been determined previously, it follows that:

$$v_A = 1.472, \quad p'_A = 400\,kN/m^2, \quad q_A = 0$$

Once the sample is unloaded then consolidated under the mean effective pressure $p'_B = 320\,kN/m^2$, the specific volume is calculated from the swelling line equation 8.10*b*:

$$v_B = v_A + \kappa \ln \frac{p'_A}{p'_B} = 1.472 + 0.035 \ln \frac{400}{320} = 1.48$$

Next, the sample is sheared under *undrained conditions*, implying that the specific volume remains constant; therefore at failure $v_D = v_B = 1.48$. The stresses at failure can thereafter be determined from the *CSL* equations 8.8 and 8.7 respectively:

$$v_D = \Gamma - \lambda \ln p'_D \quad \Rightarrow \quad p'_D = \exp\left(\frac{\Gamma - v_D}{\lambda}\right) = \exp\left(\frac{2-1.48}{0.095}\right) = 238.3\,kN/m^2$$

$$q_D = M p'_D = 0.9 \times 238.3 = 214.5\,kN/m^2$$

The complete 3-D stress path is depicted in figure 8.16 which shows that the sample follows a path from *A* (on the *NCL*) to *B* (on a swelling line), then from *B* to *C* within the elastic wall, and finally from *C* to *D* on the Roscoe surface; point *D* where failure occurs being on the *CSL*. While the precise positions of points *A, B* and *D* have been calculated, that of point *C* is yet to be determined. The shape of the stress path from *B* to *C* is of particular interest. Since it is within the elastic wall, the corresponding strains *must* be elastic. However, according to the elastic wall equation 8.19:

$$v = \Gamma + (\lambda - \kappa) \ln\left(\frac{2}{p'_o}\right) - \kappa \ln p'$$

hence: $dv = -\kappa \dfrac{dp'}{p'}$ (8.26)

so that for *undrained* shear, the specific volume remains *constant*, in other words $dv = 0$. Thus, the stress path from *B* to *C* is such that $v_C = v_B = 1.48$, and

$$dv = -\kappa \frac{dp'}{p'} = 0 \quad \Rightarrow dp' = 0$$

This indicates that, under undrained conditions, the pressure p' remains constant inside the elastic wall (*i.e.* $p'_C = p'_B = 320\,kN/m^2$), whence the vertical shape of the stress path from *B* to *C* in figure 8.16.

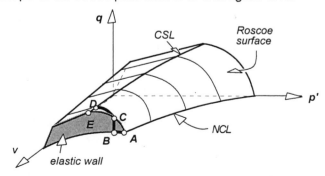

Figure 8.16 : Lightly overconsolidated clay; 3-D undrained stress path.

It is now clear from the figure that point C is where the stress path meets the yield curve, and because both the specific volume v_C and the mean effective stress p'_C are known, the value of the deviator stress q_C is obtained by rearranging the yield curve equation 8.20 :

$$q_C = Mp'_C \left(\frac{p'_A}{p'_C} - 1 \right)^{1/2} = 0.9 \times 320 \left(\frac{400}{320} - 1 \right)^{1/2} = 144 \, kN/m^2$$

Notice that because C is *also* on the Roscoe surface, it is easy to check that equation 8.18b yields a similar result. Next, the stress path from C to D is calculated from the Roscoe surface equation 8.18b in which the volume v takes the constant value $v = 1.48$:

$$q = Mp' \left[2 \exp \left(\frac{\Gamma - v - \lambda \ln p'}{\lambda - \kappa} \right) - 1 \right]^{1/2}$$

$$= 0.9p' \left[2 \exp \left(\frac{0.52 - 0.095 \ln p'}{0.06} \right) - 1 \right]^{1/2}$$

Finally, the yield curve between A and E is calculated from both equations 8.19 and 8.20 which, once rearranged, become:

$$v = \Gamma + (\lambda -) \ln \frac{2}{p'_A} - \kappa \ln p' = 1.682 - 0.035 \ln p'$$

and

$$q = Mp' \left(\frac{p'_A}{p'} - 1 \right)^{1/2} = 0.9p' \left(\frac{400}{p'} - 1 \right)^{1/2}$$

As for the position of point E, it corresponds to the intersection of the *CSL* and the yield curve where:

$$p'_E = \frac{p'_A}{2} = \frac{400}{2} = 200 \, kN/m^2$$

The *CSL* equations 8.7 and 8.8 can then be used to calculate q_E and v_E:

$$q_E = Mp'_E = 0.9 \times 200 = 180 \, kN/m^2$$

$$v_E = \Gamma - \lambda \ln p'_E = 2 - 0.095 \ln 200 = 1.497$$

The entire corresponding stress path is depicted in figure 8.17.

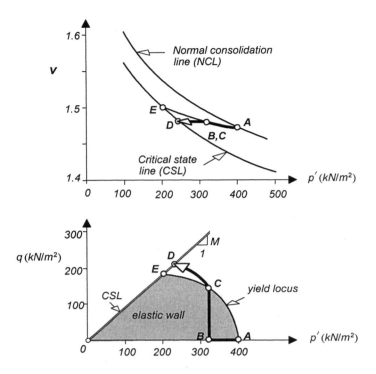

Figure 8.17: Undrained stress path for lightly overconsolidated clay.

The porewater pressure generated during the undrained shear can easily be calculated at any stage using equation 8.4 in which the quantity σ_3 is replaced by $p'_B = 320\,kN/m^2$. Whence the equation in a rearranged form is:

$$u = (320 - p') + q/3$$

so that the porewater pressure generated at point C, for instance, is:

$$u_c = (320 - p'_c) + \frac{q_c}{3} = \frac{144}{3} = 48\,kN/m^2$$

also, at point D, the porewater pressure at failure is:

$$u_D = (320 - 238.3) + \frac{214.5}{3} = 153.2\,kN/m^2$$

The variation of the porewater pressure throughout shear is depicted as the shaded area in figure 8.18.

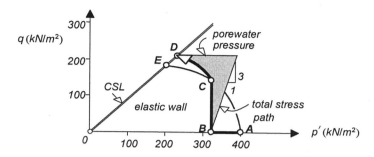

Figure 8.18: Porewater pressure generation during undrained loading.

8.4.4 Lightly overconsolidated clay: drained shear

This time, the (same) clay sample is being sheared from point *B* under *drained conditions*. The stresses and specific volumes for *A* and *B* are already known:

$$v_A = 1.47, \quad p'_A = 400 \, kN/m^2, \quad q_A = 0$$

$$v_B = 1.48, \quad p'_B = 320 \, kN/m^2, \quad q_B = 0$$

Also, the position of the yield curve (therefore that of point *E*) remains the same as under undrained conditions. However, according to equation 8.4, the *effective stress* path from the onset of *drained* shear (*i.e. u = 0*) is linear in (*q, p'*) space with a slope of 1/3:

$$p' = p'_B + q/3$$

so that, at point *D*, failure occurs when the effective stress path meets the *CSL*, whence:

$$q_D = Mp'_D \quad \text{and} \quad p'_D = p'_B + \frac{1}{3}q_D$$

and therefore:

$$p'_D = \frac{3}{(3 - M)} p'_B = \frac{3}{(3 - 0.9)} \times 320 = 457.1 \, kN/m^2$$

$$q_D = Mp'_D = 0.9 \times 320 = 411.4 \, kN/m^2$$

The specific volume at failure can now be calculated from the *CSL* equation 8.8:

$$v_D = \Gamma - \lambda \ln p'_D = 2 - 0.095 \ln 457.1 = 1.418$$

The complete stress path is sketched in figure 8.19 which shows that, as in the previous case of undrained shear, the position of point *C* corresponds to the intersection of the yield curve and the effective stress path.

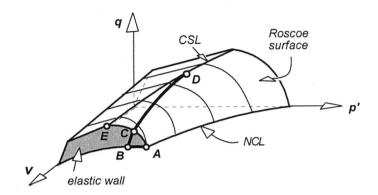

Figure 8.19: Lightly overconsolidated clay; 3-D drained stress path.

Accordingly, the yield curve equation 8.20 and the effective stress path equation at C are respectively:

$$q_C = M p_C' \left(\frac{p_A'}{p_C'} - 1 \right)^{1/2}$$

$$p_C' = p_B' + q_C/3$$

Substituting for q_C in the effective stress path equation and rearranging:

$$p_C'^2 \left(1 + \frac{M^2}{9} \right) - p_C' \left(2p_B' + \frac{M^2}{9} p_A' \right) + p_B'^2 = 0 \quad \Rightarrow \quad p_C' = 357.1 \, kN/m^2$$

Inserting this value into the yield curve equation yields the deviator stress:

$$q_C = 0.9 \times 357.1 \times \left(\frac{400}{357.1} - 1 \right)^{1/2} = 111.4 \, kN/m^2$$

The corresponding specific volume can then be calculated from the yield curve equation 8.19 in (v, p') space:

$$v_C = \Gamma + (\lambda - \kappa) \ln \frac{2}{p_A'} - \kappa \ln p_C'$$

$$= 2 + (0.095 - 0.035) \ln \frac{2}{400} - 0.035 \ln 357.1 = 1.476$$

The precise positions of the key points being determined, the stress path form B to C is calculated as follows.

- In (v, p') space, use the yield curve equation 8.19:

$$v = \Gamma + (\lambda - \kappa)\ln\frac{2}{p'_A} - \kappa\ln p' = 1.682 - 0.035\ln p'$$

- In (q, p') space, use the effective stress path equation:

$$p' = p'_B + q/3$$

or $\qquad q = 3(p' - 320)$ $\hspace{6cm}$ (a)

The stress path from C to D is determined in the following way.
- In (q, p') space, use equation (a) above.
- In (v, p') space, the stress path is on the state boundary surface, hence use both equation (a) and the Roscoe surface equation 8.18b:

$$q = 3(p' - 320)$$
$$v = \Gamma - \lambda\ln p' - (\lambda - \kappa)\ln\left[\left(\frac{q}{Mp'\sqrt{2}}\right)^2 + \frac{1}{2}\right]$$

The complete stress path is shown in figure 8.20. Notice the curvature of the stress path CD in figure 8.19, this is because of the curved nature of the Roscoe surface; the projection of the curve CD in (q, p') space results in a linear curve with a slope of 1/3 as depicted in figure 8.20. Also, because shear is undertaken under drained conditions, there is no generation of excess porewater pressure and hence the effective and total stress paths are *identical*.

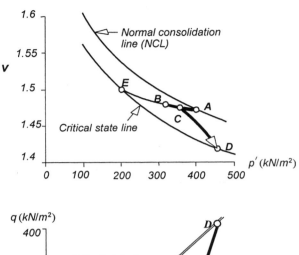

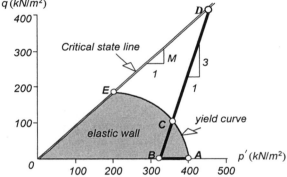

Figure 8.20: Drained stress path for lightly overconsolidated clay.

8.4.5 Heavily overconsolidated clay: undrained shear

In this instance, the sample being consolidated under an initial isotropic pressure $p_o = p'_A = 400 \, kN/m^2$ is then unloaded along a swelling line to a pressure $p'_B = 100 \, kN/m^2$, becoming in the process heavily overconsolidated with an overconsolidation ratio:

$$OCR = 400/100 = 4$$

Once consolidation under p'_B is complete, the sample is sheared under undrained conditions until failure. The initial conditions are identical to those of the previous undrained case; thus at point A, the state of the clay is such that:

$$v_A = 1.472, \quad p'_A = 400 \, kN/m^2, \quad q_A = 0$$

The unloading of the sample occurs along a swelling line, and therefore the specific volume at point B is found from the swelling line equation 8.10b which can be rearranged as follows:

$$v_B = v_A + \kappa \ln \frac{400}{100} = 1.52$$

From point B, the sample is sheared *undrained*, meaning that the specific volume remains constant throughout shear, so that at point D at failure:

$$v_D = v_B = 1.52$$

Since failure occurs on the CSL, both mean effective and deviatoric stresses at D can now be calculated from the CSL equations 8.8 and 8.7 respectively:

$$p'_D = \exp\left(\frac{\Gamma - v_D}{\lambda}\right) = \exp\left(\frac{2 - 1.52}{0.095}\right) = 155.6 \, kN/m^2$$

$$q_D = Mp'_D = 0.9 \times 155.6 = 140 \, kN/m^2$$

The entire stress path is as depicted in figure 8.21 in which point C corresponds to the intersection of the yield curve on the Hvorslev surface and the stress path BC.

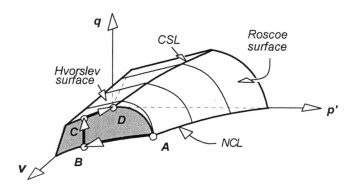

Figure 8.21: Heavily overconsolidated clay; 3-D undrained stress path.

As explained earlier, the constancy of volume between B and C implies that the corresponding stress path is vertical and hence:

$$p'_C = p'_B = 100 \, kN/m^2$$

Inserting this quantity into the yield curve equation 8.25:

$$q_C = h p'_C + \left(\frac{M-h}{2}\right) p_o \left(\frac{2p'_C}{p_o}\right)^{\kappa/\lambda}$$

$$= 0.75 \times 100 + \left(\frac{0.9-0.75}{2}\right) \times 400 \times \left(\frac{2 \times 100}{400}\right)^{0.035/0.095} = 98.2 \, kN/m^2$$

Notice that since point C is *also* on the Hvorslev surface, the same q_C value can be obtained using equation 8.23a. The precise nature of the stress path followed throughout the test is shown in figure 8.22. Of particular interest, the position of point E in the (v, p') space seems to be on the CSL. However, the (q, p') space shows clearly that point E is in fact on the swelling line (which is an isotropic line through which $q = 0$), well below the CSL.

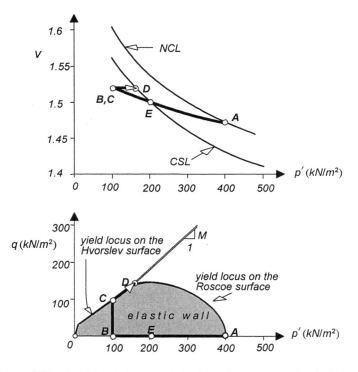

Figure 8.22: Undrained stress path for heavily overconsolidated clay.

The porewater pressure generated during shear can be calculated at any stage using equation 8.4 in which the quantity σ_3 is replaced by $p'_B = 100 \, kN/m^2$:

$$u = (100 - p') + q/3$$

Thence, at *C* for instance, the excess porewater pressure is:

$$u_C = (100 - p'_C) + \frac{q_C}{3} = \frac{98.2}{3} = 32.7 \, kN/m^2$$

whereas at *D* (*i.e.* at failure):

$$u_D = (100 - 155.6) + \frac{140}{3} = -8.9 \, kN/m^2$$

This is precisely what happens in conjunction with clays on the dry side of the *CSL*: a negative excess porewater pressure is generated during *undrained shear*. The nature of the variation of the excess porewater pressure generated throughout the undrained shear is represented by the shaded area in figure 8.23.

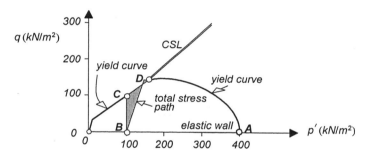

Figure 8.23: Porewater pressure generation during undrained loading.

8.4.6 Heavily overconsolidated clay: drained shear

The clay sample is now subjected to a *drained shear* after it has been unloaded from point *A* where:

$$v_A = 1.472, \quad p'_A = 400 \, kN/m^2, \quad q_A = 0$$

to point *B* for which:

$$v_B = 1.52, \quad p'_B = 100 \, kN/m^2, \quad q_B = 0$$

Because of the *drained* shear, no excess porewater pressure will be generated between point *B* (where shear starts) and point *D* (where failure occurs). Hence, according to equation 8.4, the *effective stress path* will be linear with a slope of 1/3, so that at *D*:

$$p'_D = p'_B + q_D/3$$

Also, D is on the *CSL*. Therefore, using equation 8.7:

$$q_D = Mp'_D$$

Combining the two latter equations:

$$p'_D = \frac{3}{(3-M)} \, p'_B = \frac{3}{3-0.9} \times 100 = 142.9 \, kN/m^2$$

Thence the deviator stress at failure is:

$$q_D = Mp'_D = 128.6 \, kN/m^2$$

and the specific volume at D (*i.e.* at failure), calculated from the *CSL* equation 8.8:

$$v_D = \Gamma - \lambda \ln p'_D = 2 - 0.095 \ln 142.9 = 1.53$$

The 3-D stress path corresponding to the entire test is sketched in figure 8.24.

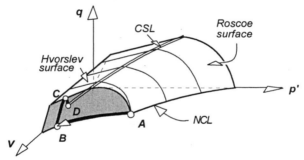

Figure 8.24: Heavily overconsolidated clay; 3-D drained stress path.

Once more, the position of point C in figure 8.24 is yet to be defined. It is however clear from the figure that point C results from the intersection of the yield curve and the effective stress path BC, whose equation is found by rearranging equation 8.4:

$$q_c = 3(p'_C - p'_B) \qquad\qquad (b)$$

Equating this equation to the equation 8.25 of the yield curve:

$$3(p'_C - p'_B) = hp'_C + \frac{M-h}{2} p_o \left(\frac{2p'_C}{p_o}\right)^{\kappa/\lambda}$$

A straightforward substitution for:

$$p'_B = 100 \, kN/m^2, \quad p_o = p'_A = 400 \, kN/m^2$$

into the above equation yields:

$$2.25p'_C - 4.26p_C^{0.368} - 300 = 0$$

hence by trial and error:

$$p'_C = 145.5 \, kN/m^2$$

The deviator stress at C is thereafter calculated from the stress path equation (b):

$$q_C = 3(145.5 - 100) = 136.5 \, kN/m^2$$

and the specific volume at C is finally obtained from the elastic wall equation 8.19:

$$v_C = \Gamma + (\lambda - \kappa) \ln\left(\frac{2}{p_o}\right) - \kappa \ln p'_C$$

$$= 2 + 0.06 \ln \frac{2}{400} - 0.035 \ln 145.5 = 1.508$$

Notice that C is *also* on the Hvorslev surface and, as such, the Hvorslev surface equation 8.23b yields precisely the same value for v_C. The complete stress path followed during the test is shown in figure 8.25.

Interestingly, the negative porewater pressure generated towards the end of the *undrained shear* in the previous example is translated into an increase in volume now that the shear is occurring under *drained* conditions. This is clearly shown in both figures 8.24 and 8.25, whereby the specific volume at point D at failure ($v_D = 1.53$) is *larger* than that at point C ($v_C = 1.508$), this type of behaviour being typical of heavily overconsolidated clays. Accordingly, points C and D are *not* on the same elastic wall as depicted unambiguously in figure 8.24.

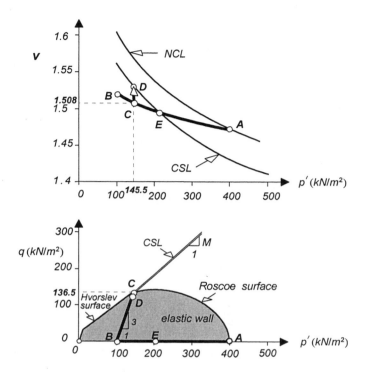

Figure 8.25: Drained stress path for a heavily overconsolidated clay.

Example 8.1

A normally consolidated clay has the following critical state parameters:
$\Gamma = 2.4$, $\lambda = 0.15$, $\kappa = 0.05$, $M = 0.9$. A sample of the clay was consolidated in a triaxial cell under an initial isotropic pressure $p'_o = 600\,kN/m^2$ (point O in figure 8.26). At the end of consolidation, the sample was unloaded under isotropic conditions (i.e. $q = 0$) until an overconsolidation ratio $OCR = 1.5$ was achieved at point A in the same figure, when the drainage tap was closed and the clay was subjected to an undrained shear phase until a mean effective stress $p'_C = 360\,kN/m^2$ was reached at point C (see figure 8.26).

Let's first claculate the specific volume v_B, the mean effective stress p'_B and the deviatoric stress q_B correponding to point B where the Roscoe surface is met. The clay sample was unloaded isotropically until the mean effective stress reached a value p'_A such that:

$$OCR = \frac{p_o'}{p_A'} = 1.5 \quad \Rightarrow \quad p_A' = \frac{600}{1.5} = 400\,kN/m^2.$$

Because the clay sample has become overconsolidated due to unloading, its initial behaviour will be elastic up to the yield curve. Also, whilst the behaviour remains elastic, the ensuing loading will be characterised by a constant specific volume, implying that within the elastic wall:

$$\delta\varepsilon_v = \frac{\delta p'}{K} = 0 \quad \Rightarrow \quad p' = \text{constant}.$$

Accordingly, the mean effective stress at point B where the yield curve is met is $p_B = 400\,kN/m^2$. The corresponding specific volume can be calculated from the elastic wall equation:

$$v_B = v_0 - \kappa \ln\left(\frac{p_A'}{p_o'}\right)$$

where the quantity v_0 represents the specific volume under the mean effective pressure p_o', estimated from the NCL equation:

$$v_0 = \Gamma + (\lambda - \kappa)\ln 2 - \lambda \ln p_o' = 1.8 + 0.05\ln 2 - 0.1\ln 600 \;=\; 1.195.$$

Whence : $v_B = 1.195 - 0.05\ln\frac{4}{6} = 1.215.$

Now that v_B and p_B' are known, the yield curve equation can be used to determine the corresponding value of deviatoric stress q_B:

$$\frac{p_B'}{p_o'} = \frac{M^2}{M^2 + \left(\frac{q_B}{p_B'}\right)^2} \quad \Rightarrow \quad q_B \approx 254.5\,kN/m^2.$$

Note that an identical q_B value could have been found using the *Roscoe* surface equation 8.18a because point B belongs to both yield and *Roscoe* surfaces.

Since the clay sample was subjected to an undrained loading until the mean effective stress reached point C in figure 8.26 at a magnitude $p_C' = 360\,kN/m^2$, the corresponding specific volume remained constant during this undrained shear phase, and thus:

$$v_C = v_B = 1.215$$

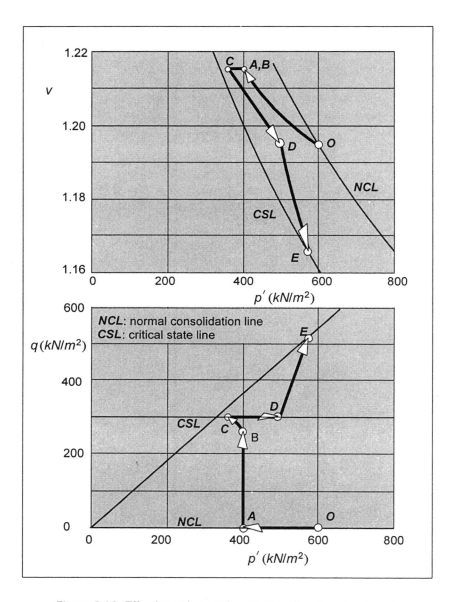

Figure 8.26: Effective stress path corresponding to example 8.1

The deviator stress at the end of this undrained shear phase can now be found from the *Roscoe* surface equation 8.18a :

$$q_c = M p_c' \left[2 \exp \frac{\left(\Gamma - v_c - \lambda \ln p_c' \right)}{\lambda - \kappa} - 1 \right]^{1/2}$$

$$= 0.9 \times 360 \left[2 \exp \frac{(1.8 - 1.215 - 0.1 \ln 360)}{0.05} - 1 \right]^{0.5} \approx 300 \, kN/m^2$$

The total mean stress corresponding to q_c is calculated from the total stress path equation 8.4:

$$p_c = p_o' + \frac{q_c}{3} = 400 + \frac{300}{3} = 500 \, kN/m^2.$$

Whence the excess porewater pressure generated under p_c':

$$u = p_c - p_c' = 500 - 360 = 140 \, kN/m^2.$$

If at this stage of test the drainage tap were opened for a long enough time to allow all excess porewater pressure to fully dissipate, then once that happens, the total mean pressure becomes an effective pressure, while the deviator stress remains constant and the effective stress path in figure 8.26 moves to point D where:

$$p_D' = p_c = 500 \, kN/m^2, \text{ and } q_D = q_c = 300 \, kN/m^2.$$

The corresponding specific volume decreases due to water expulsion from within the clay sample, and its magnitude can be calculated from the *Roscoe* surface equation 8.18b:

$$v_D = \Gamma - \lambda \ln p_D' - (\lambda - \kappa) \ln \left[\left(\frac{q_D}{M p_D' \sqrt{2}} \right)^2 + \frac{1}{2} \right]$$

$$v_D = 1.8 - 0.1 \ln 500 - 0.05 \ln \left[\left(\frac{300}{0.9 \times 500 \sqrt{2}} \right)^2 + 0.5 \right] \approx 1.195$$

Finally, were the sample to be sheared from point D under drained conditions at very low speed (so as not to generate any excess porewater pressure within the clay sample) until the occurrence of failure at point E on the critical state line, then the mean effective pressure at failure is calculated from the intersection of the effective stress path and the critical state line (equations 8.4 & 8.7):

$$p_E' = \frac{3p_o'}{3-M} = \frac{3 \times 400}{3-0.9} = 571.4\,kN/m^2$$

and the deviatoric stress and the specific volume at failure are then calculated from the critical state line equations 8.7 & 8.8:

$$q_E = Mp_E' = 0.9 \times 571.4 = 514.3\,kN/m^2$$

$$v_E = \Gamma - \lambda \ln p_E' = 1.8 - 0.1 \ln 571.4 = 1.165$$

The entire effective stress path corresponding to the full triaxial test is illustrated in figure 8.26

Example 8.2

A stiff clay is characterised by the following parameters:
$\Gamma = 2$, $\lambda = 0.1$, $\kappa = 0.04$, $h = 0.75$ and $M = 0.95$. A carefully prepared sample of the clay was initially consolidated under an isotropic effective mean pressure $p_o' = 550\,kN/m^2$ and zero back pressure. It was then unloaded isotropically (i.e. $q = 0$) to a value $p_A' = 100\,kN/m^2$ (point A in figure 8.27). The sample was thereafter subjected to an undrained shear at low speed so as to avoid generating any gradient of porewater pressure within the clay matrix. If the undrained shear was pursued until a deviator stress $q = 120\,kN/m^2$ was measured, show that yielding occurs on the Hvorslev surface, then calculate the quantities v_B, p_B' and q_B corresponding to point B in figure 8.27 at which this surface is reached.

First, the specific volume corresponding to the mean effective stress p_A' is calculated from the elastic wall equation:

$$v_A = v_o - \kappa \ln \frac{p_A'}{p_o'}.$$

where the quantity v_o is determined from the NCL equation:

$$v_o = \Gamma + (\lambda - \kappa) \ln 2 - \lambda \ln p_o' = 2 + 0.06 \ln 2 - 0.1 \ln 550 = 1.411$$

Whence the pacific volume at point A:

$$v_A = 1.411 - 0.04 \ln \frac{100}{550} = 1.479$$

Since an undrained load up to $q = 120\,kN/m^2$ is applied, the specific volume remains constant, and more importantly, the mean effective stress remains equal to p'_A until yielding occurs at point B in figure 8.27. If failure occurs under undrained conditions, then the mean effective stress at failure can be calculated from the *CSL* equation:

$$p'_h = \exp\frac{\Gamma - v_1}{\lambda} = \exp\frac{2 - 1.479}{0.1} = 183.1\,kN/m^2.$$

Since $p'_h > p'_1$, yielding occurs on the left hand side of the *CSL*, i.e. on the *Hvorslev* surface. Point B at which yielding occurs is such that:

$$v_B = v_A = 1.479 \text{ (undrained loading)},$$

and $p'_B = p'_A = 100\,kN/m^2$ (the mean effective stress is constant up to

the yield curve).
Accordingly, inserting these two quantities into the *Hvorslev* surface equation 8.23a, it follows that:

$$q_B = (M - h)\exp\left(\frac{\Gamma - v_B}{\lambda}\right) + h.p'_B$$

$$= (0.95 - 0.75)\exp\left(\frac{2 - 1.479}{0.1}\right) + 0.75 \times 100 = 111.6\,kN/m^2.$$

Note that the same value q_B is obtained from the yield curve equation 8.25, since point B in figure 8.27 is common to both *Hvorslev* and yield surfaces.

If the undrained load is pursued until $q_C = 120\,kN/m^2$ at point C, then the specific volume remains constant:

$$v_C = v_B = 1.479$$

and the mean effective stress can be found from the *Hvorslev* surface equation 8.23a:

$$p'_C = \frac{1}{h}\left[q_3 - (M - h)\exp\frac{\Gamma - v_C}{\lambda}\right] \quad \Rightarrow \quad p'_C = 111.2\,kN/m^2.$$

The corresponding total mean pressure at C being:

$$p_C = p'_A + \frac{q_C}{3} = 100 + \frac{120}{3} = 140\,kN/m^2$$

the porewater pressure generated at C is thence:

$$u_C = p_C - p'_C = 140 - 111.2 = 28.8\,kN/m^2.$$

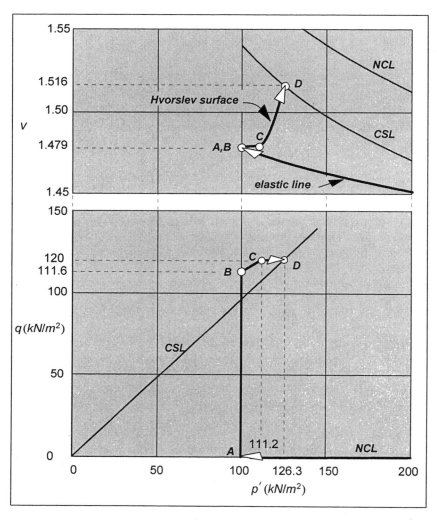

Figure 8.27: Effective stress path corresponding to example 8.2

If on reaching point C the drainage were opened, then the excess porewater pressure starts to dissipate. Accordingly, while the deviator stress remains constant at $q_C = 120\,kN/m^2$, both the mean effective pressure and the specific volume vary according to the *Hvorslev* surface equation:

$$v = \Gamma - \lambda \ln\left[\frac{q_C - hp'}{M - h}\right] = 2 - 0.1\ln\left[\frac{120 - 0.75p'}{0.2}\right]$$

Since failure occurs at point D on the CSL, it is seen that:

$$q_D = Mp'_D \quad \Rightarrow \quad p'_D = \frac{120}{0.95} = 126.3\,kN/m^2$$

and $\quad v_D = \Gamma - \lambda \ln p'_D = 2 - 0.1 \ln 126.3 = 1.516$

An identical value of the specific volume at failure could be calculated from the above *Hvorslev* surface equation, which is used to determine the co-ordinates of the stress path in the space (v, p') on figure 8.27 between the yield point B and that at failure D.

8.5 Shear strength of clays related to the critical state concept

8.5.1 Undrained shear strength

It is widely accepted that the concept of critical state does apply to natural soils and in particular to clays. Mathematically, the critical state is represented by the CSL equations 8.7 and 8.8:

$$q = Mp'$$

$$v = \Gamma - \lambda \ln p'$$

rearranging the latter equation: $p' = \exp\left(\frac{\Gamma - v}{\lambda}\right)$, then substituting for p' into the first equation:

$$q = M \exp\left(\frac{\Gamma - v}{\lambda}\right) \tag{8.27}$$

If a clay sample were subject to *undrained shear* in a triaxial test, then the deviator stress at failure will correspond to the diameter of Mohr's circle as depicted in figure 8.28:

$$q = (\sigma_1 - \sigma_3) = 2c_u$$

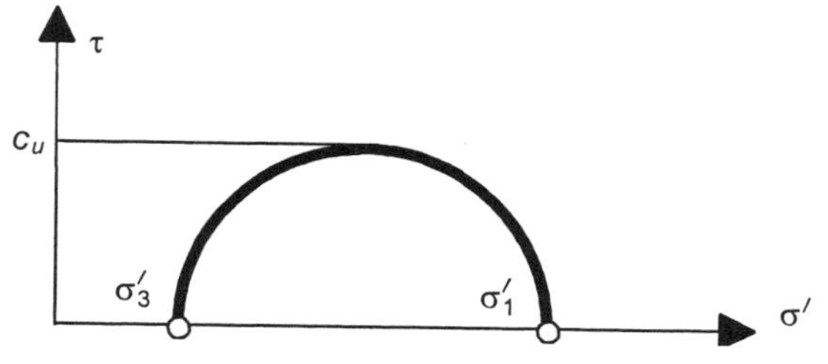

Figure 8.28: Stress field at failure during undrained shear.

Accordingly, the undrained shear strength is:

$$c_u = \frac{M}{2} \exp\left(\frac{\Gamma - v}{\lambda}\right) \tag{8.28}$$

so that the specific volume at failure can be expressed as:

$$v = \left(\Gamma - \lambda \ln \frac{2}{M}\right) - \lambda \ln c_u \tag{8.29}$$

Knowing that for a saturated clay:

$$v = 1 + e = 1 + wG_s$$

it follows that the water content at failure is related to the undrained shear strength of the clay in the following way:

$$w = A - \frac{\lambda}{G_s} \ln c_u \tag{8.30}$$

where the *constant A* corresponds to:

$$A = \frac{1}{G_s}\left(\Gamma - 1 - \lambda \ln \frac{2}{M}\right)$$

and G_s represents the specific gravity of the clay.

Equation 8.30 is a linear relationship between the water content *at failure* and the logarithm of the undrained shear strength of the clay as can be seen from figure 8.29. The constant λ can hence be determined from a set of triaxial undrained shear tests.

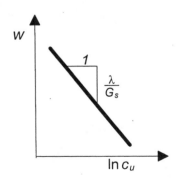

Figure 8.29: Determination of the critical state parameter λ.

8.5.2 Drained shear strength parameters

The compressive shear strength of a soil can be expressed in terms of Coulomb equation:

$$\tau_f = c' + \sigma'_f \tan \phi' \tag{8.31}$$

where the quantity c' represent the apparent cohesion of the soil. Referring to Mohr's circle depicted in figure 8.30, the co-ordinates of the centre of the circle are:

$$\tau = 0$$

$$\sigma' = \frac{1}{2}(\sigma'_1 + \sigma'_3) = \frac{1}{3}(\sigma'_1 + 2\sigma'_3) + \frac{1}{6}(\sigma'_1 - \sigma'_3) = p' + q/6$$

Thus, the expressions of the shear stress τ_f and the normal stress σ'_f at failure can now be established in a straightforward manner:

$$\tau_f = \frac{q}{2} \cos \phi'$$

$$\sigma'_f = p' + \frac{q}{6} - \frac{q}{2} \sin \phi' = p' + \frac{q}{6}(1 - 3\sin \phi')$$

Substituting for τ_f and σ'_f into equation 8.31 and rearranging:

$$q = \frac{6\cos \phi'}{3 - \sin \phi'} c' + \frac{6\sin \phi'}{3 - \sin \phi'} p' \tag{8.32}$$

but failure occurs on the *CSL* whose equation is:

$$q = Mp' \tag{8.33}$$

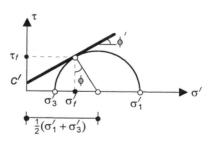

Figure 8.30: Drained behaviour of a cohesive soil at failure.

Comparing these two equations, it emerges that the critical state theory *assumes* that all soils are *frictional* (*i.e.* $c' = 0$), the critical state constant M and the angle of shearing resistance of the soil being related as follows:

$$M = \frac{6 \sin \phi'}{3 - \sin \phi'}$$

and

$$\phi' = \sin^{-1}\left(\frac{3M}{6 + M}\right) \tag{8.34}$$

Although the assumption of zero apparent cohesion tends to be on the conservative side for heavily overconsolidated clays (remember c' for normally consolidated clays), in practice however, a representative value of c' for a given clay is usually very difficult to measure with sufficient accuracy.

8.6 Calculation of elasto-plastic strains

8.6.1 Elastic deformations prior to yielding

The ensuing formulation takes into consideration the axisymmetric stress conditions of a triaxial test during which the increments of radial stresses are equal: $\delta\sigma_2 = \delta\sigma_3$, and so are the increments of radial strains: $\delta\varepsilon_2 = \delta\varepsilon_3$. The formulation can easily be extended to apply to any set of stress increments. The modified Cam-clay model assumes that, for a *saturated isotropic* soil sample subject to a set of stress increments $(\delta\sigma_1', \delta\sigma_2', \delta\sigma_3')$ so that its state remains *within* the elastic wall, the corresponding deformations are purely elastic, and as such, can be estimated from Hooke's generalised law of elasticity:

$$\begin{bmatrix} \delta\varepsilon_1 \\ \delta\varepsilon_2 \\ \delta\varepsilon_3 \end{bmatrix} = \frac{1}{E}\begin{bmatrix} 1 & -\nu & -\nu \\ & 1 & -\nu \\ sym & & 1 \end{bmatrix}\begin{bmatrix} \delta\sigma_1' \\ \delta\sigma_2' \\ \delta\sigma_3' \end{bmatrix} \tag{8.35}$$

E and ν being Young's modulus of elasticity and Poisson's ratio respectively. Under axisymmetric stress conditions, the two strain parameters, namely the *volumetric strain* and the *shear strain*, are defined as follows:

- *volumetric strain:* $\delta\varepsilon_v = \delta\varepsilon_1 + 2\delta\varepsilon_3$ (8.36)

- *shear strain:* $\delta\varepsilon_s = \frac{2}{3}(\delta\varepsilon_1 - \delta\varepsilon_3) = \delta\varepsilon_1 - \frac{\delta\varepsilon_v}{3}$ (8.37)

Hence, according to the matrix form 8.35, the volumetric strain can be expressed as follows:

$$\delta\varepsilon_v = \frac{1}{E}(1 - 2\nu)(\delta\sigma_1' + 2\delta\sigma_3') = \frac{3(1 - 2\nu)}{E}\delta p'$$

which can be written as:

$$\delta \varepsilon_v = \frac{\delta p'}{K}$$ (8.38)

where K represents the soil *bulk modulus*:

$$K = \frac{E}{3(1 - 2v)}$$ (8.39)

Similarly, a combination of equations 8.35 and 8.37 leads to:

$$\delta \varepsilon_1 - \delta \varepsilon_3 = \frac{3}{2} \delta \varepsilon_s = \frac{(1+v)}{E}(\delta \sigma_1' - \delta \sigma_3') = \frac{(1+v)}{E} \delta q$$

or $\quad \delta \varepsilon_s = \frac{2}{3} \frac{(1+v)}{E} \delta q = \frac{\delta q}{3G}$ (8.40)

where G is the soil *shear modulus*:

$$G = \frac{E}{2(1+v)}$$ (8.41)

Relating the increments of the two stress parameters $(\delta p', \delta q)$ to the strain parameters $(\delta \varepsilon_v, \delta \varepsilon_s)$, the following elastic compliance matrix is then obtained:

$$\begin{bmatrix} \delta \varepsilon_v \\ \delta \varepsilon_s \end{bmatrix} = \begin{vmatrix} \frac{1}{K} & 0 \\ 0 & \frac{1}{3G} \end{vmatrix} \begin{bmatrix} \delta p' \\ \delta q \end{bmatrix}$$ (8.42)

The latter relationship indicates that, for *isotropic* soils, a change in volume can only be generated by a change in the mean effective stress, while the shear strain depends entirely on the change in deviator stress. Consequently, under undrained conditions, the soil volume remains constant (*i.e.* $\delta \varepsilon_v = 0$), in which case equation 8.38 is rewritten as:

$$\delta \varepsilon_v = \frac{\delta p'}{K_u} = 0$$

indicating that $K_u \rightarrow \infty$. Substituting for K from equation 8.39, it follows that:

$$K_u = \frac{E}{3(1 - 2v)} \rightarrow \infty \quad \Rightarrow v_u = 0.5$$

Thus, under undrained conditions (*i.e.* short term behaviour), Poisson's ratio takes the value $v_u = 0.5$. For drained behaviour of soils, Poisson's ratio is typically in the range: $0.2 \le v \le 0.4$.

8.6.2 Calculation of plastic strains

Once the stress path reaches the yield locus, elasto-plastic strains ensue. The onset of plasticity is governed by two sets of rules, the first being Druker *stability criterion* which postulates that, for the material to be stable, an increment of stress $\delta\sigma'$ that engenders yielding then hardening *must* do a positive or zero work during the increment of plastic strain $\delta\varepsilon^p$:

$$\delta\sigma'\delta\varepsilon^p \geq 0 \qquad\qquad (8.43)$$

With reference to figure 8.31, it can be seen that the vectorial form of equation 8.43 is:

$$\delta p'\,\delta\varepsilon_v^p + \delta q\,\delta\varepsilon_s^p \geq 0 \qquad\qquad (8.44)$$

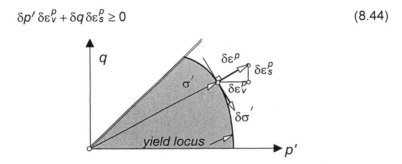

Figure 8.31: Associated flow rule.

The latter inequality means that $\delta\sigma'$ must have a component in the direction of $\delta\varepsilon^p$ and, consequently, the yield locus must have a *convex shape*. When the state of the soil is *on* the boundary surface, a strain hardening takes place through the expansion of the yield locus, and both $\delta\sigma'$ and $\delta\varepsilon^p$ become orthogonal as depicted in figure 8.31. The second and perhaps most important criterion of plastic deformations is the *flow rule*. As mentioned earlier, the critical state theory assumes an *associated flow rule* defined by equation 8.15:

$$\frac{\delta\varepsilon_v^p}{\delta\varepsilon_s^p} = \frac{M^2 - \eta^2}{2\eta}$$

From a theoretical viewpoint (Hill, 1950), a plastic flow is said to be associated if the yield locus is also a *plastic potential*, that is if the plastic strains are normal to the yield locus as is the case in figure 8.31. Hence the associated flow rule is sometimes referred to as the *normality condition*.

Note that because equation 8.15 is related exclusively to the Roscoe surface, the following formulation of plastic strains will only apply in conjunction with the state boundary surface between the NCL and the CSL (refer to figure 8.10), heavily overconsolidated clays being characterised by a brittle behaviour on the Hvorslev surface.

Consider the same stress path depicted in figures 8.32 and 8.33 corresponding to a triaxial test on a normally consolidated clay that was first subjected to a drained loading (path *AB*), followed by an undrained shear until the occurrence of failure (path *BC*). It is clear that from the onset of shear, elasto-plastic strains are generated since point *A* is *on* the Roscoe surface.

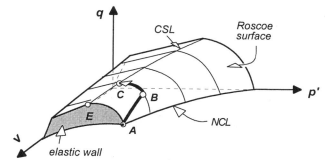

Figure 8.32: 3-D stress path on the state boundary surface.

On the other hand, figure 8.33 shows that the total volume change δv is the sum of an elastic component δv^e and a plastic component δv^p, so that:

$$\delta v^p = \delta v - \delta v^e \qquad (8.45)$$

The quantity δv^e can easily be calculated from the swelling line equation 8.10*b*:

$$v^e = v_\kappa - \kappa \ln p'$$

whence:

$$\delta v^e = -\kappa \frac{\delta p'}{p'} \qquad (8.46)$$

Moreover, the total volume change occurs on the Roscoe surface whose equation 8.18*b* has already been established:

$$v = \Gamma - \lambda \ln p' - (\lambda - \kappa) \ln\left[\left(\frac{q}{Mp'\sqrt{2}} \right)^2 + \frac{1}{2} \right]$$

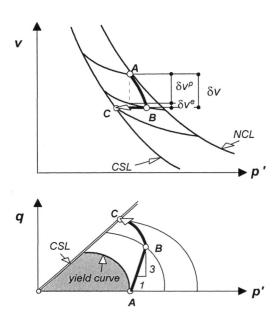

Figure 8.33: Elasto-plastic volume changes.

This equation can now be differentiated:

$$\delta v = -\lambda \frac{\delta p'}{p'} - \frac{(\lambda - \kappa)\,q}{\left[\left(\dfrac{q}{Mp'\sqrt{2}}\right)^2 + \dfrac{1}{2}\right](Mp')^2}\left(\delta q - q\frac{\delta p'}{p'}\right)$$

Inserting the quantity $\eta = q/p'$ into the latter equation and rearranging, it follows that:

$$\delta v = -\lambda \frac{\delta p'}{p'} - \frac{2\eta(\lambda - \kappa)}{p'\,(\eta^2 + M^2)}(\delta q - \eta \delta p') \qquad (8.47)$$

Substituting for δv^e and δv^p from equations 8.46 and 8.47 respectively into equation 8.45:

$$\delta v^p = \delta v - \delta v^e$$

$$= \frac{(\lambda - \kappa)}{p'\,(\eta^2 + M^2)}(\eta^2 - M^2)\delta p' - \frac{(\lambda - \kappa)2\eta}{p'\,(\eta^2 + M^2)}\delta q \qquad (8.48)$$

Knowing that the plastic *strain increment* is related to the plastic component of the volume change in the following manner:

$$\delta\varepsilon_v^p = -\frac{\delta v^p}{v}$$

(8.49)

the final expression of the plastic volumetric strain is therefore:

$$\delta\varepsilon_v^p = \frac{(\lambda-\kappa)}{vp'\,(\eta^2+M^2)}[(M^2-\eta^2)\,\delta p' + 2\eta\,\delta q]$$

(8.50)

Also, the increment of the plastic shear strain is related to the increment of the plastic volumetric strain through the associated plastic flow equation 8.15 which can be rewritten as follows:

$$\delta\varepsilon_s^p = \frac{2\eta}{M^2-\eta^2}\,\delta\varepsilon_v^p$$

(8.51)

Hence:

$$\delta\varepsilon_s^p = \frac{(\lambda-\kappa)}{vp'\,(\eta^2+M^2)}\left(2\eta\,\delta p' + \frac{4\eta^2}{M^2-\eta^2}\,\delta q\right)$$

(8.52)

Both equation 8.50 and 8.52 yield the plastic compliance matrix:

$$\begin{bmatrix}\delta\varepsilon_v^p\\\delta\varepsilon_s^p\end{bmatrix} = \frac{(\lambda-\kappa)}{vp'\,(\eta^2+M^2)}\begin{bmatrix}(M^2-\eta^2)&2\eta\\2\eta&\frac{4\eta^2}{(M^2-\eta^2)}\end{bmatrix}\begin{bmatrix}\delta p'\\\delta q\end{bmatrix}$$

(8.53)

Example 8.3

Consider, first, the case of the lightly overconsolidated clay sample subjected to an *undrained* loading as depicted in figure 8.16. Since the *state* of the sample has been defined in terms of stresses and specific volume, let us concentrate on the calculation of strains throughout the entire stress path, starting with the elastic strains within the elastic wall (stress path *ABC* in figure 8.16). Along the path *AB*, the specific volume increases and the strains are elastic. The already established state of the sample at both points is summarised below:

- point *A*: $v_A = 1.472$, $p_A' = 400\,kN/m^2$, $q_A = 0$
- point *B*: $v_B = 1.48$, $p_B' = 320\,kN/m^2$, $q_A = 0$

The increment of elastic volumetric strain is defined as:

$$\delta\varepsilon_v^e = -\frac{\delta v^e}{v}$$

(8.54)

where the elastic volume change is determined from equation 8.46:

$$\delta v^e = -\kappa \frac{\delta p'}{p'}$$

Accordingly at point B:

$$\delta \varepsilon_v^e = \kappa \frac{\delta p'}{v p'} \qquad (8.55)$$

with the quantities v and p' representing the *average values* of the specific volume and effective mean stress between the points A and B. Thus:

$$\delta \varepsilon_v^e = 0.035 \times \frac{(320 - 400)}{\left(\frac{1.472 + 1.48}{2}\right)\left(\frac{320 + 400}{2}\right)} = -5.27 \times 10^{-3}$$

Moreover, the clay *bulk modulus* is related to $\delta \varepsilon_v^e$ through equation 8.38, so that:

$$K = \frac{\delta p'}{\delta \varepsilon_v^e} = \frac{80}{5.27} \times 10^3 = 15,180 \, kN/m^2$$

Assuming that the clay is characterised by a Poisson's ratio $v = 0.38$, its elastic modulus can then be calculated from equation 8.39:

$$E = 3K(1 - 2v) = 15180 \times 3 \times (1 - 0.76) = 10,930 \, kN/m^2$$

Along the path *BC*, the volume remains constant because of the *undrained* conditions, and consequently the elastic volumetric strain is zero. Point C however marks the onset of *elastoplastic strains*. Considering that the loading along *CD* is undrained (*i.e.* no volume change), the increment of the overall volumetric strain $\delta \varepsilon_v$ must be zero. However, $\delta \varepsilon_v$ is the sum of two components:

$$\delta \varepsilon_v = \delta \varepsilon_v^e + \delta \varepsilon_v^p \qquad (8.56)$$

consequently, the elastoplastic volumetric strains corresponding to an *undrained* loading are such that the elastic and the plastic components are equal and opposite to each other:

$$\delta \varepsilon_v = 0 \quad \Rightarrow \quad \delta \varepsilon_v^e = -\delta \varepsilon_v^p$$

The stresses and specific volumes at C and D have been established previously:

- point C: $v_C = 1.48$, $p_C' = 320 \, kN/m^2$, $q_C = 144 \, kN/m^2$
- point D: $v_D = 1.48$, $p_D' = 238.3 \, kN/m^2$, $q_D = 214.5 \, kN/m^2$

Also, the stress path CD is calculated from the Roscoe surface equation 8.18b:

$$q = Mp'\left[2\exp\left(\frac{\Gamma - v - \lambda \ln p'}{\lambda - \kappa}\right) - 1\right]^{1/2}$$

with $\Gamma = 2$, $v = 1.48$, $\lambda = 0.095$, $\kappa = 0.035$ and $M = 0.9$.

Using the above equation, the following results can be obtained.

$p'(kN/m^2)$		$q(kN/m^2)$		v			average		
	$\delta p'$		δq		δv		$p'(kN/m^2)$	$q(kN/m^2)$	$\eta = q/p'$
320		145		1.48					
	−20		23.5		0		310	156.8	0.51
300		168.5		1.48					
	−20		18.3		0		290	177.7	0.61
280		186.8		1.48					
	−20		14.8		0		270	194.2	0.72
260		201.6		1.48					
	−21.7		12.9		0		249.2	208	0.84
238.3		214.5		1.48					

Because of the undrained loading conditions from C to D, the total volumetric strain is zero and, according to equation 8.56, the plastic and elastic components of the volumetric strain have the same magnitude but opposite signs. Thence, using equation 8.55:

$$\delta\varepsilon_v^e = \kappa\frac{\delta p'}{vp'}$$

where $\delta p'$ and p' correspond to the pressure increment and the *average* mean pressure respectively between two points, so that with reference to the previous table, the first increment of pressure is $\delta p' = 300 - 320 = -20\,kN/m^2$, and the corresponding average pressure is:

$$p' = \frac{300 + 320}{2} = 310\,kN/m^2$$

The ensuing increment of elastic volumetric strain is thence:

$$\delta\varepsilon_v^e = -0.035 \times \frac{20}{1.48 \times 310} = -1.53 \times 10^{-3}$$

and the increment of plastic volumetric strain is:

$$\delta\varepsilon_v^p = -\delta\varepsilon_v^e = 1.53 \times 10^{-3}$$

A similar result for $\delta\varepsilon_v^p$ can be obtained from equation 8.50 in which the quantity η corresponds to the ratio of *average stresses* as indicated in the previous table. Whence:

$$\delta\varepsilon_v^p = \frac{(\lambda - \kappa)}{vp'\,(\eta^2 + M^2)}[(M^2 - \eta^2)\delta p' + 2\eta\delta q]$$

$$= \frac{0.06}{1.48 \times 310 \times (0.506^2 + 0.9^2)}[-(0.9^2 - 0.506^2) \times 20 + 2 \times 0.506 \times 23.5]$$

$$= 1.56 \times 10^{-3}$$

Finally, the corresponding increment of plastic shear strain is computed from equation 8.51:

$$\delta\varepsilon_s^p = \frac{2\eta}{M^2 - \eta^2}\,\delta\varepsilon_v^p$$

$$= \frac{2 \times 0.506}{0.9^2 - 0.506^2} \times 1.56 \times 10^{-3} = 2.85 \times 10^{-3}$$

The results are summarised in the following table in terms of strain increments. Note that $\delta\varepsilon_v^p$ are calculated using equation 8.50.

$\delta p'\,(kN/m^2)$	$\delta q\,(kN/m^2)$	$\delta\varepsilon_v^p$	$\delta\varepsilon_s^p$	$\delta\varepsilon_v^e$
−20	23.5	1.56×10^{-3}	2.85×10^{-3}	-1.56×10^{-3}
−20	18.3	1.62×10^{-3}	4.58×10^{-3}	-1.62×10^{-3}
−20	14.8	1.75×10^{-3}	8.59×10^{-3}	-1.75×10^{-3}
−21.7	12.9	2.06×10^{-3}	3.05×10^{-2}	-2.06×10^{-3}

The *cumulative* values of different strains throughout the test can now be calculated in a straightforward way as follows:

$p'\,(kN/m^2)$	$q\,(kN/m^2)$	ε_v^e	ε_v^p	$\delta\varepsilon_s^p$
400	0	0	0	0
320	0	-5.27×10^{-3}	0	0
320	145	-5.27×10^{-3}	0	0
300	168.5	-6.83×10^{-3}	1.56×10^{-3}	2.85×10^{-3}
280	186.6	-8.45×10^{-3}	3.18×10^{-3}	7.43×10^{-3}
260	201.6	-1.02×10^{-2}	4.93×10^{-3}	1.60×10^{-2}
238.3	214.5	-1.23×10^{-2}	6.99×10^{-3}	4.65×10^{-2}

Example 8.4

Let us now tackle the case of figures 8.19 and 8.20 where the lightly overconsolidated clay is subject to a *drained* loading from point B. The calculation of strains in this case will be undertaken in a way similar to that used in the previous example. Since an identical clay sample with the same characteristics $(\Gamma = 2, \lambda = 0.095, \kappa = 0.035, M = 0.9)$ is used, the loading from point A to point B will yield precisely the same elastic strain as in the previous example:

$$\delta\varepsilon_v^e = \kappa \frac{\delta p'}{vp'} = -5.27 \times 10^{-3}$$

From B to C, the stress path is within the elastic wall and therefore all strains will be elastic. The position of point C has already been established:

$$v_C = 1.476, \quad p_C' = 357.1\,kN/m^2, \quad q_C = 111.4\,kN/m^2$$

Also, the equations of the stress path BC have been defined thus (refer to section 8.4.4):

$$v = 1.682 - 0.035\ln p' \tag{8.57}$$

$$q = 3\,(p' - 320) \tag{8.58}$$

These two equations yield the following values of the variables (p', q, v) within the elastic wall. Note that the calculations consist simply of selecting a value for p' then calculating the *corresponding values* of v and q from equations 8.57 and 8.58 respectively. The quantities $\delta\varepsilon_v^e$ are then calculated from equation 8.55: $\delta\varepsilon_v^e = \kappa \frac{\delta p'}{vp'}$ using the *average values* of p' and v.

For instance, during the first load increment in the following table, it can be seen that the pressure increased from $p' = 320 \, kN/m^2$ to $330 \, kN/m^2$; similarly, the corresponding specific volume changed from 1.48 to 1.479. Whence:

$$\delta p' = 330 - 320 = 10 \, kN/m^2,$$

and the average values:

$$p' = \tfrac{1}{2}(330 + 320) = 325 \, kN/m^2$$

and

$$v = \tfrac{1}{2}(1.48 + 1.479) = 1.4795$$

$p'(kN/m^2)$	$q(kN/m^2)$		v	average		
		$\delta p'$		$p'(kN/m^2)$	v	$\delta \varepsilon_v^e$
320	0		1.48			
		10		325	1.4795	7.28×10^{-4}
330	30		1.479			
		10		335	1.4785	7.06×10^{-4}
340	60		1.478			
		10		345	1.4775	6.87×10^{-4}
350	90		1.477			
		7.1		353.4	1.4765	4.76×10^{-4}
357.1	111.4		1.476			

The Roscoe surface is reached at point C where:

$$v_C = 1.476, \; p'_C = 357.1 \, kN/m^2, \; q_C = 111.4 \, kN/m^2$$

Also, point D where failure occurs is such that:

$$v_D = 1.418, \; p'_D = 457.1 \, kN/m^2, \; q_D = 411.4 \, kN/m^2$$

Along the path CD, the strains are elastoplastic; the corresponding stress path equations being as follows (refer to section 8.4.4):

$$q = 3(p' - 320) \tag{8.59}$$

$$v = \Gamma - \lambda \ln p' - (\lambda - \kappa) \ln \left[\left(\frac{q}{Mp' \sqrt{2}} \right)^2 + \frac{1}{2} \right] \tag{8.60}$$

Accordingly, for any selected p' value, both equation 8.59 and 8.60 yield the corresponding q and v values respectively. The results are summarised in the following table. Note that the stresses p', $\delta p'$, q and δq are expressed in kN/m^2.

p'	$\delta p'$	q	δq	v	δv	average v	average p'	average q	$\eta = q/p'$
357.1				1.476					
	22.9		68.6		−0.013	1.469	368.6	145.7	0.39
380		180		1.463					
	20		60		−0.013	1.456	390	210	0.54
400		240		1.450					
	20		60		−0.012	1.444	410	270	0.66
420		300		1.438					
	20		60		−0.011	1.432	430	330	0.77
440		360		1.427					
	17.1		51.4		−0.009	1.422	448.6	385.6	
				1.418					

The three strain components are thereafter calculated in the following way:

- increment of elastic volumetric strain (equation 8.55):

$$\delta\varepsilon_v^e = \kappa \frac{\delta p'}{vp'}$$

- increment of plastic volumetric strain (equation 8.50):

$$\delta\varepsilon_v^p = \frac{(\lambda - \kappa)}{vp(\eta^2 + M^2)}[(M^2 - \eta^2)\delta p' + 2\eta\delta q]$$

- increment of plastic shear strain (equation 8.51):

$$\delta\varepsilon_s^p = \frac{2\eta}{M^2 - \eta^2}\delta\varepsilon_v^p$$

The results are tabulated below.

$\delta p'\,(kN/m^2)$	$\delta q\,(kN/m^2)$	$\delta\varepsilon_v^e$	$\delta\varepsilon_v^p$	$\delta\varepsilon_s^p$
22.9	68.6	1.48×10^{-3}	7.93×10^{-3}	9.58×10^{-3}
20	60	1.23×10^{-3}	7.20×10^{-3}	1.49×10^{-2}
20	60	1.18×10^{-3}	7.05×10^{-3}	2.46×10^{-2}
20	60	1.14×10^{-3}	6.72×10^{-3}	4.65×10^{-2}
17.1	51.4	9.40×10^{-4}	5.44×10^{-3}	13.30×10^{-2}

Hence the *cumulative* strain values throughout the test are as follows:

$p'\,(kN/m^2)$	$q\,(kN/m^2)$	ε_v^e	ε_v^p	ε_s^p
400	0	0	0	0
320	0	-5.27×10^{-3}	0	0
330	30	-4.54×10^{-3}	0	0
340	60	-3.84×10^{-3}	0	0
350	90	-3.15×10^{-3}	0	0
357	111	-2.67×10^{-3}	0	0
380	180	-1.19×10^{-3}	7.93×10^{-3}	9.58×10^{-3}
400	240	0.04×10^{-3}	1.51×10^{-2}	2.45×10^{-2}
420	300	1.22×10^{-3}	2.22×10^{-2}	4.91×10^{-2}
440	360	2.36×10^{-3}	2.89×10^{-2}	9.56×10^{-2}
457	411	3.30×10^{-3}	3.43×10^{-2}	22.86×10^{-2}

The extent of the plastic shear strain at failure in the latter (drained) case is noticeable with a magnitude of just under 23%, compared with only 4.65% for the undrained case.

8.7 Shortcomings of Cam-clay theory and alternative models

The mathematical model developed earlier is based on the assumption that soils are isotropic. It is well known that natural soils, especially clays, are inherently *anisotropic* due to their mode of deposition. Accordingly, the properties of a natural clay differ in every direction depending on the degree (or the extent) of anisotropy. There is ample experimental evidence to suggest that, while the critical state *concept* is valid, the predictions of the model fall short of the experimental behaviour of natural (anisotropic) clays. This is not surprising considering that Cam-clay models were validated using *reconstituted isotropic clays*.

The main behavioural difference between predictions and experimental measurements on natural clays relate to the *position* rather than the *shape* of the yield loci. In this respect, most natural clays exhibit a behaviour at failure similar to that shown in figures 8.34 in the case of a natural stiff clay (Josseaume and Azizi, 1991). The figure indicates clearly that while the yield locus is elliptical, the major axis of the ellipse is *not* horizontal as predicted by Cam-clay model.

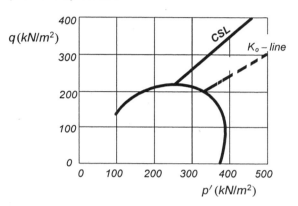

Figure 8.34: Yield locus for a natural stiff clay
(Josseaume and Azizi, 1991).

In this case, the major axis of the yield locus seems to coincide with the K_o–line (K_o being the coefficient of earth pressure at rest as defined in equations 7.38), the departure from the prediction of a horizontal major axis being mainly due to anisotropy (see for instance Wood and Graham (1990)). This is illustrated schematically in figure 8.35 representing the three-dimensional state boundary surface for *natural clays*, as opposed to figure 8.36 which corresponds to the prediction of the *modified Cam-clay model* combined with the *Hvorslev surface* for *reconstituted isotropic clays*.

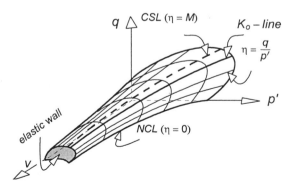

Figure 8.35: State boundary surface for anisotropic natural clays.

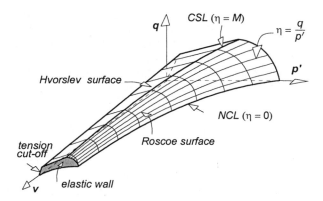

Figure 8.36: State boundary surface for reconstituted isotropic clays.

Predictive models such as the modified Cam-clay are attractive because of their simplicity. It is seen from equation 8.42 that for *isotropic soils*, only *two* independent parameters, namely the bulk and shear modulii, are required to calculate the strains generated by a set of stresses. Fully anisotropic soils, on the other hand, are characterised by no fewer than 21 independent parameters (see Graham and Houlsby, 1983) that need to be measured. However, the number can be reduced to five by assuming that soils are *transversely isotropic* or *cross-anisotropic*, in other words by assuming that their properties are identical in the two horizontal directions but different in the vertical direction. Graham and Houlsby (1983) suggested using a relationship similar in nature to equation 8.42, in which *coupling effect* is taken into account. This coupling reflects the fact that for cross-anisotropic soils, shear stress *can* generate some volumetric strain, whereas a degree of shear strain is engendered by the mean effective stress:

$$
\left| \begin{array}{c} \Delta p' \\ \Delta q \end{array} \right| = \left| \begin{array}{cc} K^* & J \\ J & G^* \end{array} \right| \left\| \begin{array}{c} \Delta \varepsilon_v \\ \Delta \varepsilon_s \end{array} \right| \qquad (8.61)
$$

with only three independent parameters, that is a modified bulk modulus K^* (as opposed to the bulk modulus K in equation 8.42), a modified shear modulus G^* (in contrast to the shear modulus G in equation 8.42), and a cross-modulus J reflecting the degree of soil anisotropy:

- *isotropic soil:* $J = 0$
- *soil stiffer horizontally:* $J < 1$
- *soil stiffer vertically:* $J > 1$.

Experimental evidence shows that shear strains measured on *heavily overconsolidated clays* may differ substantially from values predicted by modified Cam-clay. This is essentially due to the fact that the behaviour within the elastic wall is by and large non-linear and consequently, the shear modulus G does not have a constant value. Alternative models have been suggested to account for the non-linearity of the stress–strain behaviour within the elastic wall (Duncan and Chang, 1970, Jardine *et al.*, 1991). Other approaches suggest the inclusion, within the framework of Cam-clay, of kinematic surfaces inside the state boundary surface to delimit the elastic behaviour corresponding to very small strains (Al-Tabbaa and Wood, 1989, Atkinson, 1992). As mentioned earlier, Cam-clay does not take into account the time effect on soil deformation. This effect, known as *creep* depends on the soil microstructure and its stress history, as well as on loading and drainage conditions (*i.e.* on the stress path).

Creep can be modelled using the following relationship between the strain rate and time (Mitchell, 1993):

$$\frac{d\varepsilon}{dt} = A \exp\left(\frac{\alpha q}{q_c}\right)\left(\frac{t_1}{t}\right)^m \qquad (8.62)$$

with
α: the slope of the creep curve as per figure 8.37,
t_1: a reference time,
q_c: deviator stress at failure,
m: a soil parameter ≤ 1, and
A: a fictitious strain rate corresponding to a deviator stress $q = 0$.

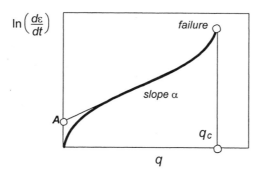

Figure 8.37: Creep curve.

A straightforward integration of equation 8.62 yields the following creep strains:

- for $m = 1$:

$$\varepsilon_c = A t_1 \exp\left(\frac{\alpha q}{q_c}\right) \ln\left(\frac{t}{t_1}\right) \qquad (8.63a)$$

- for $m \neq 1$:

$$\varepsilon_c = \frac{At_1}{1-m} \exp\left(\frac{\alpha q}{q_c}\right)\left(\frac{t}{t_1}\right)^{(1-m)} \qquad\qquad (8.63b)$$

Experimental evidence suggests that creep effect is somewhat limited, and in this respect, figure 8.37 shows that the slope α remains moderate except when the deviator stress nears its magnitude q_c. Alternatively, more sophisticated creep models based on hypo-elasticity can be used (see for instance Yin et al., 1989, 1990).

Finally, notwithstanding or perhaps because of its shortcomings, Cam-clay was and is still used as a framework for more sophisticated and more representative mathematical or numerical models. This work involves the modelling of increasingly complex soil behaviour as in the case of unsaturated soils (see Toll, 1990, Wheeler, 1991), or of thermally induced strains.

Problems

8.1 A clay sample was consolidated *isotropically* under a mean effective pressure $p'_o = 200\,kN/m^2$ and zero back pressure. Assume in what follows that the behaviour of the clay remains elastic throughout the test.

(a) Once consolidation under p'_o was achieved, the sample was then subjected to a stress increment $\delta p' = 50\,kN/m^2$ and $\delta q = 60\,kN/m^2$ under *drained conditions*. As a result, an increment of volumetric strain $\delta\varepsilon_v = 10^{-2}$ was measured. Knowing that the clay has a shear modulus $G = 10\,MN/m^2$, calculate its bulk modulus K, as well as the increments of axial and radial strains $\delta\varepsilon_1$ and $\delta\varepsilon_3$.

(b) At that state of stresses (*i.e.* $p' = 250\,kN/m^2$, $q = 60\,kN/m^2$), the drainage was closed and the deviator stress was increased by an additional increment $\delta q = 30\,kN/m^2$.

Calculate the ensuing value of $\delta\varepsilon_1$, as well as the porewater pressure that would have been generated.

(c) Were the drainage to be reopened at this stage, what would be the increment $\delta\varepsilon_v$ once all excess porewater pressure has dissipated ?

(d) Plot the effective stress path corresponding to the above stages of the test.

Ans: (a) $K = 5 \, MN/m^2$, $\delta\varepsilon_1 = 5.3 \times 10^{-3}$, $\delta\varepsilon_3 = 2.35 \times 10^{-3}$
        (b) $\delta\varepsilon_1 = 10^{-3}$, $\delta u = 10 \, kN/m^2$
        (c) $\delta\varepsilon_v = 2 \times 10^{-3}$

8.2   A normally consolidated clay has the following critical state parameters: $\Gamma = 2.4$, $\lambda = 0.15$, $\kappa = 0.05$, $M = 0.9$. A sample of the clay was first consolidated in a triaxial cell under isotropic stress conditions corresponding to $p'_o = 500 \, kN/m^2$, then unloaded to $p'_1 = 300 \, kN/m^2$, becoming in the process lightly overconsolidated. Once an equilibrium of volume was reached at the end of unloading, the sample was then sheared at a very low speed under *drained* conditions until a value $p'_2 = 350 \, kN/m^2$ was reached.

(a) Show that at the end of shearing, the stress path is well within the elastic wall.

(b) Knowing that the (measured) elastic shear and volumetric strains corresponding to p'_2 are $\varepsilon_s = 4.2 \times 10^{-3}$ and $\varepsilon_v = 7 \times 10^{-3}$ respectively, estimate both bulk and shear modulii of the clay.

(c) If, at $p'_2 = 350 \, kN/m^2$, the drainage was closed and the shearing of the sample was pursued under *undrained* conditions, calculate the specific volume, the mean effective stress, the deviator stress, as well as the porewater pressure generated at the point where the *yield curve* is attained.

(d) Calculate these same quantities at failure.

(e) Plot the entire stress path.

Ans: (a) *At yield,* $p'_y = 366.3 \, kN/m^2 > 350 \, kN/m^2$ $\Rightarrow$ *stress path is within the elastic wall.*
        (b) $K = 7.14 \, MN/m^2$, $G = 11.9 \, MN/m^2$
        (c) $v = 1.555$, $p' = 350 \, kN/m^2$, $q = 206.2 \, kN/m^2$, $u = 18.7 \, kN/m^2$
        (d) $v_f = 1.555$, $p'_f = 279.6 \, kN/m^2$,
          $q_f = 251.6 \, kN/m^2$, $u_f = 104.3 \, kN/m^2$

8.3   A clay has the following critical state parameters :
$\lambda = 0.1$, $\kappa = 0.05$, $\Gamma = 1.8$, $M = 0.9$.
A sample of the clay was consolidated *isotropically* under a cell pressure $\sigma_3 = 220 \, kN/m^2$ and zero back pressure. At the end of consolidation, the drainage tap was closed and the deviator stress was increased gradually until a value $q = 74 \, kN/m^2$ was reached, the cell pressure being kept constant.

(a) Calculate the specific volume v_1 and the mean effective pressure p'_1 corresponding to the value $q = 74\,kN/m^2$.

(b) Determine the value of the porewater pressure u generated by the same deviator stress $q = 74\,kN/m^2$.

At that stage of loading, the drainage was then opened for a period of time long enough for the excess porewater pressure generated during the undrained phase to dissipate.
(c) Calculate the values of the mean effective stress p'_2 and the deviator stress q_2, as well as the specific volume v_2 when all excess porewater pressure has dissipated.

(d) What is the increment of volumetric strain $\delta\varepsilon_v$ that would have been generated if the clay has a bulk modulus $K = 7\,MN/m^2$?

The test was thereafter resumed under *drained conditions* until the occurrence of failure on the critical state line.

(e) Calculate the values at failure of p'_f, q_f and v_f.

(f) Plot the entire stress path followed throughout the test.

Ans: (a) $v_1 = 1.295$, $p'_1 = 204.8\,kN/m^2$
        (b) $u = 39.9\,kN/m^2$
        (c) $p'_2 = 244.7\,kN/m^2$, $q_2 = 74\,kN/m^2$, $v_2 = 1.279$
        (d) $\delta\varepsilon_v = 5.7 \times 10^{-3}$
        (e) $p'_f = 314\,kN/m^2$, $q_f = 283\,kN/m^2$, $v_f = 1.225$

8.4   Consider the clay sample used in conjunction with problem 8.2. Assume that the clay was first consolidated under an isotropic pressure $p'_0 = 600\,kN/m^2$, then unloaded isotropically (*i.e.* $q = 0$) to a value $p'_1 = 400\,kN/m^2$. A *drained* shear test then ensued until the mean effective pressure reached a value $p'_3 = 500\,kN/m^2$.

(a) Calculate the specific volume v_1 corresponding to p'_1.

(b) Determine the values q_2, p'_2 and v_2 corresponding to the point at which the yield curve was met.

(c) Calculate the quantities q_3 and v_3 occurring under the mean effective pressure p'_3.

(d) Once the stresses have reached the values (p'_3, q_3), the drainage was then closed and the clay was sheared under *undrained* conditions until the advent of failure. Calculate the quantities v_f, p'_f and q_f as well as the porewater pressure u_f at failure.

(e) Plot the corresponding stress path.

Ans: (a) $v_1 = 1.215$
(b) $q_2 = 220.1 \, kN/m^2$, $p'_2 = 473.4 \, kN/m^2$, $v_2 = 1.207$
(c) $q_3 = 300 \, kN/m^2$, $v_3 = 1.195$
(d) $v_f = v_3$, $p'_f = 425 \, kN/m^2$, $q_f = 382.5 \, kN/m^2$, $u_f = 102.5 \, kN/m^2$

8.5 Rework problem *8.4* above assuming that, at the point where the yield curve was met (*i.e.* point with the co-ordinates (p'_2, q_2, v_2)), the drainage tap was closed and the clay was sheared under undrained conditions up to the failure point. Estimate then the quantities p'_f, q_f and v_f at failure as well as the corresponding excess porewater pressure u_f generated. Also, plot the entire stress path.

Ans: $v_f = v_2 = 1.207$, $p'_f = 376.2 \, kN/m^2$, $q_f = 338.5 \, kN/m^2$, $u_f = 136.6 \, kN/m^2$

8.6 Consider problem *8.2* then:

(a) estimate the total elastoplastic strains (that is ε_v and ε_s) at failure;

(b) plot the graph (q, ε_s).

Ans: (a) $\varepsilon_v = 0$, $\varepsilon_s = 8.24 \times 10^{-2}$

8.7 Calculate the elastoplastic strains along the stress path relating to problem *8.3*. Plot the corresponding graphs (p', ε_v) and (q, ε_s).

8.8 Calculate the total (*i.e.* cumulative) strains at failure in the case of the worked example *8.1*.

Ans: $\varepsilon_v = 4.2 \times 10^{-2}$, $\varepsilon_s = 24.72 \times 10^{-2}$

8.9 Assuming that the clay has a bulk modulus $K = 8200 \, kN/m^2$, estimate the elastic volumetric strain at the yield point corresponding to problem *8.4*. Calculate the variation of the elasto-plastic volumetric and shear strains along the stress path on the Roscoe surface, then plot the corresponding graphs (p', ε_v) and (q, ε_s).

Ans: *Initial elastic strain:* $\delta\varepsilon_v = 8.95 \times 10^{-3}$

References

Al-Tabbaa, A. and Wood, D. M. (1989) *An experimentally based 'bubble' model for clay*. Proceedings NUMOG III. Elsevier Applied Science, pp. 91–99.

Atkinson, J. H. (1992) *A note on modelling small strain stiffness in Cam-clay*. Predictive Soil Mechanics. Proceedings of the Wroth Memorial Symposium, Oxford. Thomas Telford, London, pp. 111–119.

Druker, D. C. (1954) *A definition of stable inelastic material*. Journal of Applied Mechanics. Trans. ASME 26, pp. 101–106.

Duncan, J. M. and Chang, C. Y. (1970) *Non-linear analysis of stress and strain in soils*. ASCE, Journal of Soil Mechanics and Foundation Engineering Division, 96 (SM5), pp. 1629–1653.

Graham, J. and Houlsby, G. T. (1983) *Elastic anisotropy of a natural clay*. Géotechnique, 33 (2), pp. 165–180.

Graham, J., Noonan, M. L. and Lew, K. V. (1983) *Yield states and stress–strain relationships in a natural plastic clay*. Canadian Geotechnical Journal, 20, pp. 502–516.

Hill, R. (1950) *The Mathematical Theory of Plasticity*. Oxford University Press. London.

Hvorslev, M. J. (1937) *Uber die fesigkeitseigenshaften gestorter bindinger boden*. Ingvidensk. Skr., A., No 45.

Jardine, R. J., Potts, D. M., St John, H. D. and Hight, D. W. (1991) *Some applications of a non-linear ground model*. Proceedings of the 10th European Conference on Soil Mechanics and Foundation Engineering. Florence. Vol. 1, pp. 223–228.

Josseaume, H. and Azizi, F. (1991) *Détermination expérimentale de la courbe d'état limite d'une argile raide très plastique*. Revue Française de Géotechnique, 54, pp. 13–25.

Mitchell, J. K. (1993) *Fundamentals of Soil Behaviour, 2nd edn.* John Wiley & Sons, New York.

Roscoe, K. H. and Burland, J. B. (1968) *On the generalised stress-strain behaviour of "wet" clay*. Engineering Plasticity. Cambridge University Press. pp. 535–609.

Schofield, A. N. and Wroth, C. P. (1968) *Critical State Soil Mechanics*. McGraw-Hill, New York.

Toll, D. G. (1990) *A framework for unsaturated soil behaviour*. Géotechnique, 40 (1), pp. 31–44.

Wheeler, S. J. (1991) *An alternative framework for unsaturated soil behaviour*. Géotechnique, 41 (2), pp. 257–261.

Wood, D. M. (1992) *Soil Behaviour and Critical State Soil Mechanics*. Cambridge University Press.

Wood, D. M. and Graham, J. (1990) *Anisotropic elasticity and yielding of a natural plastic clay.* International Journal of Plasticity, 6, pp. 377–388.

Yin, J.-H., Graham, J., Saadat F. and Azizi, F. (1989) *Constitutive modelling of soil behaviour using three modulus hypoelasticity.* Proceedings of the 12th ICSMFE, Rio de Janeiro, Brazil, pp. 143–147.

Yin, J.-H., Saadat, F. and Graham, J. (1990) *Constitutive modelling of a compacted sand-bentonite mixture using three modulus hypoelasticity.* Canadian Geotechnical Journal, 27, pp. 365–372.

CHAPTER 9

Analysis of the expansion of cylindrical cavities in an infinite soil mass

9.1 The stability of cylindrical cavities: equilibrium equations

Consider the cross-section of a *circular tunnel* subjected to a uniform pressure σ_o at the top as depicted in figure 9.1. Within the circular area surrounding the tunnel opening, both *radial* and *circumferential* (or *hoop*) stresses are assumed to be principal stresses in the absence of any shear stress.

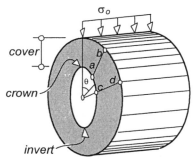

Figure 9.1: Cross-section of a circular tunnel.

Let us now analyse the equilibrium requirements of the curvilinear element *abdc*, whose axis is inclined at an angle θ with respect to the vertical. Using the different dimensions of the element shown in figure 9.2, and neglecting any shear stresses along the sides *ab* and *cd*, then the equilibrium equations can be established in a straightforward way.

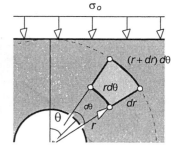

Figure 9.2: Dimensions relating to an elemental cross-section.

Thus, with reference to figure 9.3, the weight w of the element can be evaluated as follows:

$$w \approx \gamma \, r \, d\theta \, dr \tag{9.1}$$

γ being the (relevant) unit weight of soil. Resolving the forces radially in the knowledge that $\sin \frac{d\theta}{2} \approx \frac{d\theta}{2}$, it follows that:

$$(\sigma_r + d\sigma_r)(r + dr)\, d\theta - \sigma_r r \, d\theta - \sigma_\theta \, dr \frac{d\theta}{2} - (\sigma_\theta + d\sigma_\theta)\, dr \frac{d\theta}{2} + \gamma \, r \, dr \, d\theta \cos\theta = 0$$

whence: $$\frac{d\sigma_r}{dr} + \frac{(\sigma_r - \sigma_\theta)}{r} + \gamma \, \cos\theta = 0 \tag{9.2}$$

Now, resolving perpendicular to the radius:

$$\sigma_\theta \, dr + \gamma \, r \, dr \, d\theta \sin\theta - (\sigma_\theta + d\sigma_\theta)\, dr = 0$$

so that: $$\frac{d\sigma_\theta}{d\theta} - \gamma \, r \sin\theta = 0 \tag{9.3}$$

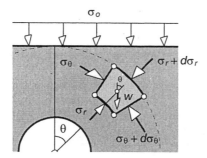

Figure 9.3: Stresses related to the elemental cross-section.

Both equations 9.2 and 9.3 represent the conditions of equilibrium of an element in the vicinity of the tunnel and, as can be seen from figure 9.3, the most unfavourable equilibrium conditions are likely to occur at the *crown* of the tunnel when $\theta = 0$. Under these circumstances, the equilibrium conditions are represented by equation 9.2 which, on substitution for $\theta = 0$, reduces to the following:

$$\frac{d\sigma_r}{dr} = \frac{\sigma_\theta - \sigma_r}{r} - \gamma \tag{9.4}$$

9.2 Stress analysis related to circular tunnels

9.2.1 Circular tunnels in cohesive soils

In the short term, clays derive their strength from their *undrained cohesion* c_u. Hence, in accordance with equation 7.53 in section 7.5.3, the failure criterion in the *passive mode* (*i.e.* $\sigma_\theta > \sigma_r$) under undrained conditions is such that:

$$(\sigma_\theta - \sigma_r) = 2c_u \tag{9.5}$$

Substituting for this quantity in equation 9.4, then integrating between the limits shown in figure 9.4, that is $\sigma_r = \sigma_a$ at $r = a$, and $\sigma_r = \sigma_o$ at $r = R$, it follows that:

$$\int_{\sigma_a}^{\sigma_o} d\sigma_r = \int_a^R \left(\frac{2c_u}{r} - \gamma\right) dr$$

or

$$\sigma_a = \sigma_o + \gamma(R - a) - 2c_u \ln\frac{R}{a} \tag{9.6}$$

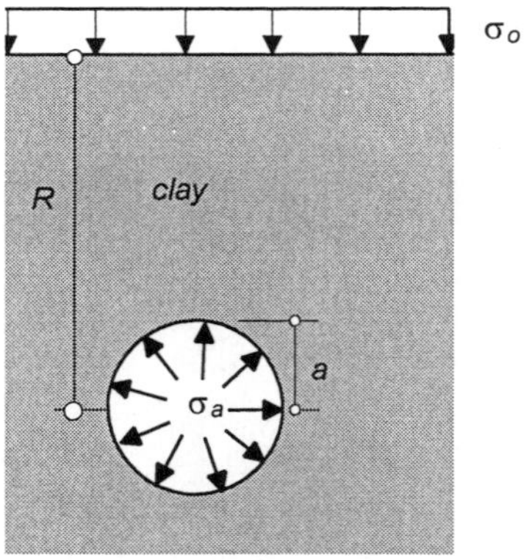

Figure 9.4: Circular tunnels in clays; boundary conditions.

Equation 9.6 yields the pressure σ_a needed in the *short term* to support an unlined tunnel in a clay with an undrained shear strength c_u and a unit weight γ; so that, for example, in the case of a tunnel with a diameter $2a = 4\,m$ and a cover $R - a = 12\,m$, executed in a firm clay characterised by a unit weight $\gamma = 20\,kN/m^3$ and an undrained shear strength $c_u = 60\,kN/m^2$, the support pressure would be, in the absence of any surcharge ($\sigma_o = 0$):

$$\sigma_a = 20 \times 12 - 2 \times 60 \times \ln\frac{14}{2} = 6.5\,kN/m^2$$

This value of (short term) support pressure is in this case surprisingly low given the depth of the tunnel, and reflects a fact known as *stress arching*.

Example 9.1

A circular tunnel is to be excavated unlined in a firm clay having an undrained shear strength $c_u = 50\,kN/m^2$ and a bulk unit weight $\gamma = 20\,kN/m^3$. It is proposed to find the maximum tunnel opening a_{max} that does not require any support pressure (*i.e.* $\sigma_a = 0$) during excavation, if the ground pressure were $\sigma_o = 60\,kN/m^2$.

Introducing the condition of zero support pressure ($\sigma_a = 0$) into equation 9.6, then rearranging, it is easy to show that:

$$a = \frac{2c_u \ln\left(\frac{R}{a}\right) - \sigma_o}{\gamma\left(\frac{R}{a} - 1\right)}$$

Accordingly, a graphical solution can be achieved by plotting the tunnel radius a *versus* the ratio R/a. The corresponding graph, depicted in figure 9.5 yields a maximum radius $a_{max} \approx 1.31\,m$, corresponding to a ratio $R/a_{max} = 4$; whence a distance $R \approx 5.24\,m$ (refer to figure 9.4).

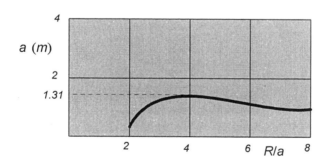

Figure 9.5: Graphical solution to the tunnel opening.

9.2.2 Circular tunnels in cohesionless soils

For soils without cohesion, an effective stress analysis is needed, and for a passive mode of failure, both radial and hoop effective stresses are related at failure through the coefficient of passive earth pressure defined as follows:

$$\sigma'_\theta = K_p \sigma'_r \tag{9.7}$$

$$K_p = \frac{1 + \sin\phi'}{1 - \sin\phi'}$$

In the absence of porewater pressure (*i.e.* dry soil), then $\sigma'_\theta \equiv \sigma_\theta$ and $\sigma'_r \equiv \sigma_r$. Thus substituting for the hoop stress σ_θ from equation 9.7 in the equilibrium equation 9.4, and rearranging:

$$\frac{d\sigma_r}{dr} = \frac{(K_p - 1)\sigma_r}{r} - \gamma \tag{9.8}$$

Using the following change of variables $r\xi = \sigma_r$, so that $d\sigma_r = r\,d\xi + \xi\,dr$, then substituting for the quantities σ_r and $d\sigma_r$ in equation 9.8, it is seen that:

$$\frac{dr}{r} = \frac{d\xi}{(K_p - 2)\xi - \gamma} \tag{9.9}$$

The limits of integration for the above equation are such that (refer to figure 9.4):

$$r = a \implies \xi = \frac{\sigma_a}{a}, \text{ and } r = R \implies \xi = \frac{\sigma_o}{R}$$

Thus:

$$\int_{\sigma_a/a}^{\sigma_o/R} \frac{d\xi}{(K_p - 2)\xi - \gamma} = \int_a^R \frac{dr}{r}$$

On integration, it is easy to establish that:

$$\sigma_a = \frac{a}{(K_p - 2)}\left\{\left(\frac{a}{R}\right)^{K_p - 2}\left[(K_p - 2)\left(\frac{\sigma_o}{R} - \frac{\gamma}{(K_p - 2)}\right)\right] + \gamma\right\} \tag{9.10}$$

Example 9.2

A laboratory experiment is undertaken in a small transparent tank $0.5\,m \times 0.5\,m$ in cross section and $1\,m$ in depth to simulate the collapse of a cylindrical cavity. The experiment consists of burying a thin plastic tube in a uniform sand having a unit weight $\gamma = 20\,kN/m^3$ and an angle $\phi' = 37°$. Considering the dimensions indicated in figure 9.6, and assuming the tube radial stiffness is equivalent to $\sigma_a = 0.3\,kN/m^2$, estimate the maximum static stress σ_o needed to cause collapse of the tube.

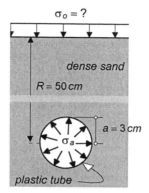

Figure 9.6: Dimensions of opening.

The maximum pressure σ_o capable of causing the opening to collapse is calculated from equation 9.10, which in the circumstances is rearranged as follows:

$$\sigma_o = \left\{ \left[(K_p - 2) \frac{\sigma_a}{a} - \gamma \right] \left(\frac{R}{a} \right)^{K_p-2} + \gamma \right\} \frac{R}{(K_p - 2)}$$

with the coefficient of passive earth pressure: $K_p = \frac{1+\sin 37}{1-\sin 37} = 4.02$.

Substituting for the numerical values into the above equation yields :

$$\sigma_o = \left[\left(\frac{2.02}{0.03} \times 0.3 - 20 \right) \times \left(\frac{0.5}{0.03} \right)^{2.02} + 20 \right] \times \frac{0.5}{2.02} = 19.5\,kN/m^2$$

This pressure is equivalent to a force $F = 478\,kg$ applied across the top surface of the tank, indicating plainly that the collapse of very small openings in sand necessitates large static pressures. This is why vibration is used in conjunction with sand compaction, to generate a state nearing *quick conditions* (refer to section 3.2) whereby the shear strength of sand is minimised, thus allowing the solid particles to be optimally positioned with respect to one another, and reducing in the process the void ratio and hence increasing the density of sand.

It is essential to bear in mind that in practice, the support pressure for cohesionless soils must be provided by structural elements such as concrete or steel linings, since the application of an *air pressure* in this case would increase the total and porewater pressures equally, thus leaving the effective stresses unchanged. More importantly perhaps, *the use of large air pressures for tunnelling in clays at depth can potentially be a health hazard.* Under any circumstances, the air pressure should not exceed $350\,kN/m^2$ (*i.e.* 3.5 *bars*), under which the maximum duration of work is limited to a mere one hour per day considering that, in this case, the time of decompression (about 50 *min*) is longer than the maximum time per shift (around 30 *min*) then, most importantly, a 6 *hour* rest interval is needed to recover physically (Tschebotarioff, 1973). Remember that an air pressure of $350\,kN/m^2$ is equivalent to a 35 *m* head of water.

Also, the previous closed-form solutions relates to circular openings executed in simple soil conditions (essentially homogeneous clays and sands), and cannot therefore be extended to more complex soil strata which are likely to be encountered *in situ,* nor can it apply to rocks which are characterised by different constitutive stress–strain relationships and different boundary conditions (see Brady and Brown (1993), Timoshenko and Goodier (1970), Jaeger (1979)). For such complex soil conditions and for different shapes of tunnel opening, the stress analysis is usually undertaken numerically through finite element modelling (see for instance Mestat (1997), Smith and Griffiths (1998), Assadi and Sloan (1991), Zienkiewicz and Taylor (1991)).

9.3 The pressuremeter test analogy

9.3.1 The pressuremeter equipment

The *pressuremeter* was first invented as an *in situ* testing tool in the mid-1950s by Louis Ménard, who then went on to develop a semi-empirical design method for foundations based on pressuremeter test results (Ménard, 1962, 63). The testing equipment and the related design techniques have been continuously refined since and have now become, in France at least, a standard design method for shallow and deep foundations (MELT, 1993).

The equipment itself has undergone considerable technical changes since Ménard's time and different types of pressuremeters are now available, two of which are widely used: the *prebored pressuremeter* (*PBP*) and the *self-boring pressuremeter* (*SBP*). Figure 9.7 represents a detailed sketch of the *Cambridge in situ* high pressure dilatometer, a PBP that needs to be inserted into a prebored 2.0 *m* long NX-size hole (*i.e.* $\approx 76\,mm$ in diameter) as shown in the figure. The test consists of applying a radial pressure to the soil by inflating a *rubber membrane* and measuring the ensuing radial deformation under conditions of axial symmetry and plane strain.

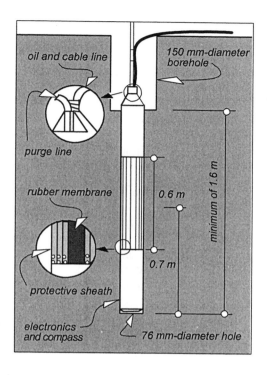

Figure 9.7: Cambridge in situ high pressure dilatometer.

The rubber membrane is inflated by means of hydraulic or gas pressure and the *radial displacement* is averaged from the readings of six strain gauges placed in the same plane about halfway along the membrane height. The *Casing* of the borehole depends on the type of soil tested and the depth at which the test is undertaken. A bentonite mud may be needed to prevent the collapse of the borehole walls. While a PBP such as the one depicted in figure 9.7 is equipped with highly sensitive sensors to detect a borehole wall displacement of 10^{-6} *mm* (or $1\,\mu m$), corresponding to a hoop strain $\varepsilon_\theta \approx 0.003\%$, it is obvious that the quality of measurement depends on the degree of soil disturbance which is bound to occur during the preboring of the hole. The disturbance is largely due to the scouring of the cavity wall by the high pressure drilling fluid. In order to *minimise* these effects, the self boring pressuremeter (*SBP*) was developed independently in France (Baguelin *et al.,* *1972*, 74) and in Britain (Hughes, 1973). A thorough discussion of the technical details of different types of pressuremeter equipment, as well as the practical aspects related to their use can be found in Clarke (1995).

The pressuremeter test, coupled with the elegant theory of the expansion of cylindrical cavities, can provide the designer with reliable values of soil variables such as the variation with depth of horizontal stresses and shear modulii, as well as the undrained shear strength and porewater pressures (for clays) and the angle of dilation (for sands).

9.3.2 The pressuremeter test in clays

The soil behaviour described in the following analysis is assumed to be elastic–perfectly plastic. Moreover, the ensuing mathematical formulation is based on the analysis by Gibson and Anderson (1961) (also, refer to Baguelin *et al.* (1978)).

Because a pressuremeter test in a clay can be performed very quickly (a test can be practically finished in a matter of minutes), the clay behaviour is therefore undrained for the test duration since the excess water pressure due to the expansion of the borehole remains virtually unchanged. Consequently, the analysis that follows, applicable to clays, is based on total stresses.

Referring to figure 9.8, the equilibrium of horizontal forces, applied to an element of soil at a distance r from the centre of cavity, having a radial thickness dr, requires that:

$$\sigma_r r d\theta - (\sigma_r + d\sigma_r)(r + dr)\, d\theta + 2dr\sigma_\theta \frac{d\theta}{2} = 0 \qquad (9.11)$$

or $\quad \dfrac{(\sigma_r - \sigma_\theta)}{r} + \dfrac{d\sigma_r}{dr} = 0 \qquad\qquad\qquad (9.12)$

Notice that the equilibrium equation 9.12 is similar to equation 9.4 established earlier, except that the weight of the element becomes irrelevant to its equilibrium in the case of a radial stress field such as the one generated by a pressuremeter test.

A solution to equation 9.12 can be established in conjunction with the elasto–plastic behaviour of the clay; starting first, with the assumed initial linear elastic behaviour.

Prior to testing, the *in situ* stresses are such that: $\sigma_r = \sigma_\theta = \sigma_{ho} = K_o \sigma_v$, where:

σ_{ho} : the total horizontal *in situ* stress
K_o : the coefficient of earth pressure at rest
σ_v : the total vertical *in situ* stress.

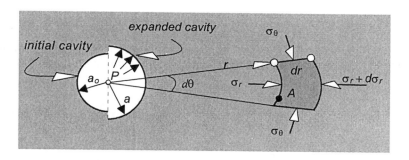

*Figure 9.8: Plan view of the stress field applied to an
element in the vicinity of an expanded cavity.*

This state of stress indicates that, for any deformation to occur, the pressure P applied through the membrane of the pressuremeter (refer to figure 9.7) must exceed σ_{ho}. Accordingly, the radial and circumferential *total* stress increments, resulting from a pressure $P = \sigma_{ho} + \Delta P$ would be such that:

$$\Delta\sigma_r = \sigma_r - \sigma_{ho} \qquad (9.13)$$

$$\Delta\sigma_\theta = \sigma_\theta - \sigma_{ho} \qquad (9.14)$$

Let the displacement undergone by point A in figure 9.8 be w. The principal strains at A can then be expressed in terms of w, so that when *plane strain conditions* are taken into account (*i.e.* $\varepsilon_z = 0$), the following relationships apply:

- *radial strain*: $\qquad \varepsilon_r = \dfrac{dr - (dr + dw)}{dr} = -\dfrac{dw}{dr} \qquad (9.15a)$

- *hoop strain*: $\qquad \varepsilon_\theta = \dfrac{2\pi r - 2\pi(r + w)}{2\pi r} = -\dfrac{w}{r} \qquad (9.15b)$

Applying Hooke's law of elasticity, and taking into account the *axial symmetry* of the problem, it follows that:

$$\begin{bmatrix} \varepsilon_r \\ \varepsilon_\theta \\ 0 \end{bmatrix} = \begin{bmatrix} -dw/dr \\ -w/r \\ 0 \end{bmatrix} = \frac{1}{E}\begin{bmatrix} 1 & -\nu & -\nu \\ -\nu & 1 & -\nu \\ -\nu & -\nu & 1 \end{bmatrix}\begin{bmatrix} \Delta\sigma_r \\ \Delta\sigma_\theta \\ \Delta\sigma_z \end{bmatrix} \quad (9.16)$$

Moreover, the shear modulus G and the elasticity modulus E of the clay are linked through Poisson's ratio n as follows:

$$G = \frac{E}{2(1 + v)} \qquad (9.17)$$

Thus, substituting for the different strains from equation 9.15 into the matrix system 9.16, the increments of radial and circumferential stresses can now be determined:

$$\Delta\sigma_r = -\frac{2G}{1-2v}\left[(1-v)\frac{dw}{dr} + v\frac{w}{r}\right] \qquad (9.18)$$

$$\Delta\sigma_\theta = -\frac{2G}{1-2v}\left[v\frac{dw}{dr} + (1-v)\frac{w}{r}\right] \qquad (9.19)$$

In addition, the quantity $d(\Delta\sigma_r)/dr$ can easily be derived from equation 9.18:

$$\frac{d(\Delta\sigma_r)}{dr} = -\frac{2G}{1-2v}\left[(1-v)\frac{d^2w}{dr^2} + \frac{v}{r}\left(\frac{dw}{dr} - \frac{w}{r}\right)\right] \qquad (9.20)$$

Substituting for $\Delta\sigma_r$, $\Delta\sigma_\theta$ and $d(\Delta\sigma_r)/dr$ from equations 9.18, 9.19 and 9.20 respectively into the incremental form of the equilibrium equation 9.12 yields the following second order differential equation:

$$r.\frac{d^2w}{dr^2} + \frac{dw}{dr} - \frac{w}{r} = 0 \qquad (9.21)$$

for which the boundary conditions are, with reference to figure 9.8:

$$r \to \infty, \quad w \to 0$$
$$r = a, \qquad \Delta\sigma_r = \Delta P$$

Hence the solution to equation 9.21:

$$w = \frac{a^2}{r}\frac{\Delta P}{2G} \qquad (9.22)$$

Now, substituting for w from the latter equation into equations 9.18 and 9.19, then rearranging:

$$\Delta\sigma_r = \frac{a^2}{r^2}\Delta P \qquad (9.23)$$

$$\Delta\sigma_\theta = -\frac{a^2}{r^2}\Delta P = -\Delta\sigma_r \qquad (9.24)$$

Knowing that $P = \sigma_{ho} + \Delta P$, and inserting $\Delta\sigma_r$ and $\Delta\sigma_\theta$ from equations 9.13 and 9.14 into the above equations, it is straightforward to show that the elastic distribution of both radial and circumferential stresses are as follows:

$$\sigma_r = \frac{a^2}{r^2}P + \sigma_{ho}\left(1 - \frac{a^2}{r^2}\right) \qquad (9.25)$$

$$\sigma_\theta = -\frac{a^2}{r^2}P + \sigma_{ho}\left(1 + \frac{a^2}{r^2}\right) \qquad (9.26)$$

Moreover, according to equation 9.22, the strain at the borehole wall where the radial displacement is measured is:

$$\varepsilon = \frac{w_{(r=a)}}{a} = \frac{\Delta P}{2G} \qquad (9.27)$$

so that at the borehole wall, the *elastic* strain is, in theory, related linearly to the applied pressure P as follows:

$$P = \sigma_{ho} + 2G\,\varepsilon_{(r=a)} \qquad (9.28)$$

where G represents the shear modulus of the clay. In practice, however, the clay behaviour is more identifiable with figure 9.9(*b*), which indicates that, *a priori*, the shear modulus cannot be determined from the early elastic response of soil to the applied pressure. This difficulty is overcome by undertaking an unload–reload cycle and measuring G from the corresponding loop as indicated in the figure. *During the unloading phase, care must be taken so as to avoid the collapse of the borehole walls. This may occur when the radial stress becomes a minor stress, in other words, when the amplitude of unloading exceeds* $2c_u$.

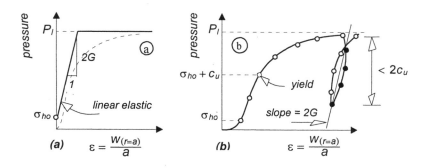

Figure 9.9 : (a) Assumed and (b) experimental aspects of a pressuremeter test in clay.

If the clay were further pressurised at the end of the elastic behaviour, then a plastic annulus with a radius R will start to form around the borehole as soon as the failure criterion is reached, *i.e.*, when:

$$(\sigma_r - \sigma_\theta) = (\Delta\sigma_r - \Delta\sigma_\theta) = 2c_u \qquad (9.29)$$

Thus, substituting for σ_r and σ_θ from equations 9.25 and 9.26 into equation 9.29, it is easy to show that, *on yielding*, which first occurs at the borehole wall (*i.e.* $r = a$), the undrained shear strength c_u of the clay is related to the applied pressure P as follows:

$$P = \sigma_{ho} + c_u \qquad (9.30)$$

Moreover, at the onset of plasticity, the incremental form of the equilibrium equation still holds:

$$\frac{\Delta\sigma_r - \Delta\sigma_\theta}{r} + \frac{d\Delta\sigma_r}{dr} = 0 \qquad (9.31)$$

Whence, substituting for $(\Delta\sigma_r - \Delta\sigma_\theta)$ from equation 9.29, it follows that:

$$\frac{2c_u}{r} + \frac{d\Delta\sigma_r}{dr} = 0 \qquad (9.32)$$

On integration: $\Delta\sigma_r = -2c_u \ln r + C \qquad (9.33)$

The boundary conditions shown in figure 9.10 are such that at $r = R$ (R being the radius of the plastic annulus):

$$\Delta\sigma_r = \Delta\sigma_\theta + 2c_u \quad \text{(plastic boundary)}$$
$$\Delta\sigma_r = -\Delta\sigma_\theta \qquad \text{(elastic boundary)}$$

Hence, combining these two conditions:

$$r = R \;\rightarrow\; \Delta\sigma_r = c_u$$

whence the value of the constant C in equation 9.33:

$$C = c_u + 2c_u \ln R \qquad (9.34)$$

The radial and circumferential total stress increments in the plastic range are therefore:

$$\Delta\sigma_r = c_u + 2c_u \ln \frac{R}{r} \qquad (9.35)$$

$$\Delta\sigma_\theta = -c_u + 2c_u \ln \frac{R}{r} \qquad (9.36)$$

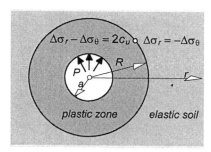

*Figure 9.10: Boundary conditions related
to the plastic behaviour of clays.*

The radius R of the plastic annulus can be determined using the boundary condition at $r = a$ (*a* being the current radius of the borehole):

$$r = a \rightarrow \quad \Delta\sigma_r = \Delta P = P - \sigma_{ho}$$

where P is the applied pressure.

Inserting this condition into equation 9.35, then rearranging:

$$R = a \exp\left(\frac{P - \sigma_{ho} - c_u}{2c_u}\right) \qquad (9.37)$$

Finally, substituting for R from the above equation into equations 9.35 and 9.36, it is seen that the variation of both radial and circumferential stresses in the *plastic range* is:

$$\sigma_r = P + 2c_u \ln\frac{a}{r} \qquad (9.38)$$

$$\sigma_\theta = P - 2c_u(1 - \ln\frac{a}{r}) \qquad (9.39)$$

Notice that the stresses σ_r and σ_θ are related to the stress increments $\Delta\sigma_r$ and $\Delta\sigma_\theta$ through equations 9.13 and 9.14. The stress variations both in the elastic and the plastic range are depicted in figure 9.11.

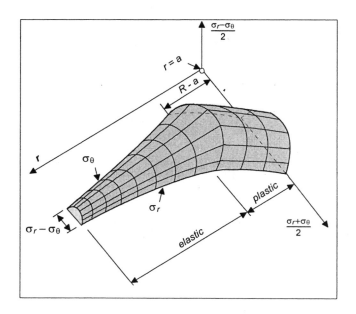

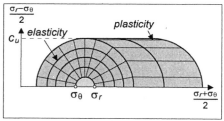

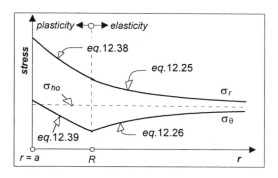

Figure 9.11: Variation of radial and circumferential stresses during a pressuremeter test in a clay.

Because the pressuremeter test is undrained, the radial displacement w related to the formation and expansion of the plastic annulus is such that the volume of the plastic zone remains constant as shown in figure 9.12. Thus, equating the volumes at any two different stages of pressure amounts to:

$$z\pi\left[(R-w)^2 - a_0^2\right] = z\pi(R^2 - a^2) \tag{9.40}$$

Neglecting the quantity w^2 in the above equation then rearranging:

$$a^2 - a_0^2 = 2Rw \tag{9.41}$$

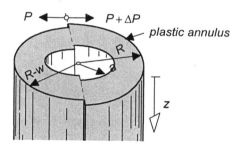

Figure 9.12: Constant volume test.

With reference to figure 9.12, it is clear that both elastic and plastic conditions are simultaneously verified at any point located on the outer boundary of the plastic annulus $r = R$. The elastic condition is obtained from Hooke's law (matrix system 9.16) which yields:

$$w = -\frac{R}{2G}[(1 - v)\Delta\sigma_\theta - v\Delta\sigma_r] \tag{9.42}$$

Since the test is undrained, Poisson's ratio $v = 0.5$, and equation 9.42 then reduces to:

$$w = \frac{R}{4G}(\Delta\sigma_r - \Delta\sigma_\theta) \tag{9.43}$$

Now, inserting the plastic condition from equation 9.29 into the above, it follows that:

$$w = \frac{Rc_u}{2G} \tag{9.44}$$

Replacing R by its value from equation 9.37, then substituting for w from equation 9.44 into equation 9.41 yields:

$$\frac{a^2 - a_o^2}{a^2} = \frac{c_u}{G} \exp\left(\frac{\Delta P - c_u}{c_u}\right) \tag{9.45}$$

The left-hand side of equation 9.45 is in fact the *shear strain* expressing the changes in volume of the expanding membrane:

$$\varepsilon_s = \frac{\Delta V}{V} = \frac{a^2 - a_o^2}{a^2} = 1 - \frac{a_o^2}{a^2} \tag{9.46}$$

so that, once rearranged, equation 9.45 becomes:

$$\Delta P = c_u\left(1 + \ln\frac{G}{c_u}\right) + c_u \ln \varepsilon_s \tag{9.47}$$

Note that some authors refer (unjustifiably?) to the strain in equation 9.46 as volumetric strain. This cannot be the case since the actual volume of soil is constant due to the undrained nature of the test.

It can readily be seen from the latter equation that the yielding of clay is characterised by a linear relationship between the applied pressure and the natural logarithm of the shear strain. The corresponding graph is depicted in figure 9.13, where the linear portion representing equation 9.47 and corresponding to the plastic range is characterised by a slope c_u.

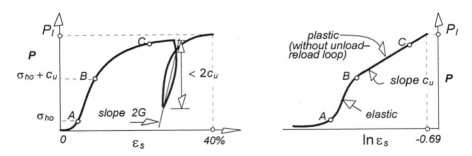

Figure 9.13: Relationship between applied pressure and shear strain during a pressuremeter test in clays.

In practice, the variation in time of the radial displacement at the borehole wall is usually recorded during a pressuremeter test rather than the volume change of the borehole. However, the relationship between the hoop and shear strains can easily be established. Considering the sign convention which stipulates that compressive strains are positive, the hoop strain can be expressed as:

$$\varepsilon_\theta = -\frac{a_o - a}{a_o} = \frac{a}{a_o} - 1 \qquad (9.48)$$

thence:
$$\frac{a_o}{a} = \frac{1}{1 + \varepsilon_\theta} \qquad (9.49)$$

Inserting the above quantity into equation 9.46 yields the relationship between shear and hoop strains:

$$\varepsilon_s = 1 - \frac{1}{(1 + \varepsilon_\theta)^2} \qquad (9.50)$$

Also, equation 9.47 can be rewritten as follows:

$$\Delta P = P_l + c_u \ln(\varepsilon_s) \qquad (9.51)$$

where the *limit pressure* P_l is defined as follows:

$$P_l = c_u\left(1 + \ln\frac{G}{c_u}\right) \qquad (9.52)$$

According to equation 9.51, P_l is the *theoretical* pressure needed to induce a shear strain $\varepsilon_s = \Delta V/V = 1$ (or 100%). However, it is an accepted practice to assume that P_l is the pressure under which a hoop strain $\varepsilon_\theta \approx 40\%$ is measured, in which case it is easy to establish from equations 9.50 and 9.51 that P_l corresponds to a shear strain $\varepsilon_s \approx 50\%$, hence the value -0.69 on the logarithmic scale of figure 9.13.

Example 9.3

Results measured from a pre-bored pressuremeter test, undertaken in a firm to stiff clay at a depth of 1.6 m from the bottom of a wide excavation are illustrated in figures 9.14 & 9.15. Although the borehole depth was some 3 metres below the excavation surface, the actual measurements of radial displacements (averaged from six diametrically opposed sensors) were undertaken at 1.6 m depth. Figure 9.14, representing the variation of the pressure versus the shear strain of equation 9.50, shows that the in situ horizontal pressure σ_{ho} (which corresponds to the lift-off point A of the pressure diagram) has a magnitude of $20\,kN/m^2$. The clay being characterised by a saturated unit weight $\gamma_{sat} \approx 20\,kN/m^3$, its coefficient of earth pressure at rest can then be calculated (refer to equation 7.37, chapter 7) :

$$K_o = \frac{\sigma'_{ho}}{\sigma'_v} = \frac{20 - 10}{1.6 \times (20 - 10)} = 0.625$$

Furthermore, the clay's shear modulus can be calculated from the slope of the unload-relaod cycle as per figure 9.13, and the reader may wish to check that, according to figure 9.14, the shear modulus of the clay is:

$$G \approx 2483 \, kN/m^2$$

The undrained shear strength of the clay can be measured from the slope of the linear portion of the $(P, \ln\varepsilon_s)$ graph in figure 9.15. Once more, it is left to the reader to show that the magnitude of the undrained shear strength of the clay is:

$$c_u \approx 72 \, kN/m^2$$

Finally, it is easy to show that, although the test was not conducted up to a 50% shear strain, the projection of the linear portion of the graph in figure 9.14 yields a limit pressure:

$$P_l \approx 207 \, kN/m^2$$

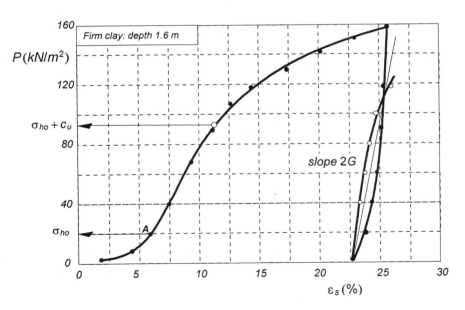

Figure 9.14: Pressuremeter test results in the case of a firm clay.

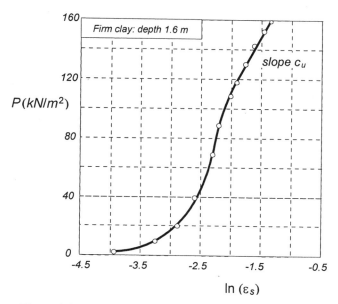

Figure 9.15: Undrained shear strength of a firm clay derived
from a pressuremeter test.

9.3.3 The Pressuremeter test in sands

A pressuremeter test undertaken in a sandy soil does not generate excess porewater pressures because of the high permeability of such materials. Consequently, any increase in the applied pressure is transferred to the soil skeleton, and the analysis in this case is made in terms of effective stresses. The behaviour of sand is assumed to be elastic–perfectly plastic.

As far as the elastic behaviour is concerned, the analysis undertaken previously relating to the elastic behaviour of clays is valid for sands, provided that effective stresses are used instead of total stresses. Therefore, only the plastic behaviour will be analysed in what follows.

Once the elastic limit is exceeded, the sand fails and its volume is no longer constant. When expressed in terms of effective stresses, the equilibrium equation 9.12 established earlier becomes:

$$\frac{\sigma_r' - \sigma_\theta'}{r} + \frac{d\sigma_r'}{dr} = 0 \qquad\qquad (9.53)$$

Moreover, the effective stress ratio at failure (in the active mode) is given by:

$$\frac{\sigma'_\theta}{\sigma'_r} = \frac{1 - \sin\phi'}{1 + \sin\phi'} = \tan^2\left(\frac{\pi}{4} - \frac{\phi'}{2}\right) = K_a \tag{9.54}$$

On substitution for σ'_θ from equation 9.54 into equation 9.53, it follows that:

$$-\frac{d\sigma'_r}{\sigma'_r} = (1 - K_a)\frac{dr}{r} \tag{9.55}$$

The above equation is then integrated using both boundary conditions at the limit of the failed sand zone $(r = R)$ depicted in figure 9.16. Since the effective stress increments are related to the effective horizontal stress *in situ* as follows:

$$\Delta\sigma'_r = \sigma'_r - \sigma'_{ho} \tag{9.56}$$

$$\Delta\sigma'_\theta = \sigma'_\theta - \sigma'_{ho} \tag{9.57}$$

the distribution of the radial and circumferential effective stresses with r can be established effortlessly:

$$\sigma'_r = \frac{2\sigma'_{ho}}{1 + K_a}\left(\frac{R}{r}\right)^{1-K_a} \tag{9.58}$$

$$\sigma'_\theta = K_a\sigma'_r \tag{9.59}$$

where the radius of the plastic annulus R can be determined by using the following boundary condition in conjunction with equation 9.58: $r \to a$ (a being the current radius of the borehole), $\sigma_r = P$ (P is the applied pressure). Thence equation 9.58 yields:

$$R = a\left[\frac{P(1 + K_a)}{2\sigma'_{ho}}\right]^{1/(1-K_a)} \tag{9.60}$$

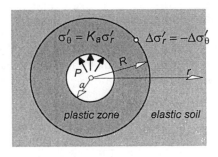

Figure 9.16: Limiting conditions.

Finally, a substitution for R in equations 9.58 and 9.59 yields the expressions of both effective radial and hoop stresses in the plastic range where $a \leq r \leq R$:

$$\sigma'_r = P\left(\frac{a}{r}\right)^{1-K_a}$$

(9.61)

$$\sigma'_\theta = K_a P\left(\frac{a}{r}\right)^{1-K_a}$$

(9.62)

The corresponding patterns of stress changes are shown in figure 9.17.

Because at failure the volume is not constant, *Hughes et al.* (1977) assumed the sand to be failing at a constant dilation rate:

$$\sin \upsilon = -\frac{(\varepsilon_r + \varepsilon_\theta)}{(\varepsilon_r - \varepsilon_\theta)}$$

(9.63)

where υ is the *angle of dilation* of sand. They then argued that both dilatancy and internal angle of friction are constant over the strain range of a pressuremeter test once failure has occurred. Under such circumstances, the following relationship based on the Rowe (1962) stress dilatancy theory applies:

$$\frac{1 + \sin \phi'}{1 - \sin \phi'} = \left(\frac{1 + \sin \phi'_c}{1 - \sin \phi'_c}\right)\left(\frac{1 + \sin \upsilon}{1 - \sin \upsilon}\right) = N\left(\frac{1 + \sin \upsilon}{1 - \sin \upsilon}\right)$$

(9.64)

ϕ'_c being the critical state angle of shearing resistance.

Next, *Hughes et al.* (1977) integrated the equilibrium equation 9.55 using the boundary condition $\sigma'_r = \sigma'_R$ at the outer boundary $r = R$ in figure 9.16, where σ'_R represents the effective radial stress associated with the onset of failure. On integration, it is easy to show that within the failed area in the figure:

$$\ln\left(\frac{\sigma'_r}{\sigma'_R}\right) = (1 - K_a) \ln(R/r)$$

(9.65)

In general, the linear graph corresponding to equation 9.63 has an intercept, and accordingly, the equation can be expressed as follows:

$$-(\varepsilon_r + \varepsilon_\theta) = (\varepsilon_r - \varepsilon_\theta) \sin \upsilon - c$$

(9.66)

where the negative intercept c corresponds to a compressive volumetric strain in the absence of any dilatancy.

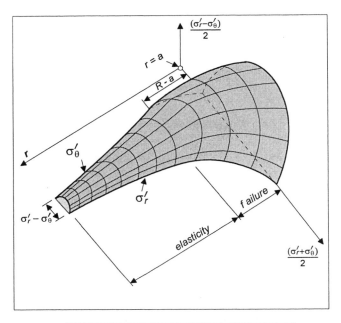

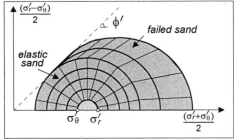

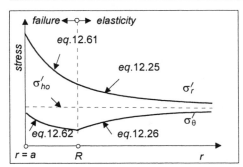

Figure 9.17: Variation of radial and circumferential stresses during a pressuremeter test in a sand.

Equation 9.66 can easily be rearranged as follows:

$$-\varepsilon_r = n\,\varepsilon_\theta - c\frac{(n+1)}{2}$$

(9.67)

with: $\quad n = \dfrac{1 - \sin\upsilon}{1 + \sin\upsilon}$

(9.68)

Substituting for both radial and hoop strains from equations 9.15 into equation 9.67, it is seen that:

$$\frac{dw}{dr} = -n\frac{w}{r} - c\frac{(n+1)}{2}$$

(9.69)

This equation can be solved by making a change of variable similar to that used in conjunction with equation 9.8. Let $\xi = wr^n$ so that:

$$\frac{d\xi}{dr} = \frac{dw}{dr}r^n + nwr^{(n-1)}$$

A straightforward integration then yields:

$$\xi = -\frac{c}{2}.r^{(n+1)} + b$$

so that when the change of variable is taken into account, it is seen that:

$$wr^n = -\frac{c}{2}.r^{(n+1)} + b$$

(9.70)

The constant b in equation 9.70 can be found from the outer boundary:

$$r = R, \quad w/R = \varepsilon_R = constant.$$

Thus:

$$b = R^{(n+1)}\left(\varepsilon_R + \frac{c}{2}\right)$$

(9.71)

The complete solution to equation 9.70 can then be established:

$$\frac{w}{r} = \left(\frac{R}{r}\right)^{n+1}\left(\varepsilon_R + \frac{c}{2}\right) - \frac{c}{2}$$

(9.72)

Substituting for the ratio R/r from equation 9.65 into equation 9.72, then writing at $r = a$, $\quad w/a = \varepsilon_{r=a}$ and $\sigma'_r = P$, where P is the applied pressure and $\varepsilon_{r=a}$ is the measured hoop strain:

$$\left(\varepsilon_{r=a} + \frac{c}{2}\right) = (P/\sigma'_R)^{(n+1)/(1-K_a)}\left(\varepsilon_R + \frac{c}{2}\right)$$

so that:

$$\log\left(\varepsilon_{r=a} + \frac{c}{2}\right) = \frac{n+1}{1-K_a}\log(P) + constant \qquad (9.73)$$

The constant c in equation 12.73 is according to *Hughes et al.* (1977) very small, and therefore can safely be discarded. Consequently, when plotted as the variation of $\log P$ *versus* $\log \varepsilon_\theta$, equation 9.73 yields a linear graph (refer to figure 9.18) with a slope:

$$s = \frac{1-K_a}{n+1} = \frac{(1+\sin\upsilon)\sin\phi'}{1+\sin\phi'} \qquad (9.74)$$

On substitution for the quantity N from equation 9.64, the slope s can be related both to the critical state angle ϕ'_c and the angle of dilation υ of the sand in the following way :

$$\sin\phi' = \frac{(N+1)\,s}{(N-1)\,s+2} \qquad (9.75)$$

$$\sin\upsilon = \frac{2Ns - N + 1}{N+1} \qquad (9.76)$$

$$N = \tan^2\left(\frac{\pi}{4} + \frac{\phi'_c}{2}\right) \qquad (9.77)$$

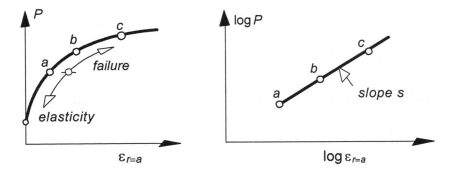

Figure 9.18: Stress–strain relationship at failure during a pressuremeter test in a sand.

9.4 Practical aspects related to the use of the pressuremeter

A successful application of the theoretical basis for the pressuremeter test developed earlier depends, by and large, on how representative are the measured stiffness parameters of the soil. It must be emphasised that, however careful an operator can be, some soil disturbance is bound to occur during testing. Moreover, the results profile depends on the type of equipment used for the test. In this respect, figure 9.19 illustrates typical stress–strain graphs corresponding to the same soil tested using a *prebored PBP* and a *sef-boring SBP* pressuremeters. It has been already mentioned that, in practice, the expansion of cavity during a *PBP* test is limited to a shear strain $\varepsilon_s \approx 50\%$. In contrast, the expansion curve of an *SBP* test tends to have a more realistic form of the initial part of the graph, reflecting the lower levels of disturbance associated with the insertion process. In both tests, the limit pressure for clays which, in theory, corresponds to a ratio $\Delta V/V = 1$, where V represents the expanded volume of the membrane, reflects the assumption that the clay was loaded to a limiting stress condition.. Leaving aside the empirical correlation between these graphs, the question that arises at this stage is how representative are these stiffness parameters (that is σ_{ho}, P_l, c_u, ϕ') that have been measured from a pressuremeter test. It is useful to remember that the pressuremeter theory detailed earlier is based on the *assumption* that the soil behaviour is best described as *elastic–perfectly plastic*, and that the expansion of the cavity occurs under conditions of *axial symmetry* and *plane strain* (refer to section 9.3.1). This implies that the pressuremeter membrane (see figure 9.7) is presumed to be *infinitely long*. In practice however, most (self-boring) pressuremeters used commercially are characterised by a *typical ratio L/D $\approx$ 6* (L and D are the membrane length and diameter respectively), and therefore any measured parameter can potentially be affected by the *end effects* due to the limited length of membrane (*i.e.* the ratio *L/D*). These effects were examined by Houlsby and Carter (1993), who undertook a finite element simulation of (self-boring) pressuremeter tests in clay. The results suggest that, while the clay shear modulus G is unaffected by the ratio *L/D*, the undrained shear strength c_u, derived from central strain measurements using a self-boring pressuremeter with a typical ratio *L/D* = 6, may be slightly overestimated. However, such a conclusion should be considered carefully since the finite element analysis in question was undertaken on a linear elastic medium, in other words on an ideal soil.

Furthermore, the assumption related to linear elasticity becomes arguable in the case of tests on clays performed using an *SBP*, for which the initial elastic behaviour is markedly non-linear as illustrated in figure 9.19. Under such circumstances, the clay behaviour is best modelled as *non-linear elastic–perfectly plastic*. Accordingly, applying the previous linear elastic analysis in conjunction with results measured from an SBP test can result in noticeably erroneous stiffness parameters. As an alternative, some authors suggest the use of a power law to describe the variation during the (non-linear) elastic phase of the stiffness with deformation   (Bolton and Whittle, 1999):

$$\tau = a\gamma^b \tag{9.78}$$

where the shear stress corresponds to $\tau = (\sigma_r - \sigma_\theta)$, and the shear strain is defined as $\gamma = (\varepsilon_r - \varepsilon_\theta)$, both the parameter a and the power exponent b being soil constants.

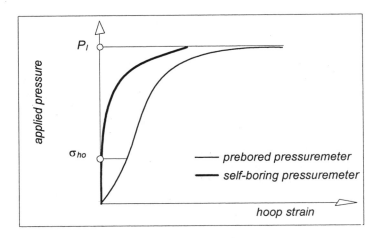

Figure 9.19: Typical PBP and SBP expansion graphs.

It can readily be shown that, were such a power law to be adopted, then the increase in *radial pressure* (*i.e.* $\Delta P = P - \sigma_{ho}$) in the elastic range will be related to the *shear strain* expressed in terms of the *current volume V* (as per equation 9.46) as follows:

$$\Delta P = \frac{a}{b}(\varepsilon_s)^b \tag{9.79}$$

Thus a plot of the pressure applied at the borehole walls versus the shear strain calculated from equation 9.50 in the space ($\ln \Delta P$, $\ln \varepsilon_s$) yields a line with an intercept a/b and a slope b. Figure 9.20 corresponds to results measured from an *SBP* on London clay by Bolton and Whittle (1999). These results were averaged from three unload–reload cycles, where the reversal point in each cycle was taken as an origin. In all three cycles, the clay behaviour was very accurately fitted with a power law type equation, yielding an exponent $b \approx 0.57$ (the corresponding coefficient of correlation in all case was $R^2 = 0.999$). In the *plastic range*, the applied pressure becomes related to the undrained shear strength of the clay and to the current volume change as follows:

$$\Delta P = P_l + c_u \ln \varepsilon_s \qquad (9.80)$$

the *limit pressure* being this time defined as:

$$P_l = c_u \left(\frac{1}{b} + \ln \frac{G}{c_u} \right) \qquad (9.81)$$

where the G represents the *secant shear modulus* corresponding to the *yield shear strain* (*i.e.* the shear strain corresponding to the onset of plasticity). Notice that for a *linear* elastic behaviour, the exponent b in equation 9.78 is 1, and equation 9.81 becomes identical to equation 9.52 derived from the Gibson and Anderson theory presented earlier. Similarly, the undrained shear strength c_u of clay is *not* affected by the assumption made in relation to the initial elastic behaviour, since c_u can be obtained using both equations 9.80 and 9.51, and corresponds to the slope of the linear portion of the graph plotted in a semi-logarithmic space as illustrated in figure 9.21 in the case of London clay.

These experimental results highlight the need for a cautious approach when interpreting measured data corresponding to a markedly non-linear elastic behaviour. One has to bear in mind that the quality of the outcome of any analysis is a reflection of the assumptions used: unrealistic assumptions yield erroneous results.

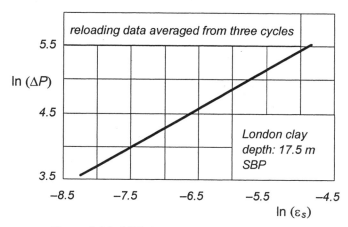

Figure 9.20: SBP data corresponding to three reload cycles, London clay (from Bolton and Whittle (1999), by permission).

Based on these conclusions, and judging from the amount of data amassed through the use of the pressuremeter in different ground conditions and on different soil types thus far, the following facts emerge:

(a) although data related to the undrained shear strength c_u of clays measured from pressuremeter tests seem to indicate a considerable scatter, they are heavily dependent on the boundary conditions.

(b) An *average* effective angle of friction ϕ'_{av} *can* be measured from *SBP* tests on sands.

(c) The total *in situ* horizontal stress σ_{ho} is sensitive to insertion disturbance. However a good estimate of σ_{ho} can be obtained through the use of an appropriate analysis.

(d) Provided that the non-linearity during the elastic phase of a pressuremeter test is taken into account, the soil shear modulus G compares favourably with those measured using other *in situ* testing techniques.

(e) Although the limit pressure P_l is not constant for a given soil, and is rather intricately related to the stiffness parameters σ_{ho}, G, c_u or ϕ', its value can be reliably determined.

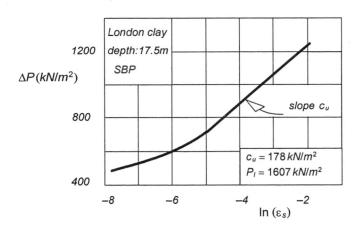

Figure 9.21: Determination of the undrained shear strength of London clay from an SBP test (from Bolton and Whittle (1999), by permission).

Several semi-empirical methods of design (which generally tend to be grossly conservative), especially concerning shallow and deep foundations, have been developed and are being regularly updated. The details of such methods are out of the scope of this textbook, but can be found in Clarke (1995) for instance. These developments, however, are a clear indication of an increasing reliability of the pressuremeter method and of the willingness of practising engineers to use them with ever growing confidence.

References

Assadi, A. and Sloan, S. W. (1991) *Undrained stability of shallow square tunnels.* ASCE Geotechnical Engineering Division, 117, pp. 1152–1173.

Baguelin, F., Jézéquel, J. F. and Le Méhauté, A. (1972) *Expansion of cylindrical probes in cohesive soils.* Journal of Soil Mechanics, Foundations Division, ASCE, 98 (SM11), pp. 1129–1142.

Baguelin, F., Jézéquel, J. F. and Le Méhauté, A. (1974) *Self-boring placement method of soil characteristics measurement.* Proceedings of Speciality Conference on Subsurface Exploration of Underground Excavation and Heavy Construction, Henniker, pp. 312–332.

Baguelin, F., Jézéquel, J. F. and Shields, D. H. (1978) *The Pressuremeter and Foundation Engineering.* Trans Tech. Publication, Germany.

Bolton, D. M. and Whittle, R. W. (1999) *A non-linear elastic-perfectly plastic analysis for plane strain undrained expansion tests.* Géotechnique, 49 (1), pp. 133–141.

Brady, B. H. G. and Brown, E. T. (1993) *Rock Mechanics for Underground Mining,* 2nd edn. Chapman & Hall, London.

Clarke, B. G. (1995) *Pressuremeters in Geotechnical Design.* Blackie Academic and Professional, London.

Gibson, R. E. and Anderson, W. F. (1961) *In situ measurement of soil properties with the pressuremeter.* Civil Engineering and Public Works Review, 56, pp. 615–618.

Houlsby, G. T and Carter, J. P. (1993) *The effects of pressuremeter geometry on the results of tests in clay.* Géotechnique, 43 (4), pp. 567–576.

Hughes, J. M. O. (1973) *An instrument for in situ measurement in soft clays.* PhD Thesis, University of Cambridge.

Hughes, J. M. O, Wroth, C. P. and Windle, D. (1977) *Pressuremeter test in sand.* Géotechnique, 27 (4), pp. 455–477.

Jaeger, C. (1979) *Rock Mechanics and Engineering,* 2nd edn. Cambridge University Press.

MELT (1993) *Ministère de l'Equipement, du Logement et des Transports: Règles Techniques de Conception et de Calcul des Fondations des Ouvrages de Génie Civil.* Projet de Fascicule 62, Titre 5, CCTG.

Ménard, L. (1962). *Comportement d'une fondation profonde soumise à des efforts de renversement.* Sol Soils, 3, pp. 9–27.

Ménard, L. (1963) *Calcul de la force portante des fondations sur la base des résultats des essais pressiométriques.* Sol Soils, 5, pp. 9–32.

Mestat, P. (1997) *Maillage d'éléments finis pour les ouvrages de géotechnique:*

conseils et recommondations. Bulletin des Laboratoires des Ponts et Chaussées, 212, pp. 39–64.

Rowe, P. W. (1962) *The stress-dilatancy relation for static equilibrium of an assembly of particles in contact.* Proceedings of the Royal Society, A.269, pp. 500–527.

Smith, I. M. and Griffiths, D. V. (1998) *Programming the Finite Element Method.* 3rd edn. John Wiley, New York.

Timoshenko, S. P. and Goodier, J. N. (1970) *Theory of Elasticity,* 3rd edn. McGraw-Hill, International Edition, Singapore.

Tchebotarioff, G. P. (1973) *Foundations, Retaining and Earth Structures,* 2nd edn. McGraw-Hill, New York.

Zienkiewicz, O. C. and Taylor, R. (1991) *The Finite Element Method* (2 volumes), 4th edn. McGraw-Hill, London.

CHAPTER 10

Centrifuge modelling of soil behaviour

10.1 Introduction

Physical modelling of soil behaviour has always played a pivotal role in helping the designer acquire a better understanding of the *actual* behaviour under *similar* stress conditions in the field. In this respect, laboratory tests such as triaxial, consolidation and shear box tests are still used extensively and *do* provide reliable data provided that adequate testing procedures are adhered to. Centrifuge testing of soils constitutes another (recent) development in the field of physical modelling, which has taken off quite rapidly. More and more research laboratories are equipped with centrifuge centres, and the research outcome in this field is becoming widely available so that comparative studies can be undertaken, leading to the development of ever more sophisticated instrumentation equipment. As in the case of triaxial testing, for instance, a centrifuge test is undertaken on a small size sample of soil, referred to as the *model,* in a way that stress conditions corresponding to a particular event (such as subjecting a pile to a lateral load for example), or to a particular process (as in the case of the execution of an excavation, or the construction of an embankment) are recreated *via* an *inertial acceleration field*. Under such loading conditions, the behaviour of the *model* should be, in theory, a replica of that of the *actual* soil (often referred to as the *prototype*), when subjected to a *similar state of stresses*. Notwithstanding the practical difficulties related to model preparation and instrumentation, centrifuge modelling is regarded as a valuable means of testing that enhances markedly the understanding of the physical behaviour of soils under complex static or dynamic stress fields (see for instance the paper by Schofield (1980)). Examples vary widely and include (classical) problems such as the stability of slopes, retaining structures, embankments, foundations and tunnels, as well as heat transfer (that is conduction and convection), diffusion (*i.e.* consolidation), seepage, earthquakes, wave loading, contaminant transport, freeze/thaw and the effects of deep mining.

10.2 Modelling principles, stress similarities

The basic principle of centrifuge testing consists of creating stress conditions which are similar to those applied through gravity in the field to a prototype, *in* or *on* a model, with dimensions which are much smaller than those of the prototype. This can be achieved by placing the model in a basket at the end of a centrifuge boom, then subjecting it to an inertial acceleration field. The main features of a centrifuge equipment are depicted in figure 10.1, corresponding to an *Acutronic 680* centrifuge, capable of developing a maximum acceleration of 200g (g being the acceleration due to gravity), and whose technical details can be found for instance in the book *Centrifuge 88* edited by Corté (1988).

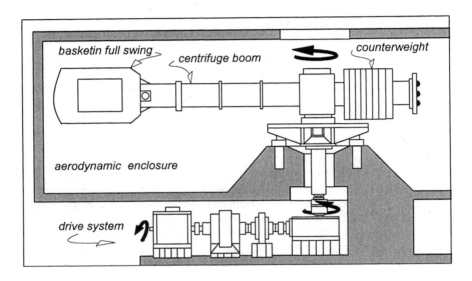

Figure 10.1: Acutronic 680 centrifuge.

In the following analysis, the subscript m refers to the model and the subscript p is used in conjunction with the prototype. Thus, assuming that all soil properties, including those of the porewater, are identical for the prototype and for the model, and referring to figure 10.2, it is seen that, for a model with a dimension R/n (n being an integer), placed at a distance R (which can be the effective radius of a centrifuge, for instance) from the centre of rotation, and subjected to an acceleration Ng (*i.e.* N times the acceleration due to gravity g), the *centrifugal stress* σ_{vm} is, in theory, *similar* to the vertical stress σ_{vp} due to the self weight of soil in a prototype having a dimension NR/n. Accordingly, if the respective dimensions of the model and prototype were:

$$h_m = \frac{R}{n} \quad \text{and} \quad h_p = N\frac{R}{n}$$

then the vertical stress σ_{vm} at a depth h_m in the model, induced by an acceleration $N.g$ will be:

$$\sigma_{vm} = N\rho g h_m \tag{10.1}$$

Similarly, the vertical stress σ_{vp} at depth h_p in the prototype is:

$$\sigma_{vp} = \rho g h_p \tag{10.2}$$

ρ, in both equations, being the soil density.

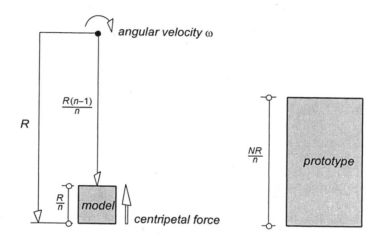

*Figure 10.2: Effect of inertial forces on stress
similarities between model and prototype.*

If the stresses are similar, then clearly the dimensions of the model and prototype are such that:

$$h_m = \frac{h_p}{N} \tag{10.3}$$

In practice however, the similarity between σ_{vm} and σ_{vp} is affected to a certain degree by the negative *centripetal* (or inertial) *forces* applied to the model due to the variation of the angular velocity ω with the radius r. Referring once more to figure 10.2, it can be seen that the stress σ_{vm} at the base of the model can be evaluated as follows:

$$\sigma_{vm} = \int_{R(n-1)/n}^{R} \rho\omega^2 r\, dr = \rho\omega^2 \frac{R^2}{2}\left(\frac{2n-1}{n^2}\right) \tag{10.4}$$

Moreover, the vertical stress due to gravity at the base of the prototype is:

$$\sigma_{vp} = \rho g N \frac{R}{n} \tag{10.5}$$

Consequently, for these two stresses to be *similar*, equations 10.4 and 10.5 must be equal. Whence:

$$\sigma_{vm} = \sigma_{vp} \quad \Rightarrow \quad \frac{Ng}{\omega^2 R} = 1 - \frac{1}{2n} \tag{10.6}$$

It can be shown that if the stresses σ_{vm} at a depth R/n and σ_{vp} at a depth NR/n are similar, then the maximum stress difference (*i.e.* error) defined as:

$$\Delta S = \frac{\sigma_{vp} - \sigma_{vm}}{\sigma_{vm}} \tag{10.7}$$

occurs at a depth $R/2n$ in the model and $NR/2n$ in the prototype (see for instance Taylor (1995)). Thus, evaluating the stresses at these respective depths, it follows that:

$$\sigma_{vm} = \int_{R(1-1/n)}^{R(1-1/2n)} \rho\omega^2 r\, dr = \rho\omega^2 \frac{R^2}{8n^2}(4n-3) \tag{10.8}$$

and

$$\sigma_{vp} = \rho g N \frac{R}{2n} \tag{10.9}$$

Consequently, it is easy to show that the error corresponding to equation 10.7 is such that:

$$\Delta S = \frac{4nNg}{\omega^2 R(4n-3)} - 1 \tag{10.10}$$

Hence, substituting for the quantity $Ng/\omega^2 R$ from equation 10.6 in equation 10.10 and rearranging, it follows that:

$$\Delta S = \frac{1}{4n-3} \tag{10.11}$$

Moreover, assuming there is similarity of stresses at two-thirds model depth as depicted in figure 10.3, then the graph corresponding to the maximum error ΔS calculated from equation 10.11, and shown in figure 10.4, indicates that for an n value larger than 10, the ensuing error (*i.e.* the shaded area in figure 10.4) is smaller than 3% and therefore negligible.

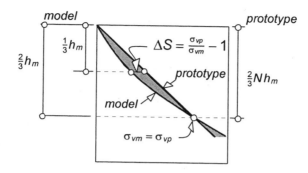

Figure 10.3: Scaling errors due to inertial forces in the model.

In practice, a value $n = 10$ is typical in geotechnical centrifuge testing, so that the model height corresponds to one tenth of the effective centrifuge radius (measured from the centre of rotation to one third the model depth).

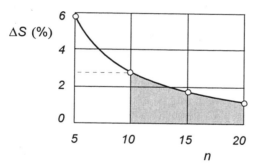

Figure 10.4: Error magnitude related to model dimensions.

10.3 Scale effects

The previous analysis of stress similarities between model and prototype serves as a reminder of the fact that physical (especially centrifuge) modelling of soils is affected by the reduction in dimensions of the tested volume of soil. The *scale effects* are not, however, limited to the model size, since two more phenomena related to centrifuge testing can, in principle, cause the behaviour of the model to be appreciably different from that of the prototype of an identical soil. These two phenomena are associated with (*a*) the particle size and (*b*) the rotational acceleration field.

It has been established previously (refer to equation 10.3) that the stress similarity necessitates the use of a model with dimensions N times smaller than the prototype, with Ng being the acceleration to which the model is subjected in the centrifuge. Moreover, an equivalent dimensional analysis indicates that, for the same soil, the ratio d/L (d being the *average* grain size of the soil, and L a typical boundary dimension) must, in theory, be identical for both the prototype and the model, so that:

$$\frac{d_m}{L_m} = \frac{d_p}{L_p}$$

Substituting for the length $L_m \equiv h_m$ from equation 10.3, and rearranging, it is seen that:

$$d_m = \frac{d_p}{N} \tag{10.12}$$

Equation 10.12 therefore indicates the need to use a model comprising a soil with an average grain size N-times smaller than that of the same soil used for the prototype. Manifestly, this conclusion has, in practice, the potential of generating problems since, for instance, a model tested at an acceleration of $100g$, constituted of fine sand that has in the field an average grain size of $d_p = 0.1\,mm$, must have an average grain size of $d_p/100 = 0.001\,mm$ which, according to table 2.1 of section 2.2 corresponds to a clay, with all the implications related to the void ratio, permeability and stress–strain behaviour. Although no simple answer can be provided as to how the grain size might affect in any appreciable way the behaviour observed during a centrifuge test (see for example Ovesen (1979), Bolton and Lau (1988), Tatsuoka *et al.* (1991)), it seems logical, though, that the grain size effect decays with decreasing grain dimensions, so that while it appears necessary to reduce the grain size in proportion to the centrifuge acceleration when testing a gravel, the adverse effects of not doing so when testing a fine sand, a silt or a clay appear to be minimal. Evidently, these effects need be (or are already in the process of being) investigated thoroughly, and thus an engineering judgement has to be made in conjunction with the soil used for a model and the type of problem to be physically simulated. Therefore some caution must be exercised, so that the above analysis and guidelines are not used in a mechanical way.

Let us now establish the effects of the rotational acceleration field, better known as the *Coriolis effects*. In this respect, it is easier to establish all acceleration components related to a soil element, rotated at a steady velocity V, much in the way that a model contained in a centrifuge basket is subjected to an acceleration Ng. Thus, with reference to figure 03.5, it is seen that the radial co-ordinates of point A, a distance r far from the centre of rotation, are as follows:

$$X = r \cos \theta$$

$$Y = r \sin \theta$$

(10.13)

The components of velocity are therefore:

$$V_x = \frac{dX}{dt} = \cos\theta \frac{dr}{dt} - r\sin\theta \frac{d\theta}{dt}$$

$$\dot{V}_y = \frac{dY}{dt} = \sin\theta \frac{dr}{dt} + r\cos\theta \frac{d\theta}{dt}$$

(10.14)

whence the following accelerations:

$$\frac{d^2 X}{dt^2} = \cos\theta \frac{d^2 r}{dt^2} - 2\sin\theta \frac{dr}{dt}\frac{d\theta}{dt} - r\sin\theta \frac{d^2\theta}{dt^2} - r\cos\theta \left(\frac{d\theta}{dt}\right)^2$$

$$\frac{d^2 Y}{dt^2} = \sin\theta \frac{d^2 r}{dt^2} + 2\cos\theta \frac{dr}{dt}\frac{d\theta}{dt} + r\cos\theta \frac{d^2\theta}{dt^2} - r\sin\theta \left(\frac{d\theta}{dt}\right)^2$$

(10.15)

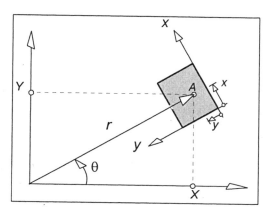

Figure 10.5: Radial co-ordinate system.

Moreover, when the *local co-ordinates system (x, y)* is used, then with reference to figure 10.6, the position of A is such that:

$$x = C_1 \qquad\qquad y = C_2 - r$$

(10.16)

where C_1 and C_2 are constants.

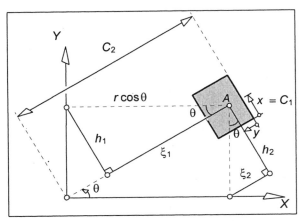

Figure 10.6: Local co-ordinate system.

Referring to figure 10.6, it is seen that:

$$h_1 = r \cos\theta \sin\theta = X \sin\theta$$

$$h_2 = h_1 = Y \cos\theta$$

$$\xi_1 = X \cos\theta$$

$$\xi_2 = Y \sin\theta$$

and $\quad r = \xi_1 + \xi_2$

Accordingly, equations 10.16 can now be expressed as follows:

$$x = C_1 - h_1 + h_2$$

$$y = C_2 - \xi_1 - \xi_2$$

and so, inserting for the quantities h_1, h_2, ξ_1 and ξ_2, it follows that:

$$x = C_1 - X \sin\theta + Y \cos\theta$$

$$y = C_2 - X \cos\theta - Y \sin\theta$$

(10.17)

The accelerations, expressed in the local co-ordinates system can then be derived:

$$\frac{d^2x}{dt^2} = -\left(\frac{d^2X}{dt^2}\right)\sin\theta + \left(\frac{d^2Y}{dt^2}\right)\cos\theta$$

$$\frac{d^2y}{dt^2} = -\left(\frac{d^2X}{dt^2}\right)\cos\theta - \left(\frac{d^2Y}{dt^2}\right)\sin\theta$$

Thus, substituting for the quantities derived in equation 10.15 and rearranging:

$$\frac{d^2x}{dt^2} = 2\frac{dr}{dt}\frac{d\theta}{dt} + r\frac{d^2\theta}{dt^2}$$

$$\frac{d^2y}{dt^2} = -\frac{d^2r}{dt^2} + r\left(\frac{d\theta}{dt}\right)^2$$

(10.18)

Equations 10.18 yield the four components of acceleration:

- *the horizontal shaking:* $\Gamma_h = r\frac{d^2\theta}{dt^2}$

- *the vertical shaking:* $\Gamma_v = \frac{d^2r}{dt^2}$

- *the inertial acceleration:* $\Gamma_i = r\left(\frac{d\theta}{dt}\right)^2 = \omega^2 r = \frac{V^2}{r}$
    where ω is the angular velocity

- *the Coriolis acceleration:* $\Gamma_c = 2\frac{dr}{dt}\frac{d\theta}{dt}$

It is noticeable that the first two components Γ_h and Γ_v only apply to *dynamic models* (to simulate quakes for instance). Also, the Coriolis acceleration Γ_c which translates the velocity $v = dr/dt$ of a particle within the model, relative to the velocity of the model centrifuge *in flight* $tV = rd\theta/dt$, can be rewritten as follows:

$$\Gamma_c = 2v\frac{d\theta}{dt} = 2v\frac{V}{r}$$

(10.19)

In practice, it is accepted that, for slow moving particles, in other words for a *steady model flight* where no shaking takes place, the error due to Coriolis acceleration is negligible for ratios $\Gamma_c/\Gamma_i < 0.1$, meaning:

$$v < 0.05V$$

(10.20)

However, for faster particles, the path of a moving particle within a model becomes curved, with a radius of curvature r_c defined as follows:

$$r_c = \frac{v^2}{\Gamma_c} \tag{10.21}$$

Substituting for Γ_c from equation 10.19, it is seen that:

$$\frac{r_c}{r} = \frac{v}{2V} \tag{10.22}$$

Since r represents the *effective radius of centrifuge* (refer to figure 10.5), equation 10.22 implies that the curvature effect becomes less significant when $r_c > r$. Accordingly, it is suggested that for fast particles (such as in a blast simulation for instance), the errors related to Coriolis acceleration are no longer appreciable as long as the velocities in equation 10.22 are such that:

$$v > 2V \tag{10.23}$$

Thus, both equations 10.20 and 10.23 yield the range *within* which Coriolis effects *must* be taken into account:

$$0.05V < v < 2V \tag{10.24}$$

10.4 Scaling laws

10.4.1 Static models

• *Length*

In accordance with equation 10.3, the stress similarities between a model subjected to an acceleration of Ng and a prototype subjected to the acceleration due to gravity g imply that the model dimensions are N *times smaller* than those of the prototype. Thus, using the (same) subscript m for model and p for prototype, it follows that:

$$L_m = L_p N^{-1} \tag{10.25}$$

• *Unit weight*

The densities of the model and the prototype being identical, the corresponding unit weights are as follows:

$$\gamma_p = \rho g$$
and $$\gamma_m = \rho N g = N \gamma_p \tag{13.26}$$

Therefore, the unit weight of the model is N *times larger* than that of the prototype.

• Hydraulic gradient

With reference to figure 4.4 in section 4.2 (chapter 4), it is seen that the hydraulic gradient can be thought of as a pressure gradient, because it is defined as the ratio of the total head loss Δh to the length of the flow path along which Δh is lost through friction, so that at the limit:

$$i = \frac{dh}{dl} \tag{10.27}$$

But the porewater pressure is identical in both the model and the prototype, and therefore:

$$i_p = \frac{dh}{(dl)_p} \qquad \text{and} \qquad i_m = \frac{dh}{(dl)_m}$$

Thus, making use of equation 10.25, it follows that:

$$i_m = \frac{dh}{(dl)_p(1/N)} = Ni_p \tag{10.28}$$

Hence, the hydraulic gradient in the centrifuge model is *N times larger* than the one in the prototype.

• Seepage velocity

Darcy's law, expressed in terms of seepage velocity in the centrifuge model is as follows:

$$v_m = Ki_m \tag{10.29}$$

Knowing that the model and prototype have identical permeabilities, and substituting for the hydraulic gradient from equation 10.28 into equation 10.29, it follows that:

$$v_m = KNi_p = Nv_p \tag{10.30}$$

which shows that, as in the case of the hydraulic gradient, the seepage velocity is *N times larger* in the centrifuge model than in the prototype.

• Seepage time

The seepage time can be expressed as the ratio of the length of the flow path to the seepage velocity. So, for the model:

$$t_m = \frac{L_m}{V_m} \qquad (10.31)$$

A straight substitution for L_m and v_m from equations 10.25 and 10.30 respectively into the above equation yields:

$$t_m = \frac{L_p}{N} \times \frac{1}{N v_p} = \frac{1}{N^2} t_p \qquad (10.32)$$

Accordingly, water seeps N^2 *times faster* in the centrifuge model than that in the prototype.

• *Seepage flow*

Using Darcy's law, the flow quantity *per unit length* in the centrifuge model can be expressed as follows:

$$q_m = L_m v_m t_m \qquad (10.33)$$

where L_m represents the length across the flow path. Making good use of equations 10.25, 10.30 and 10.32, it is easy to establish that:

$$q_m = \frac{1}{N^2} q_p \qquad (10.34)$$

The above equation shows that the flow quantity *per unit length* in the centrifuge model is N^2 *times smaller* than the one in the prototype. Note that, if the scaling law between *total flow* quantities in a centrifuge model and in a prototype were sought, then one must remember that:

$$Q_m = A_m v_m t_m \qquad (10.35)$$

with A_m being the *area* of flow. An approach similar to that used previously leads to the following:

$$Q_m = \frac{1}{N^3} Q_p \qquad (10.36)$$

indicating that the *total flow quantity* (in $L^3 T^{-1}$) in a model is N^3 *times smaller* than that occurring in the prototype.

• *Diffusion problems*

The governing parabolic equation of a consolidation process (*i.e.* porewater pressure dissipation with time) can be written as:

$$\frac{\partial^2 u}{\partial z^2} = \frac{1}{c_v}\frac{\partial u}{\partial t} \tag{10.37}$$

The solution to the above equation contains the following time factor written in the case of the centrifuge model as follows:

$$T_v = c_v \frac{t_{cm}}{L_m^2} \tag{10.38}$$

where L represents the drainage path and t is the time, the coefficient of consolidation c_v being identical for both prototype and model. Substituting for t_{cm} and L_m from equations 10.32 and 10.25 respectively, then cancelling appropriate terms:

$$t_{cm} = \frac{1}{N^2}t_p \tag{10.39}$$

This equation being identical to equation 10.32 in the case of seepage, indicates that the same s*tage* of consolidation occurs N^2 *times faster* in a centrifuge model than in a prototype.

• *Reynolds number*

The Reynolds number is of particular interest in centrifuge modelling, because its value is linked to the flow regime. It is well established that for soils, the regime of flow is assumed *laminar* as long as the Reynolds number is kept smaller than 10 (refer to section 4.1, chapter 4). Let us examine the effect that this condition has on the centrifuge model. The dimensionless Reynolds number corresponding to the centrifuge model is defined as:

$$Re_m = v_m \frac{d}{\mu} \tag{10.40}$$

where v_m represents the model seepage velocity, d is the average diameter of soil particles and μ is the kinematic viscosity of water. Since d and μ are identical for both prototype and centrifuge model, equation 10.40 can then be rearranged after introducing the scaling law for seepage velocities from equation 10.30:

$$Re_m = Nv_p \frac{d}{\mu} = NRe_p \tag{10.41}$$

which implies that the Reynolds number is N *times higher* in a centrifuge model than in a prototype. Consequently, in order to maintain a *laminar regime of flow* in the model, provisions must be made to keep the Reynolds number smaller than 10. It is of interest to note that, according to equation 10.41, an *identical* Reynolds number for both model and prototype can be achieved by using for the centrifuge model: (*a*) a soil characterised by an average grain diameter that is *N times smaller* than the average diameter in the prototype or (*b*) a fluid *N times more viscous* than water. Clearly the first suggestion is unworkable, however, a variety of oils with differing viscosities can be used as a pore fluid in the model instead of water. One has to bear in mind, though, that the use of a pore fluid other than water may cause the surface properties of the solid particles to change, which may, in turn, affect the behaviour of the model.

10.4.2 Dynamic models

Dynamic events such as quakes can be simulated in a centrifuge, and the scaling laws related to the corresponding models are derived in a manner similar to that used in conjunction with static models. Figure 10.7 depicts a typical horizontal shear wave generated by an earthquake, which is represented by the following differential equation:

$$x = a \sin \omega t \tag{10.42}$$

where x represents the *cyclic motion*, a is the *amplitude of the motion*, and ω corresponds to the *angular velocity*. Obviously, both velocity and acceleration can be derived from equation 10.42:

$$\frac{dx}{dt} = a\omega \cos \omega t \tag{10.43}$$

$$\frac{d^2x}{dt^2} = -a\omega^2 \sin \omega t \tag{10.44}$$

As the quantity $a\omega^2$ in equation 10.44 defines the *magnitude of acceleration*, and because the centrifuge model is subjected to an acceleration *N*-times larger than that of the prototype, it is clear that:

$$a_m\omega_m^2 = Na_p\omega_p^2 \tag{10.45}$$

also, according to equation 10.25:

$$a_m = \frac{a_p}{N} \tag{10.46}$$

Thus inserting a_m into equation 10.45, and rearranging, it is easy to establish that:

$$\omega_m = N\omega_p \tag{10.47}$$

and because the *angular velocity* is related to the *motion frequency*, it follows that:

$$\omega = 2\pi f \quad \Rightarrow \quad f_m = N f_p \qquad (10.48)$$

More importantly perhaps, the quantity $a\omega$ in equation 10.43, which corresponds to the *magnitude of velocity*, is identical for both model and prototype. In fact, substituting for a_m and ω_m from equations 10.46 and 10.47 respectively into equation 10.43, it is seen that:

$$a_m \omega_m \cos(\omega_m t) = a_p \omega_p \cos(N\omega_p t) \qquad (10.49)$$

Because the velocity magnitude corresponds to the ratio of a length to a time, and knowing that in a centrifuge model the length is reduced by a factor N (see equation 10.25), equation 10.49 therefore implies that the time for dynamic models is reduced by a factor N as opposed to a factor N^2 for seepage or diffusion problems (refer to equations 10.31 and 10.39).

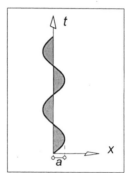

Figure 10.7: Vertically propagating shear wave.

Example 10.1

A model with a volume $V_m = 3 \times 10^{-2}\,m^3$ is subjected to 10 cycles at a frequency $f_m = 100\,Hz$ and with an amplitude $a_m = 1.5\,mm$, while being accelerated in a centrifuge at 100g. Obviously, the duration of shaking is calculated in a straightforward way: $t_m = 10/100 = 0.1s$.

The magnitude of acceleration due to the shaking can be estimated as follows:

$$a_m \omega_m^2 = a_m(2\pi f_m)^2 = 1.5 \times 10^{-3} \times 4\pi^2 \times 10^4$$

$$= 592\,m/s^2 \approx 60.3g$$

This test simulates an earthquake in a prototype, having a volume:

$$V_p = N^3 V_m = 30,000\,m^3$$

subjected to 10 cycles at a frequency: $f_p = \frac{1}{N} f_m = 1\,Hz$, and with an amplitude: $a_p = N a_m = 0.15\,m$.

The duration of the earthquake is such that: $t_p = Nt_m = 10\,s$, and the magnitude of acceleration in the prototype is, with reference to figure 10.8:

$$a_p(2\pi f_p)^2 = 0.15 \times 4\pi^2 \times 1 = 5.92\,m/s^2 \approx 0.6\,g$$

Assuming that, during the shaking, the steady centrifuge velocity is $V = 30\,m/s$, then the error due to Coriolis acceleration at maximum velocity of shaking, corresponding to the ratio of the inertial acceleration $\Gamma_i = V^2/r$ to the Coriolis acceleration $\Gamma_c = 2vV/r$ is estimated as follows:

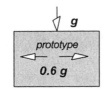

Figure 10.8: Earthquake accelerations.

$$v = a_m 2\pi f_m = 1.5 \times 2\pi \times 10^{-1} = 0.94\,m/s$$

whence: $\qquad \dfrac{\Gamma_c}{\Gamma_i} = \dfrac{2v}{V} = \dfrac{2 \times 0.94}{30} = 0.062$

Obviously, in this case, the error due to Coriolis acceleration is only 6.2%, and is therefore negligible.

The scaling laws for different physical quantities are summarised in table 13.1 in the case of a model subject to an acceleration $N.g$.

10.5 Practical aspects of centrifuge modelling

Every engineer or researcher would recognise that the outcome of a centrifuge test in geotechnics depends on the meticulous model preparation prior to testing, which is, alas, time consuming. In this respect, the paper by Phillips (1995) constitutes excellent reading as it describes in some detail the potential pitfalls related to model preparation, testing and monitoring. The one aspect that must always be considered first in relation to centrifuge testing is safety. Centrifuges such as the one depicted in figure 13.1 are powerful machines that must be handled by adequately trained staff. Furthermore, centrifuge testing is unquestionably a multi-disciplinary activity, since the modeller has to be at least conversant in (if not knowledgeable about!) mechanical engineering, electronics equipment, control systems and data acquisition, before even contemplating interpreting the test results from a geotechnical viewpoint. No wonder that such tests are generally intensively resourced, therefore expensive and time consuming. Manifestly, undertaking a centrifuge test implies spending the majority of time and effort on the careful preparation of the model. This includes the following.

• The selection of the appropriate container depending on the type of soil tested and the type of behaviour to be simulated (static or dynamic) with specific boundary conditions requirements that need to be fulfilled. For instance, modelling a static event such as the consolidation of a clay layer requires the walls of the container to be *ideally* frictionless, whereas the simulation of the creep behaviour of a frozen soil necessitates a strict thermal control within the container.

• The selection of the appropriate soil conditions for the model, in particular, the restrictions related to the flow of pore fluid and the size of the model must always be taken into account.

It was established earlier that the Reynolds number in the model must be kept below 10 for laminar flow conditions to prevail. This requirement is most likely to be fulfilled through the use of a pore fluid that is N times more viscous than water in conjunction with the model (Ng being the acceleration to which the model is subjected). Also, in order to minimise the scaling errors due to inertial forces (refer to figures 13.3 and 13.4), the model height must be kept to within one tenth of the effective centrifuge radius (measured from the centre of rotation to one third the model depth). On the other hand, the model may have to be protected against any temperature changes or any air movements that can potentially be generated within the aerodynamic enclosure (see figure 13.1) during testing.

• The reconstitution of the model under laboratory conditions must allow for the effective stress profile to be recreated in the case of cohesive soils, or for the change in soil behaviour to be taken into account when interpreting test results. In particular, remoulded samples of clay and silt can be created from a slurry by tamping. Alternatively, the slurry can be consolidated in the centrifuge, in which case, care must be taken not to induce a *differential consolidation* of the slurry mass through the generation of preferential drainage paths due to the high pore pressure within the soil mass (refer to section 5.6). For granular soils, sophisticated techniques such as tamping and pluviation can be used to create a density controlled model.

• Instrumentation and actuation of the model can potentially create problems since neither the instruments, nor the actuator are scaled. Pore pressure, total stress and displacement transducers, as well as thermocouples, that are buried within the model should be placed in a way that minimises any reinforcement effect of the soil. Also, there is a need to insulate strain gauges and lead wires embedded in the model. The restrictive effects on the model behaviour of the actuator (*i.e.* the system that sets off the model to simulate the behaviour of the prototype) must be reduced to a

minimum.
• A data acquisition system that can store a large amount of data in a short period of time is needed to conduct a centrifuge test successfully. In this respect, sophisticated systems combining the latest electronics and digital technologies are commercially available.

These points, important though they may be, are only an *aperçu* of the acumen, hard work, and vision required by a modeller to conduct a sophisticated and technically challenging test such as a geotechnical centrifuge test. A thorough analysis which tackles more detailed practical aspects of centrifuge modelling can be found in Phillips (1995).

Table 13.1: Scaling laws for different physical quantities
in the case of a model subject to an acceleration N.g.

quantity	scaling law		scaling factor
acceleration	g_m	$= Ng_p$	N^{-1}
mass, density	ρ_m	$= \rho_p$	1
stress	σ_m	$= \sigma_p$	1
strain	ε_m	$= \varepsilon_p$	1
velocity	V_m	$= V_p$	1
temperature	θ_m	$= \theta_p$	1
length	L_m	$= L_p/N$	N
time (static event)	t_m	$= t_p/N^2$	N^2
time (dynamic event)	t_m	$= t_p/N$	N
displacement, amplitude	d_m	$= d_p/N$	N
unit weight	γ_m	$= N\gamma_p$	N^{-1}
frequency	f_m	$= Nf_p$	N^{-1}
hydraulic gradient	i_m	$= Ni_p$	N^{-1}
seepage velocity	v_m	$= Nv_p$	N^{-1}
Reynolds number	Re_m	$= NRe_p$	N^{-1}
heat flux	h_{xm}	$= Nh_{xp}$	N^{-1}
seepage flow per unit length	q_m	$= q_p/N^2$	N^2
total seepage flow	Q_m	$= Q_p/N^3$	N^3
diffusion (consolidation)	t_{cm}	$= t_{cp}/N^2$	N^2
heat transfer(conduction, convection)	$(\partial\theta/\partial t)_m = (\partial\theta/\partial t)_p/N^2$		N^2

References

Bolton, M. D. and Lau, C. K. (1988) *Scale Effects Arising from Particle Size.*
    Centrifuge 88 (ed. *J. F. Corté*). A.A. Balkema, Rotterdam, pp. 127–134.
Corté, J. F. (Ed.) (1988) *Centrifuge 88.* A.A. Balkema, Rotterdam.
Ovesen, N. K. (1979) *The scaling law relationship.* Panel discussion.
    Proceeding of the 7th European conference on Soil Mechanics
    and Foundation Engineering, Brighton, 4, pp. 319–323.
Phillips, R. (1995) *Centrifuge modelling: practical considerations.*
    Geotechnical Centrifuge Technology, Blackie, London, pp. 34–60.
Schofield, A. N. (1980) *Cambridge geotechnical centrifuge operations.*
    Géotechnique, 20, pp. 227–268.
Tatsuoka, F., Okahara, M., Tanaka, T., Tani, K., Morimoto, T. and Siddiquee,
    M. S. A. (1991) *Progressive failure and particle size effect in bearing
    capacity of a footing in sand.* ASCE Geotechnical Engineering Congress,
    Vol. 2 (Geotechnical special publication 27), pp. 788–802.
Taylor, R. N. (1995) *Centrifuges in modelling: principles and scale effects.*
    Geotechnical Centrifuge Technology, Blackie, London, pp. 19–33.

Subject index

Author index

The quadratic formula
The roots of the quadratic equation $ax^2 + bx + c = 0$ are given by:

$$x = \frac{-b \pm \sqrt{b^2 - 4ac}}{2a}$$

Determinants

$$\begin{vmatrix} a_1 & b_1 \\ a_2 & b_2 \end{vmatrix} = a_1 b_2 - a_2 b_1$$

$$\begin{vmatrix} a_1 & b_1 & c_1 \\ a_2 & b_2 & c_2 \\ a_3 & b_3 & c_3 \end{vmatrix} = a_1 b_2 c_3 + a_2 b_3 c_1 + a_3 b_1 c_2 - a_1 b_3 c_2 - a_2 b_1 c_3 - a_3 b_2 c_1$$

Laws of logarithms (where $\log_a x = y$ means $x = a^y$)

$$\log_a(M.N) = \log_a M + \log_a N, \qquad \log_a\left(\tfrac{M}{N}\right) = \log_a M - \log_a N$$

$$\log_a(M^x) = x. \log_a M$$

Analytic geometry
straight line: $\quad y = mx + b \quad ; \qquad$ slope $= m = \dfrac{y_2 - y_1}{x_2 - x_1}$

Circle: $\qquad x^2 + y^2 = r^2; \quad (x-h)^2 + (y-k)^2 = r^2$

Parabola: Vertical axis: $\qquad x^2 = 4ay \;\; ; (x-h)^2 = 4a(y-k)$

Horizontal axis: $\qquad y^2 = 4ax \;\; ; (y-k)^2 = 4a(x-h)$

Ellipse: vert major axis: $\qquad \dfrac{x^2}{b^2} + \dfrac{y^2}{a^2} = 1 \;\; ; \dfrac{(x-h)^2}{b^2} + \dfrac{(y-k)^2}{a^2} = 1$

hor. major axis: $\qquad \dfrac{x^2}{a^2} + \dfrac{y^2}{b^2} = 1 \;\; ; \dfrac{(x-h)^2}{a^2} + \dfrac{(y-k)^2}{b^2} = 1$

Hyperbola: vert. transverse axis $\qquad \dfrac{y^2}{a^2} - \dfrac{x^2}{b^2} = 1 \;\; ; \dfrac{(y-k)^2}{a^2} - \dfrac{(x-h)^2}{b^2} = 1$

hor. transverse axis $\qquad \dfrac{x^2}{a^2} - \dfrac{y^2}{b^2} = 1 \;\; ; \dfrac{(x-h)^2}{a^2} - \dfrac{(y-k)^2}{b^2} = 1$

Trigonometry

Area of a triangle: $\quad A = \sqrt{s(s-a)(s-b)(s-c)} \quad$ with $\quad s = \frac{1}{2}(a+b+c)$

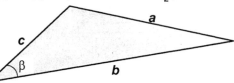

$$a^2 = b^2 + c^2 - 2bc\cos\beta$$

Pythagoras theorem: for $\beta = 90°$:
$$a^2 = b^2 + c^2$$

Trigonometry identities

$\sin(A+B) = \sin A \cos B + \cos A \sin B \qquad \sin(A-B) = \sin A \cos B - \cos A \sin B$

$\cos(A+B) = \cos A \cos B - \sin A \sin B \qquad \cos(A-B) = \cos A \cos B + \sin A \sin B$

$$\tan A = \frac{\sin A}{\cos A} \qquad\qquad \cot A = \frac{\cos A}{\sin A} \qquad\qquad \sin^2 A + \cos^2 A = 1$$

$$\tan(A+B) = \frac{\tan A + \tan B}{1 - \tan A \tan B} \qquad\qquad \tan(A-B) = \frac{\tan A - \tan B}{1 + \tan A \tan B}$$

$$\sin 2A = 2\sin A \cos A$$

$$\cos 2A = \cos^2 A - \sin^2 A = 2\cos^2 A - 1 = 1 - 2\sin^2 A$$

$$\tan 2A = \frac{2\tan A}{1 - \tan^2 A} \qquad\qquad \sin\tfrac{1}{2}A = \pm\sqrt{(1-\cos A)/2}$$

$$\cos\tfrac{1}{2}A = \pm\sqrt{(1+\cos A)/2} \qquad\qquad \tan\tfrac{1}{2}A = \frac{\sin A}{1 + \cos A}$$

$$\sin A + \sin B = 2\sin\tfrac{1}{2}(A+B)\cos\tfrac{1}{2}(A-B)$$

$$\sin A - \sin B = 2\cos\tfrac{1}{2}(A+B)\sin\tfrac{1}{2}(A-B)$$

$$\cos A + \cos B = 2\cos\tfrac{1}{2}(A+B)\cos\tfrac{1}{2}(A-B)$$

$$\cos A - \cos B = -2\sin\tfrac{1}{2}(A+B)\sin\tfrac{1}{2}(A-B)$$

$$\sin A \cos B = \tfrac{1}{2}[\sin(A+B) + \sin(A-B)]$$

$$\cos A \sin B = \tfrac{1}{2}[\sin(A+B) - \sin(A-B)]$$

$$\cos A \cos B = \tfrac{1}{2}[\cos(A+B) + \cos(A-B)]$$

$$\sin A \sin B = \tfrac{1}{2}[\cos(A-B) - \cos(A+B)]$$

Derivative formulae

$$\frac{d}{dx}(c) = 0 \qquad\qquad \frac{d}{dx}(x) = 1 \qquad\qquad \frac{d}{dx}[af(x)] = a\frac{d}{dx}[f(x)]$$

$$\frac{d}{dx}[f(x) \pm g(x)] = \frac{d}{dx}[f(x)] \pm \frac{d}{dx}[g(x)]$$

$$\frac{d}{dx}[f(x)\,g(x)] = f(x)\,g'(x) + g(x)\,f'(x)$$

$$\frac{d}{dx}\left[\frac{f(x)}{g(x)}\right] = \frac{g(x)\,f'(x) - f(x)\,g'(x)}{[g(x)]^2}$$

$$\frac{d}{dx}(x^n) = n x^{n-1} \qquad\qquad \frac{d}{dx}(u^n) = n u^{n-1}\frac{du}{dx}$$

$$\frac{d}{dx}\left[\log_a u\right] = \frac{1}{u}\frac{du}{dx}\log_a e \qquad\qquad \frac{d}{dx}[\ln u] = \frac{1}{u}\frac{du}{dx}$$

$$\frac{d}{dx}[a^u] = a^u\frac{du}{dx}\ln a \qquad\qquad \frac{d}{dx}[e^u] = e^u\frac{du}{dx}$$

$$\frac{d}{dx}[\sin u] = \cos u\frac{du}{dx} \qquad\qquad \frac{d}{dx}[\cos u] = -\sin u\frac{du}{dx}$$

$$\frac{d}{du}[\tan u] = \sec^2 u\frac{du}{dx} \qquad\qquad \frac{d}{dx}[\cot u] = -\csc^2 u\frac{du}{dx}$$

$$\frac{d}{dx}[\sec u] = \sec u \tan u\frac{du}{dx} \qquad\qquad \frac{d}{dx}[\csc u] = -\csc u \cot u\frac{du}{dx}$$

$$\frac{d}{dx}[Arc\sin u] = \frac{1}{\sqrt{1-u^2}}\frac{du}{dx} \qquad\qquad \frac{d}{dx}[Arc\cos u] = -\frac{1}{\sqrt{1-u^2}}\frac{du}{dx}$$

$$\frac{d}{dx}[Arc\tan u] = \frac{1}{1+u^2}\frac{du}{dx}$$

Integration formulae

$$\int u^n du = \frac{u^{n+1}}{n+1} + C \ , \qquad n \neq -1 \qquad\qquad \int u^{-1} du = \int \frac{du}{u} = \ln u + C$$

$$\int e^u du = e^u + C \qquad\qquad\qquad\qquad \int u e^u du = e^u(u-1) + C$$

$$\int \sin u \, du = -\cos u + C \qquad\qquad\qquad \int \cos u \, du = \sin u + C$$

$$\int \tan u \, du = \ln \sec u + C \qquad\qquad\qquad \int \cot u \, du = \ln \sin u + C$$

$$\int e^{au} \sin mu \, du = \frac{e^{au}(a \sin mu - m \cos mu)}{m^2 + a^2} + C$$

$$\int e^{au} \cos mu \, du = \frac{e^{au}(m \sin mu + a \cos mu)}{m^2 + a^2} + C$$

$$\int \sec u \, du = \ln(\sec u + \tan u) + C \qquad\qquad \int \csc u \, du = \ln(\csc u - \cot u) + C$$

$$\int \sec^2 u \, du = \tan u + C \qquad\qquad\qquad \int \csc^2 u \, du = -\cot u + C$$

$$\int \sec u \tan u \, du = \sec u + C \qquad\qquad \int \csc u \cot u \, du = -\csc u + C$$

$$\int \frac{du}{\sqrt{a^2 - u^2}} = \arcsin \frac{u}{a} + C \qquad\qquad \int \frac{du}{a^2 + u^2} = \frac{1}{a} \arctan \frac{u}{a} + C$$

$$\int \frac{du}{\sqrt{u^2 \pm a^2}} = \ln\left(u + \sqrt{u^2 \pm a^2}\right) + C \qquad \int \frac{du}{a^2 - u^2} = \frac{1}{2a} \ln\left(\frac{a+u}{a-u}\right) + C$$

$$\int u \sin u \, du = \sin u - u \cos u + C \qquad\qquad \int u \cos u \, du = \cos u + u \sin u + C$$

$$\int u^n \ln u \, du = u^{n+1}\left[\frac{\ln u}{n+1} - \frac{1}{(n+1)^2}\right] + C$$

$$\int \sin^2 u \, du = \frac{1}{2}u - \frac{1}{4}\sin 2u + C \qquad\qquad \int \cos^2 u \, du = \frac{1}{2}u + \frac{1}{4}\sin 2u + C$$

$$\int \tan^2 u \, du = \tan u - u + C \qquad\qquad\qquad \int u \, dv = uv - \int v \, du + C$$